RAND McNALLY

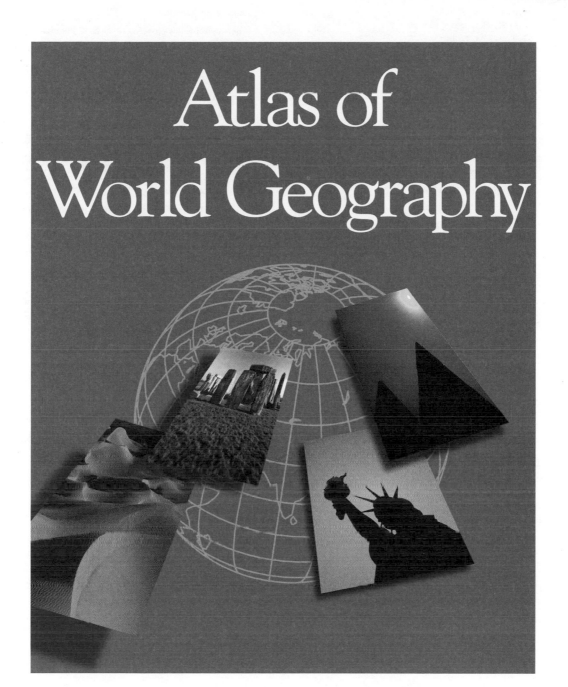

Atlas of World Geography

Editors
Brett R. Gover
Margaret McNamara
Ann T. Natunewicz

Design
Donna M. McGrath
Peggy Hogan

Cover Design
Brian C. Doherty

Design Production
DePinto Graphic Design

Cartographic Direction
V. Patrick Healy

Cartographic Staff
Nina Lusterman
Robert K. Argersinger
Lynn Jasmer
Patty A. Porter
James A. Purvis
L. Charlene Smith
James A. Wooden
David C. Zapenski

Research
Susan K. Hudson

Continental Thematic Maps
Thomas F. Vitacco
Marzee L. Eckhoff
Gwynn A. Lloyd
Robert L. Merrill
David R. Simmons
Ashley James Snyder
Barbara Benstead-Strassheim
Dara L. Thompson

Photo Research
Feldman and Associates, Inc.

Photograph Credits:

Front cover images provided by © 1997 PhotoDisc, Inc.

H. Armstrong Roberts: © R. Kord, 7, 31 (b); © Zefa, 100; © M. Schneiders, 108; © Smith/Zefa, 150 (b)

© Randall Hyman: 101

© PhotoDisc, Inc.: 135

Odyssey Chicago: © R. Frerck, 152

Tony Stone Images: © K. Wood, 29 (t); © Mark Segal, 68; © David Frazier, 69; © Jacques Jangoux, 98 (t); © John Warden, 98 (b); © Owen Franken, 110; © John Lamb, 122 (t); © Yann Layma, 134; © Paul Chelsey, 153

Information Credits:

Volcano data, pages 29, 32, and 36: Tom Simkin, Smithsonian Institution Global Volcanism Program

Earthquake data, page 37: Paula Dunbar, National Geophysical Data Center, National Oceanic and Atmospheric Administration

Australia information, page 38: Australian Tourist Commission

Much of the information on the destruction of the Amazonian rain forest, page 101, was provided by Fred Engel of the Center for Earth and Planetary Science, National Air and Space Museum, Smithsonian Institution, Washington, D.C.

Atlas of World Geography

Published and printed in the United States of America

ISBN: 0-528-17790-0

For information about ordering *Atlas of World Geography*, call 1-800-678-7263; or visit our website at:

www.K12online.com

Table of Contents

Using the Atlas

Maps and Atlases

Today, satellite images (Figure 1) and aerial photography show us the face of the Earth in precise detail. It is hard to imagine how difficult it once was to ascertain what our planet looked like—even small parts of it. Yet from earliest history we have evidence of humans trying to depict the world through maps and charts.

Figure 1

Twenty-five hundred years ago, on a tiny clay tablet the size of a hand, the Babylonians inscribed the earth as a flat disk (Figure 2) with Babylon at the center. The section of the Cantino map of 1502 (Figure 3) is an example of a portolan chart used by mariners to chart the newly discovered Americas. Handsome and useful maps have been produced by many cultures. The Mexican map (Figure 4) drawn in 1583 marks hills with wavy lines and roads with footprints between parallel lines. The methods and materials used to create these maps were dependent upon the technology available, and their accuracy suffered considerably. The maps in this atlas show the detail and accuracy that cartographers are now able to achieve. They benefit from our ever-increasing technology, including satellite imagery and computer-assisted cartography.

Figure 2

In 1589, Gerardus Mercator used the word "atlas" to describe a collection of maps. Atlases have become a unique and indispensable reference for graphically defining the world and answering the question "Where?" Only on a map can the countries, cities, roads, rivers, and lakes covering a vast area be simultaneously viewed in their relative locations. Routes between places can be traced, trips planned, boundaries of neighboring states and countries examined, distances between places measured, the meandering of rivers and streams and the sizes of lakes visualized, and remote places imagined.

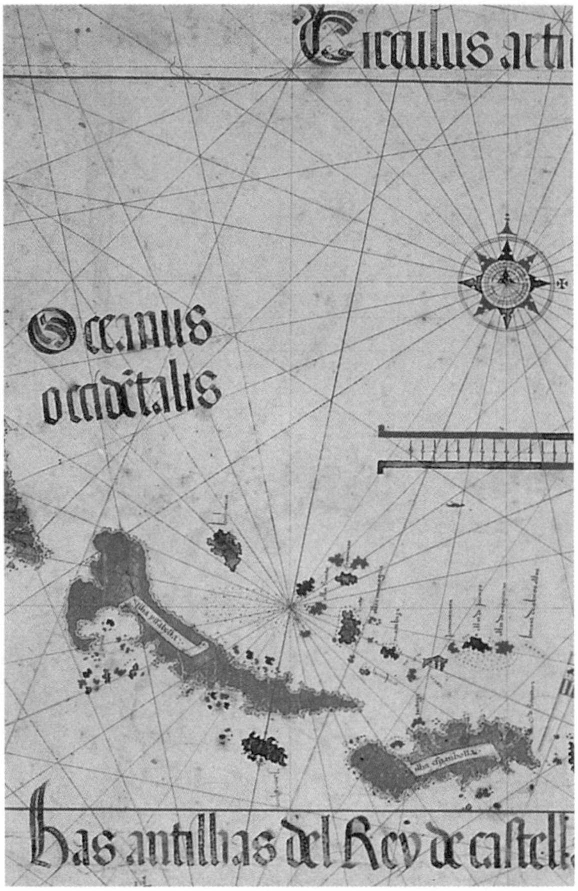

Figure 3

Figure 4

Getting the Information

An atlas can be used for many purposes, from planning a trip to finding hot spots in the news and supplementing world knowledge. To realize the potential of an atlas, the user must be able to:

1) Find places on the maps
2) Measure distances
3) Determine directions
4) Understand map symbols

Finding Places

One of the most common and important tasks facilitated by an atlas is finding the location of a place in the world. A river's name in a book, a city mentioned in the news, or a potential vacation spot may prompt your need to know where the place is located. The illustrations and text below explain how to find Lagos, Nigeria.

1) Look up the place-name in the index at the back of the atlas. Lagos, Nigeria can be found in the map on page 128, and it can be located on the map by its latitude and longitude, expressed in degrees: 7 North Latitude, 3 East Longitude (Figure 5).

La Fayette, In., U.S.	40N	87W	**90**
Lafayette, La., U.S.	30N	92W	**95**
Laghouat, Alg.	34N	3E	**128**
Lagos, Nig.	7N	3E	**128**
La Grande, Or., U.S.	45N	118W	**82**
LaGrange, Ga., U.S.	33N	85W	**92**
Lahore, Pak.	32N	74E	**143**
Lahti, Fin.	61N	26E	**116**

Figure 5

2) Turn to the map of Northern Africa on page 128. Note that the latitude appears in the right and left margins of the map, and the longitude in the upper and lower margins.

3) To find Lagos on the map, place your left index finger on the left margin at 7 degrees (between 5 and 10); and your right index finger in the top margin at 3 degrees East (between 0 and 5). Move your left finger across the map and your right finger down the map. Your fingers will meet in the area in which Lagos is located (Figure 6).

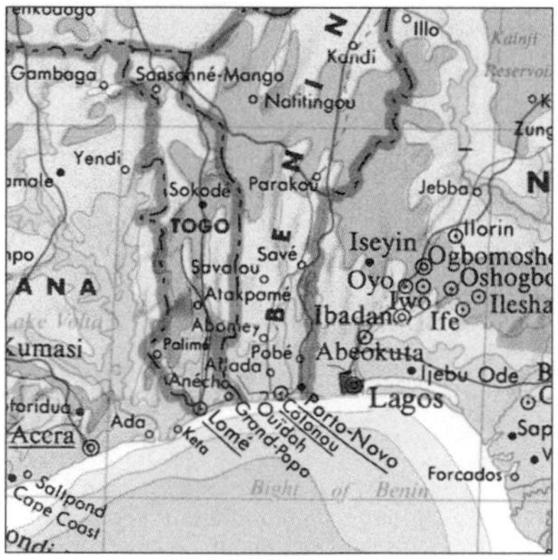

Figure 6

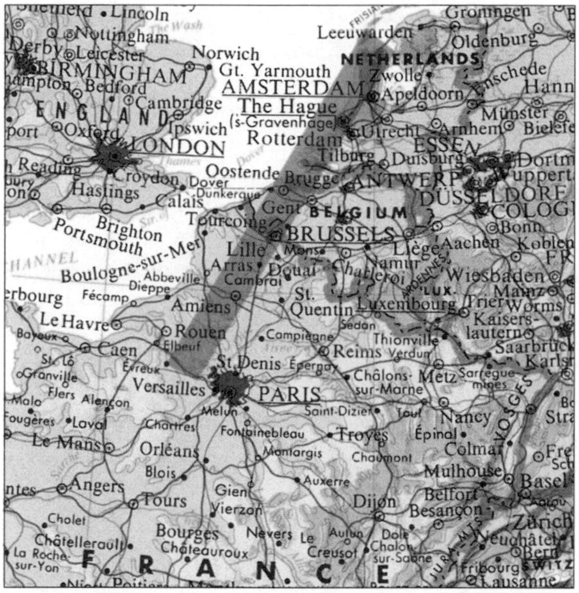

Figure 7

Measuring Distances

In planning trips, determining the distances between two places is essential, and an atlas can help in travel preparation. For instance, to determine the approximate distance between Paris, France and Amsterdam, Netherlands, follow these three steps:

1) Lay a slip of paper on the map on page 117 so that its edge touches the two cities. Adjust the paper so only one corner touches Paris. Mark the paper directly at the spot where Amsterdam is located (Figure 7).

2) Place the paper along the scale of miles beneath the map. Position the corner at 0 and line up the edge of the paper along the scale. The pencil mark on the paper indicates Amsterdam is between 250 and 300 miles from Paris (Figure 8).

3) To find the exact distance, make a second pencil mark at the 250-mile point of the scale. Then slide the paper to the left so that this second mark is lined up with 0 on the scale (Figure 9). The Amsterdam mark now falls at the third 10-mile point on the scale. This means that the Paris and Amsterdam are approximately 250 plus 30—or 280—miles apart.

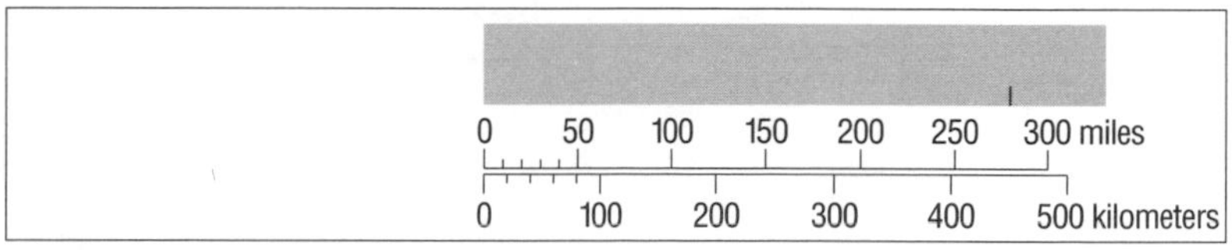

Figure 8

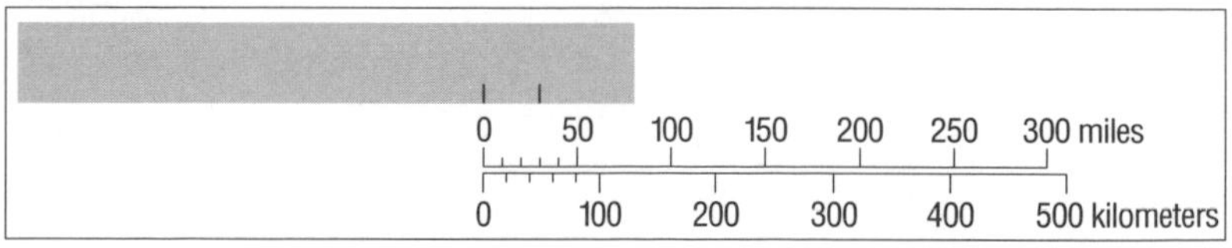

Figure 9

Determining Directions

Most of the maps in the atlas are drawn so that when oriented for normal reading, north is at the top of the map, south is at the bottom, west is at the left, and east is at the right. Most maps have a series of lines drawn across them—the lines of latitude and longitude. Lines of latitude, or parallels of latitude, are drawn east and west. Lines of longitude, or meridians of longitude, are drawn north and south (Figure 10, at bottom of page).

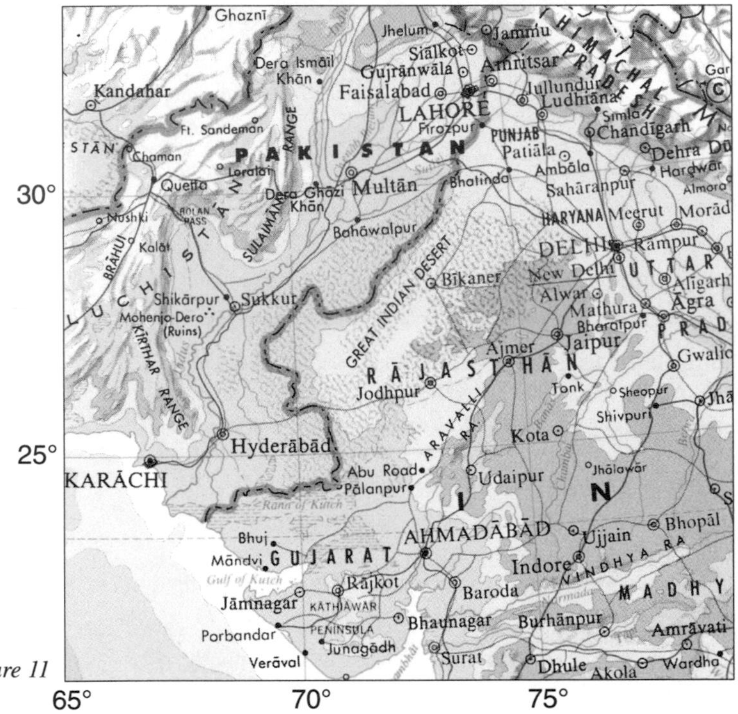

Figure 11

Parallels and meridians appear as either curved or straight lines. For example, in the section of the map of Southwestern Asia (Figure 11), from page 143, the parallels of latitude appear as curved lines. The meridians of longitude are curved vertical lines.

Latitude and longitude lines help locate places on maps. Parallels of latitude are numbered in degrees north and south of the Equator. Meridians of longitude are numbered in degrees east and west of a line called the Prime Meridian, running through Greenwich, England, near London. Any place on Earth can be located by the latitude and longitude lines running through it.

To determine directions or locations on the map, you must use the parallels and meridians. For example, suppose you want to know which is farther north, Karachi, Pakistan or Delhi, India. The map in Figure 11 shows that Karachi is south of the 25° parallel of latitude and that Delhi is north of it. Therefore Delhi is farther north than Karachi. By looking at the meridians of longitude, you can determine which city is farther east. Karachi is approximately 2° east of the 65° meridian, and Delhi is about 2° east of the 75° meridian. Delhi is farther east than Karachi.

Understanding Map Symbols

In a very real sense, every map is a symbol representing the world or part of it. It is a reduced representation of the Earth: each of the world's features—cities, rivers, etc.—is represented by a symbol. Map symbols may take the form of points, such as dots or squares (often used for cities, capital cities, or points of interest) or lines (roads, railroads, rivers). Symbols may also occupy an area, showing extent of coverage (terrain, forests, deserts). They seldom look like the feature they represent and therefore must be identified and interpreted. For instance, some of the maps in this atlas define political units by a colored line depicting their boundaries. Neither the colors nor the boundary lines are actually found on the surface of the Earth, but because countries and states are such important political components of the world, strong symbols are used to represent them. The Legend on page 51 of this atlas identifies the symbols used on the maps.

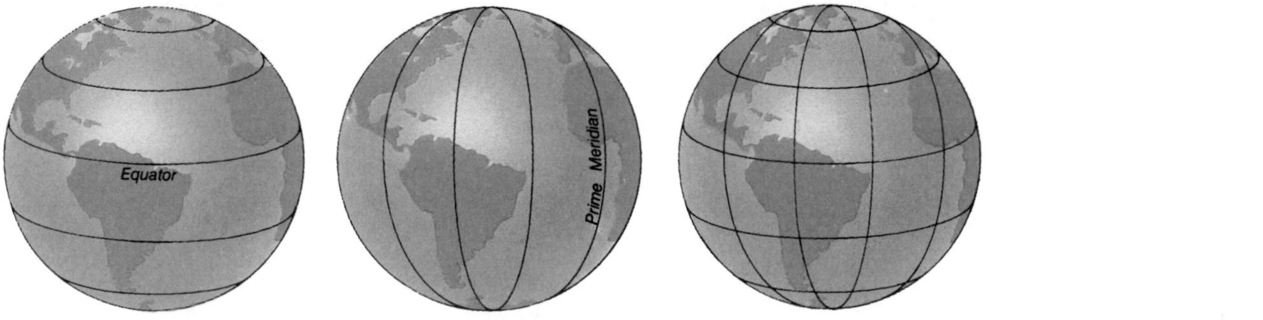

Figure 10

Introduction to Geographic Tables, Charts, and Graphs

The Universe and Solar System

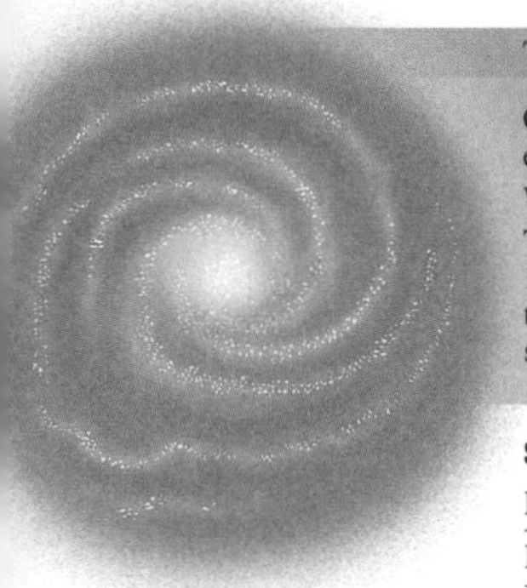

The Milky Way Galaxy

Our star, the Sun, is one of 200 billion stars banded together in the enormous gravitational spiral nebula called the Milky Way Galaxy, which is but one of millions of known galaxies in the universe.

The Milky Way is huge; it would take light — which travels at 186,000 miles per second — 100,000 years to go from one end of the galaxy to the other. In addition to the billions of stars, Earth shares the Milky Way with eight other known planets.

Statistical Data for the Milky Way Galaxy

Diameter: 100,000 light-years	
Mass: About 200 billion suns	
Distance between spiral arms: 6,500 light years	
Thickness of galactic disk: 1,300 light-years	
Satellite galaxies: 2 (visible only in the southern sky)	

Sun

The Sun's diameter — more than 865,000 miles — is 109 times greater than that of the Earth. Even so, the Sun is actually a fairly small star. Somewhere in the vastness of the universe astronomers have located a star that is 3,500 times larger than the Sun.

Diameter: 865,000 miles (1,392,000 km)
Mass: 333,000 times that of the Earth
Surface temperature: 10,300° F (5,700° C)
Central temperature: 27 million° F (15 million° C)
Composition: 70% hydrogen, 27% helium
Spin (at equator): 26 days, 21 hours

Earth

Distance from the Sun: 92,960,000 miles (149,598,000 km)
Diameter: 7,926 miles (12,756 km)
Average surface temperature: 58° F (14° C)
Surface pressure: 1 atmosphere
Atmosphere: 78% nitrogen, 21% oxygen
Length of day: 23 hours, 56 minutes and 4 seconds
Length of year: 365.25 days
Satellites: 1

The Moon

The Moon is the Earth's only natural satellite. About 2,160 miles (3,746 km) across, the Moon is an airless, waterless world just one-fourth the size of the Earth. It circles the planet once every 27 days at an average distance of about 238,000 miles (384,000 km).

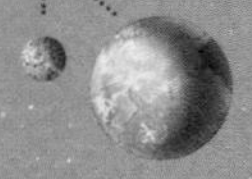

Jupiter

By any measure, Jupiter is the solar system's giant. To equal Jupiter's bulk would take 318 Earths. Over 1,300 Earth-sized balls could fit within this enormous planet.

Distance from the Sun: 483,631,000 miles (778,292,000 km), or 5.2 times that of the Earth
Diameter: 88,700 miles (142,800 km), or 11.3 times that of the Earth
Temperature at cloud tops: –234° F (–148° C)

Mercury

Distance from the Sun: 35,985,000 miles (57,909,000 km), or 39% that of the Earth
Diameter: 3,031 miles (4,878 km), or 38% that of the Earth
Average surface temperature: 340° F (171° C)
Atmosphere: Extremely thin, contains helium and hydrogen
Length of day: 58 days, 15 hours, 30 minutes
Length of year: 87.97 days
Satellites: None

Venus

Distance from the Sun: 67,241,000 miles (108,209,000 km), or 72% that of the Earth
Diameter: 7,521 miles (12,104 km), or 95% that of the Earth
Surface temperature: 867° F (464° C)
Surface pressure: 90 times that of the Earth, equivalent to the pressure at a water depth of 3,000 feet (900 meters)
Atmosphere: 96% carbon dioxide
Length of day: 243 days, 14 minutes. The planet spins opposite to the rotation of the Earth.
Length of year: 224.7 days
Satellites: None

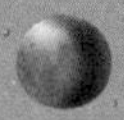

Mars

Distance from the Sun: 141,642,000 miles (227,940,000 km), about 1.5 times that of the Earth
Diameter: 4,222 miles (6,794 km), or 53% that of the Earth
Average surface temperature: –13° F (–25° C)
Surface pressure: 0.7% (1/150 th) that of the Earth
Atmosphere: 95% carbon dioxide, 2.7% nitrogen
Length of day: 24 hours, 37 minutes
Length of year: 1 year, 321.73 days
Satellites: 2

Spatial Relationships of the Sun and the Planets

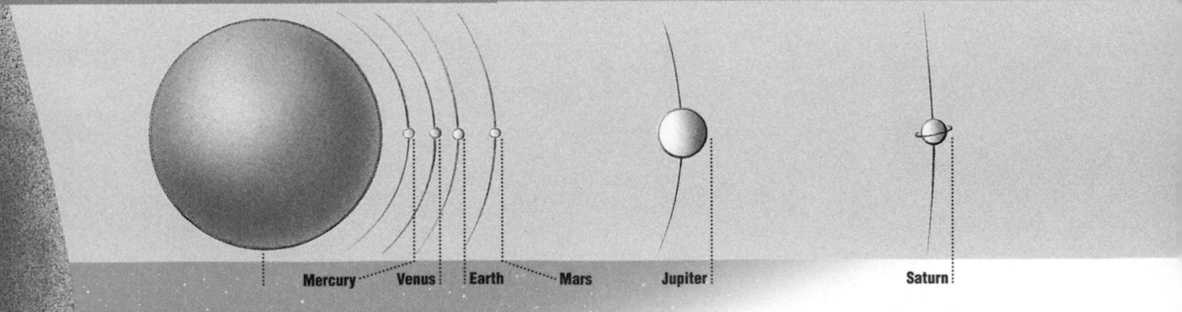

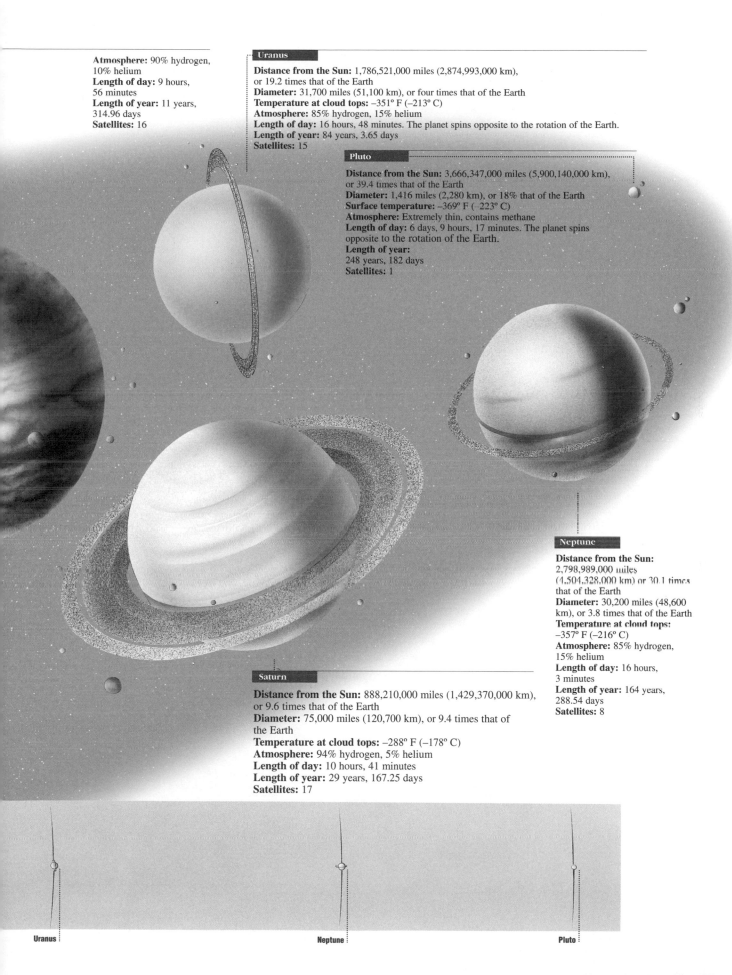

Atmosphere: 90% hydrogen, 10% helium
Length of day: 9 hours, 56 minutes
Length of year: 11 years, 314.96 days
Satellites: 16

Uranus

Distance from the Sun: 1,786,521,000 miles (2,874,993,000 km), or 19.2 times that of the Earth
Diameter: 31,700 miles (51,100 km), or four times that of the Earth
Temperature at cloud tops: –351° F (–213° C)
Atmosphere: 85% hydrogen, 15% helium
Length of day: 16 hours, 48 minutes. The planet spins opposite to the rotation of the Earth.
Length of year: 84 years, 3.65 days
Satellites: 15

Pluto

Distance from the Sun: 3,666,347,000 miles (5,900,140,000 km), or 39.4 times that of the Earth
Diameter: 1,416 miles (2,280 km), or 18% that of the Earth
Surface temperature: –369° F (–223° C)
Atmosphere: Extremely thin, contains methane
Length of day: 6 days, 9 hours, 17 minutes. The planet spins opposite to the rotation of the Earth.
Length of year: 248 years, 182 days
Satellites: 1

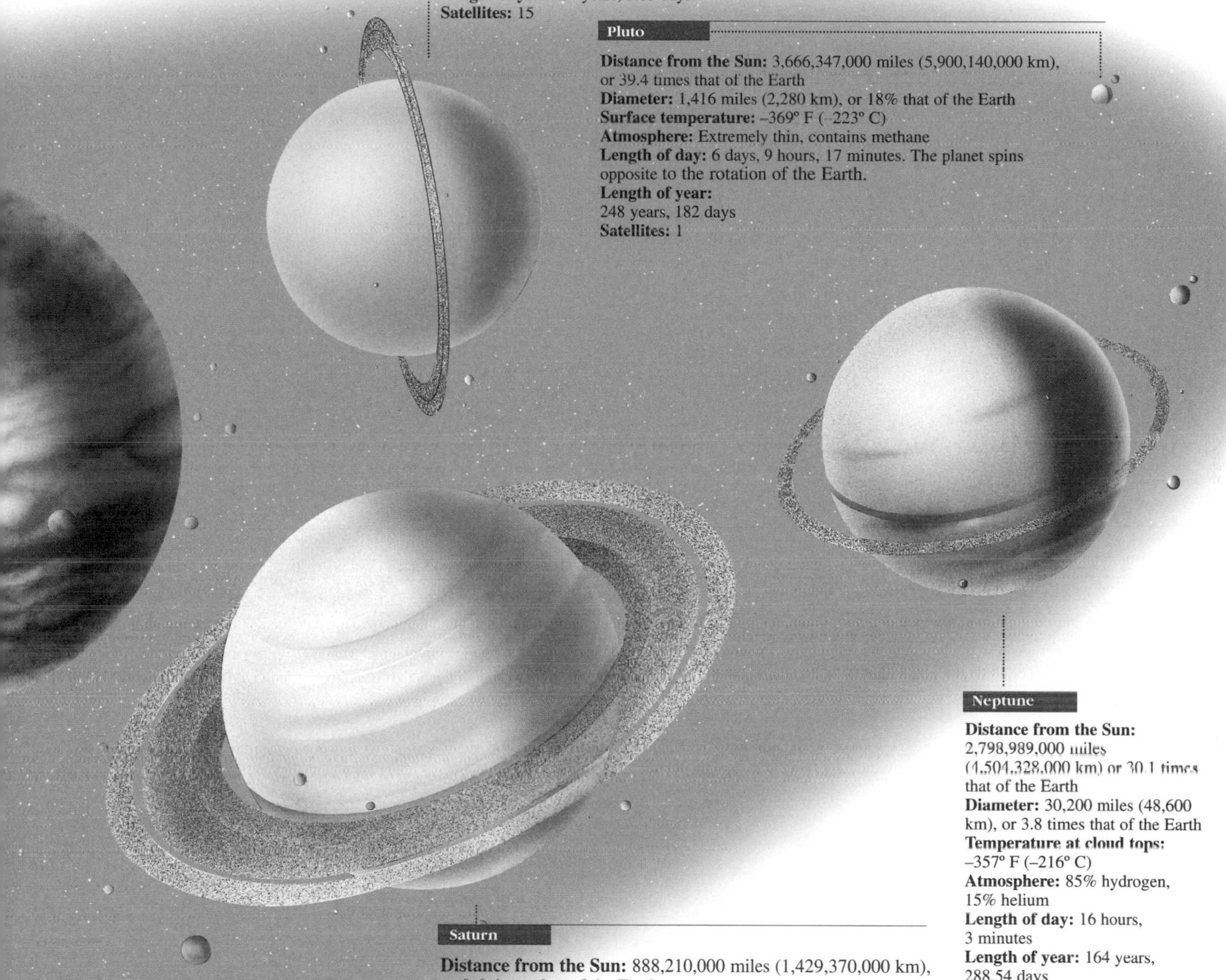

Neptune

Distance from the Sun: 2,798,989,000 miles (4,504,328,000 km) or 30.1 times that of the Earth
Diameter: 30,200 miles (48,600 km), or 3.8 times that of the Earth
Temperature at cloud tops: –357° F (–216° C)
Atmosphere: 85% hydrogen, 15% helium
Length of day: 16 hours, 3 minutes
Length of year: 164 years, 288.54 days
Satellites: 8

Saturn

Distance from the Sun: 888,210,000 miles (1,429,370,000 km), or 9.6 times that of the Earth
Diameter: 75,000 miles (120,700 km), or 9.4 times that of the Earth
Temperature at cloud tops: –288° F (–178° C)
Atmosphere: 94% hydrogen, 5% helium
Length of day: 10 hours, 41 minutes
Length of year: 29 years, 167.25 days
Satellites: 17

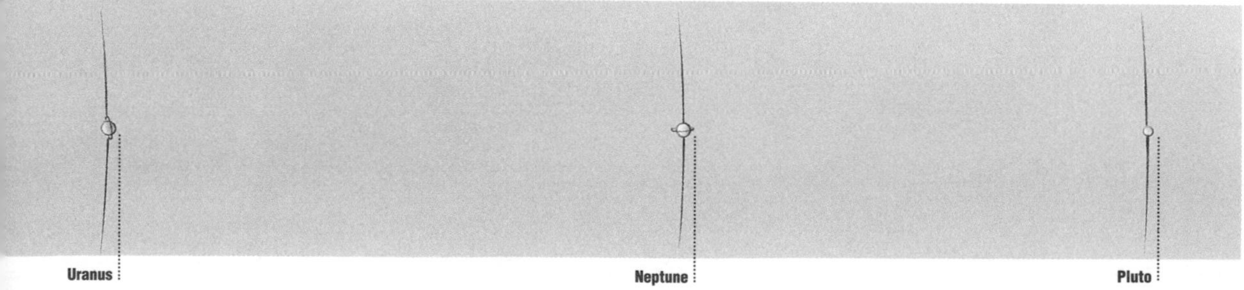

The Earth

History of the Earth

Estimated age of the Earth:
At least 4.6 billion (4,600,000,000) years.

Formation of the Earth:
It is generally thought that the Earth was formed from a cloud of gas and dust (A) revolving around the early Sun. Gravitational forces pulled the cloud's particles together into an ever denser mass (B), with heavier particles sinking to the center. Heat from radioactive elements caused the materials of the embryonic Earth to melt and gradually settle into core and mantle layers. As the surface cooled, a crust formed. Volcanic activity released vast amounts of steam, carbon dioxide and other gases from the Earth's interior. The steam condensed into water to form the oceans, and the gases, prevented by gravity from escaping, formed the beginnings of the atmosphere (C).

The calm appearance of our planet today (D) belies the intense heat of its interior and the violent tectonic forces which are constantly reshaping its surface.

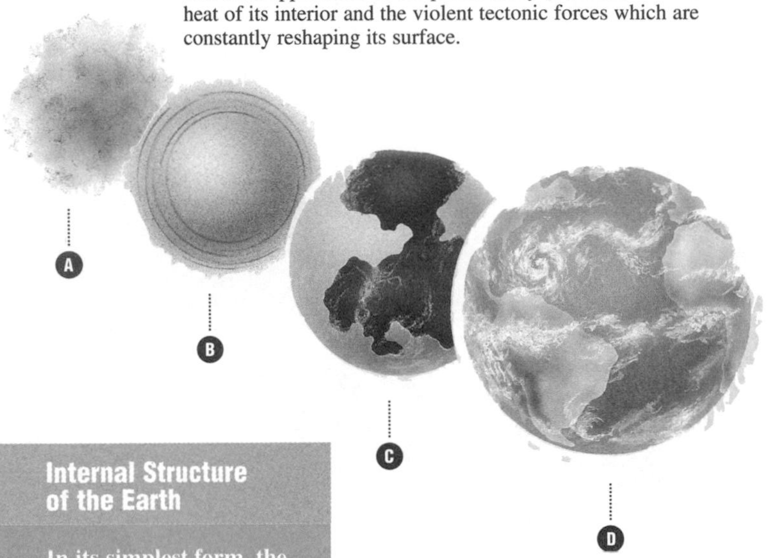

Periods in Earth's history

Earth's history is divided into different **eras**, which are subdivided into **periods**.

The most recent periods are themselves subdivided into **epochs**. The main divisions and subdivisions are shown below.

	Began (million years ago)	Ended (million years ago)	
Precambrian Era			
Archean Period	3,800	2,500	Start of life
Proterozoic Period	2,500	590	Life in the seas
Paleozoic Era			
Cambrian Period	590	500	Sea life
Ordovician Period	505	438	First fishes
Silurian Period	438	408	First land plants
Devonian Period	408	360	Amphibians
Carboniferous Period	360	286	First reptiles
Permian Period	286	248	Spread of reptiles
Mesozoic Era			
Triassic Period	248	213	Reptiles and early mammals
Jurassic Period	213	144	Dinosaurs
Cretaceous Period	144	65	Dinosaurs, dying out at the end
Cenozoic Era			
Tertiary Period			
Paleocene	65	55	Large mammals
Eocene	55	38	Primates begin
Oligocene	38	25	Development of primates
Miocene	25	5	Modern-type animals
Pliocene	5	2	*Australopithecus* ape, ancestor to the human race
Quaternary Period			
Pleistocene	2	0.01	Ice ages; true humans
Holocene	0.01	Present	Modern humans

Source: *Atlas of the Universe* by Patrick Moore, Reed International Books Limited, 1994.

Internal Structure of the Earth

In its simplest form, the Earth is composed of a crust, a mantle with an upper and lower layer, and a core, which has an inner region.

Temperatures in the Earth increase with depth, as is observed in a deep mine shaft or bore-hole, but the prediction of temperatures within the Earth is made difficult by the fact that different rocks conduct heat at different rates: rock salt, for example, has 10 times the heat conductivity of coal. Also, estimates have to take into account the abundance of heat-generating atoms in a rock. Radioactive atoms are concentrated toward the Earth's surface, so the planet has, in effect, a thermal blanket to keep it warm. The temperature at the center of the Earth is believed to be approximately 5,400° F (3,000° C).

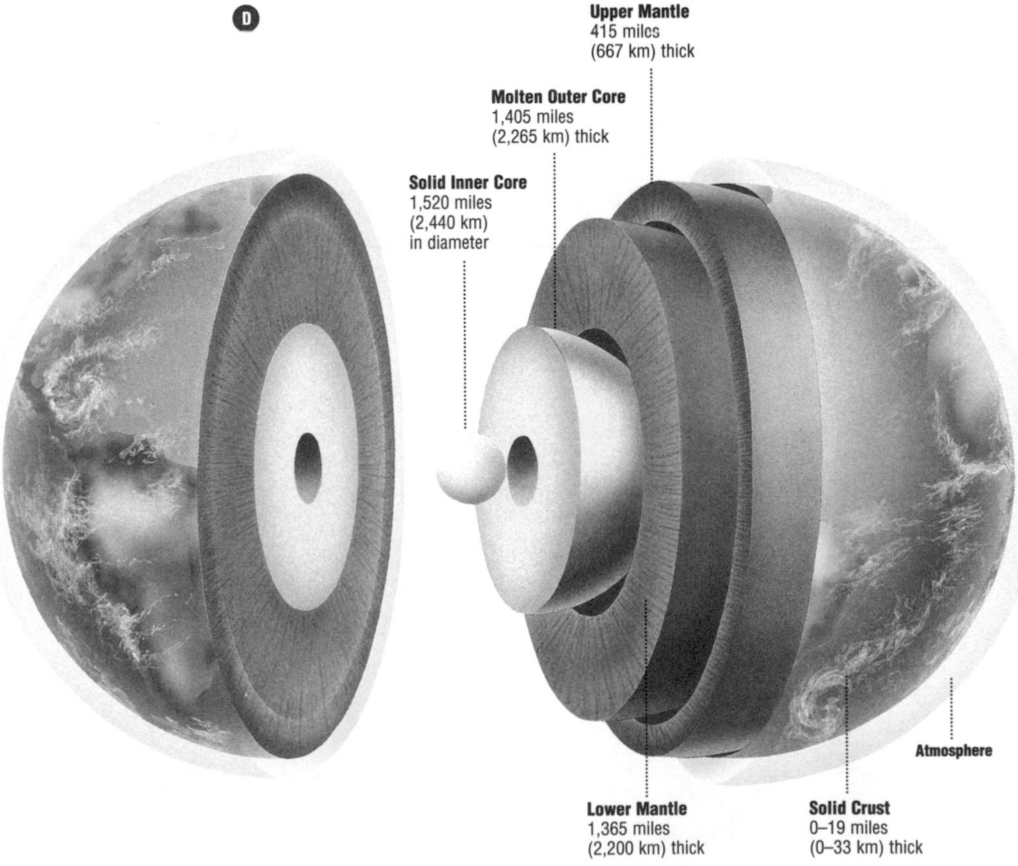

Chemical composition of the Earth:

The chemical composition of the Earth varies from crust to core. The upper crust of continents, called sial, is mainly granite, rich in aluminum and silicon. Oceanic crust, or sima, is largely basalt, made of magnesium and silicon. The mantle is composed of rocks that are rich in magnesium and iron silicates, whereas the core, it is believed, is made of iron and nickel oxides.

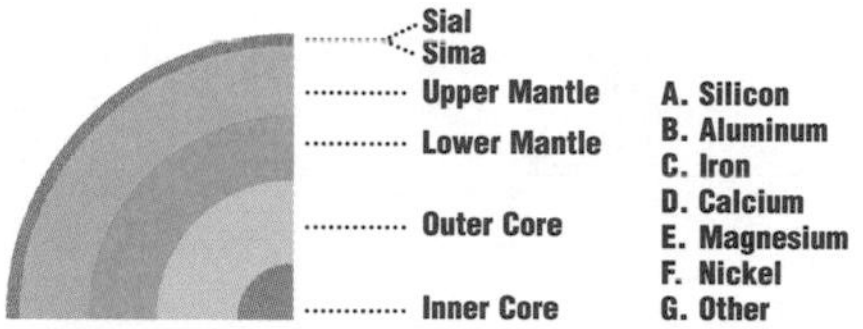

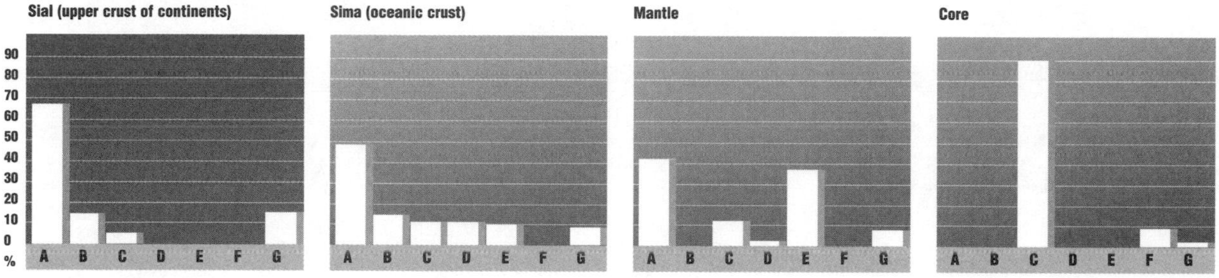

Measurements of the Earth

Equatorial circumference of the Earth: 24,901.45 miles (40,066.43 km)

Polar circumference of the Earth: 24,855.33 miles (39,992.22 km)

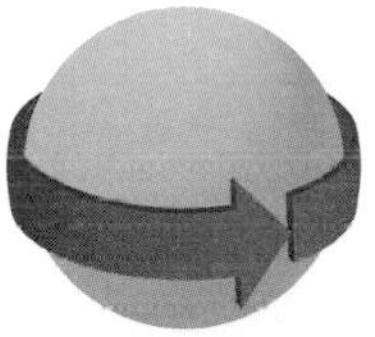

Equatorial diameter of the Earth: 7,926.38 miles (12,753.54 km)

Polar diameter of the Earth: 7,899.80 miles (12,710.77 km)

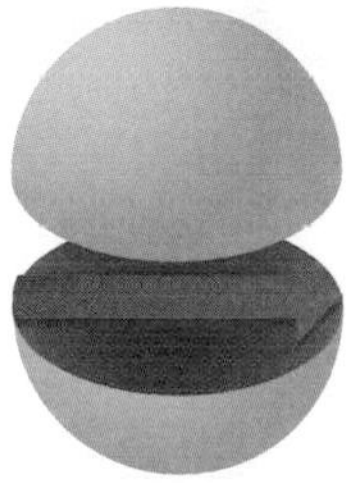

Equatorial radius of the Earth: 3,963.19 miles (6,376.77 km)

Polar radius of the Earth: 3,949.90 miles (6,355.38 km)

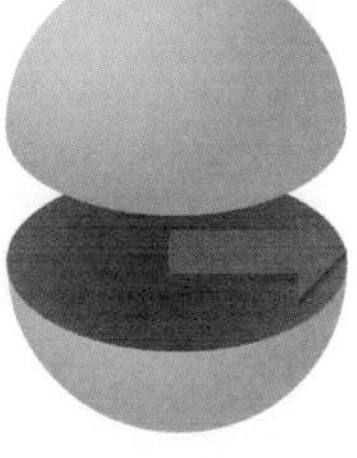

Estimated weight of the Earth: 6,600,000,000,000,000,000,000 tons, or 6,600 billion billion tons (5,940 billion billion metric tons)

Total surface area of the Earth: 197,000,000 square miles (510,230,000 sq km)

Total land area of the Earth (including inland water and Antarctica): 57,900,000 square miles (150,100,000 sq km)

Total ocean area of the Earth: 139,200,000 square miles (360,528,000 sq km), or 70% of the Earth's surface area

Total area of the Earth's surface covered with water (oceans and all inland water): 147,750,000 square miles (382,672,500 sq km), or 75% of the Earth's surface area

Types of water: 97% of the Earth's water is salt water; 3% is fresh water

Life on Earth

Number of plant species on Earth: About 350,000

Number of animal species on Earth: More than one million

Estimated total human population of the Earth: 6,195,885,000

Movements of the Earth

Mean distance of the Earth from the Sun: About 93 million miles (149.6 million km)

Period in which the Earth makes one complete orbit around the Sun: 365 days, 5 hours, 48 minutes, and 46 seconds

Speed of the Earth as it orbits the Sun: 66,700 miles (107,320 km) per hour

Period in which the Earth makes one complete rotation on its axis: 23 hours, 56 minutes and 4 seconds

Equatorial speed at which the Earth rotates on its axis: More than 1,000 miles (1,600 km) per hour

The Shape of the Earth

Comparing the Earth's equatorial and polar dimensions reveals that our planet is actually not a perfect sphere but rather an oblate spheroid, flattened at the poles and bulging at the equator. This is the result of a combination of gravitational and centrifugal forces.

An even more precise term for the Earth's shape is "geoid" — the actual shape of sea level, which is lumpy, with variations away from spheroid of up to 260 feet (80 m). This lumpiness reflects major variations in density in the Earth's outer layers.

The Seasons (Northern Hemisphere)

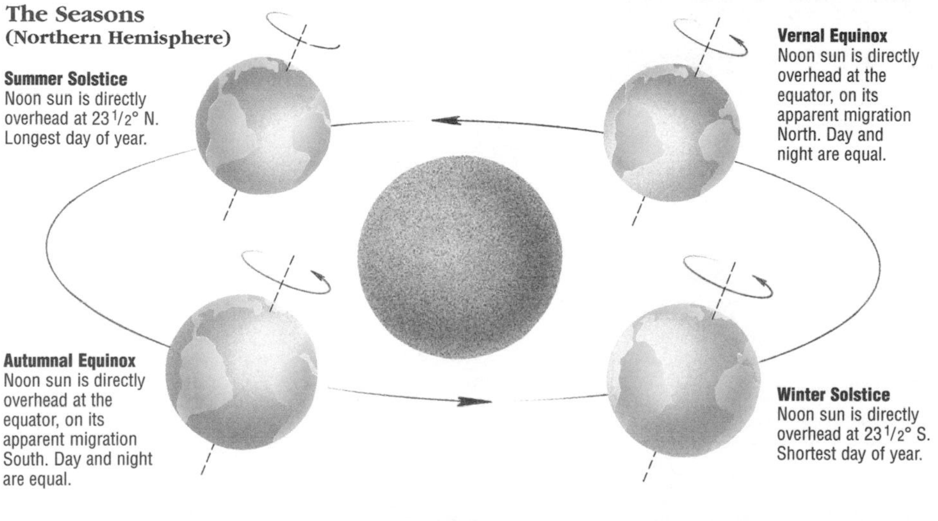

Summer Solstice
Noon sun is directly overhead at 23 1/2° N. Longest day of year.
Vernal Equinox
Noon sun is directly overhead at the equator, on its apparent migration North. Day and night are equal.
Autumnal Equinox
Noon sun is directly overhead at the equator, on its apparent migration South. Day and night are equal.
Winter Solstice
Noon sun is directly overhead at 23 1/2° S. Shortest day of year.

Plate Tectonics

Continental Drift

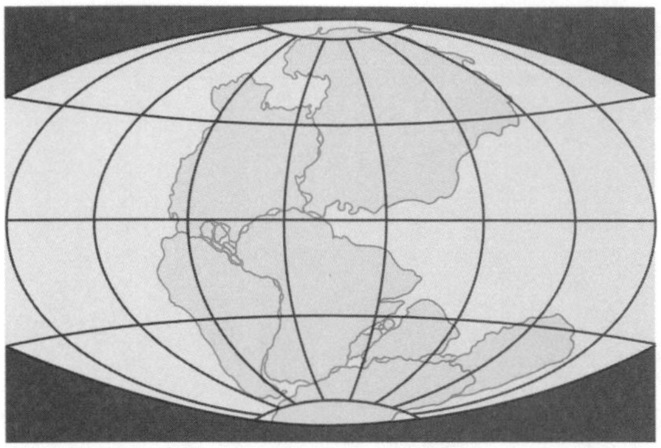

225 million years ago the supercontinent of Pangaea exists and Panthalassa forms the ancestral ocean. Tethys Sea separates Eurasia and Africa.

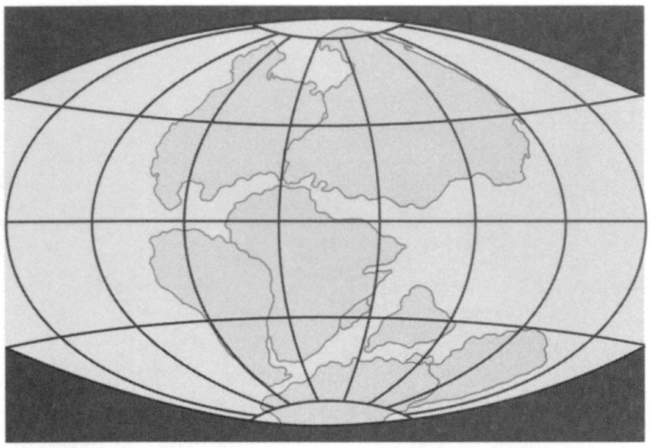

180 million years ago Pangaea splits, Laurasia drifts north. Gondwanaland breaks into South America/Africa, India, and Australia/Antarctica.

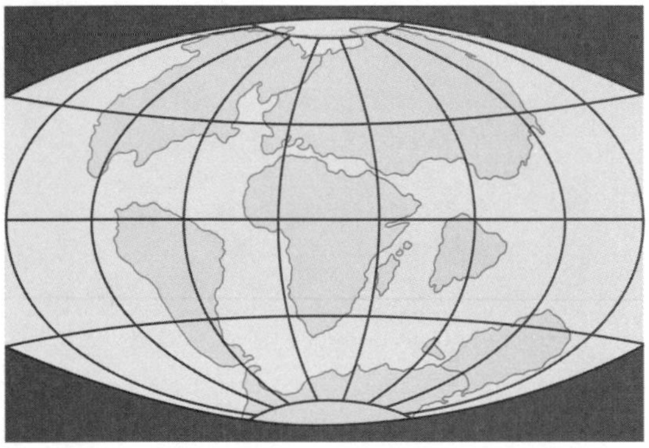

65 million years ago ocean basins take shape as South America and India move from Africa and the Tethys Sea closes to form the Mediterranean Sea.

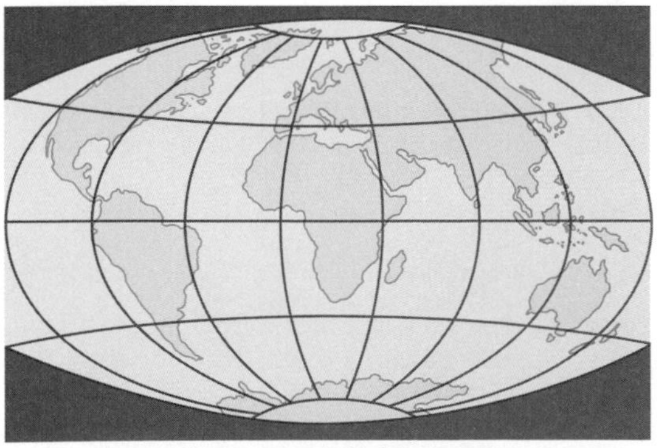

The present day: India has merged with Asia, Australia is free of Antarctica, and North America is free of Eurasia.

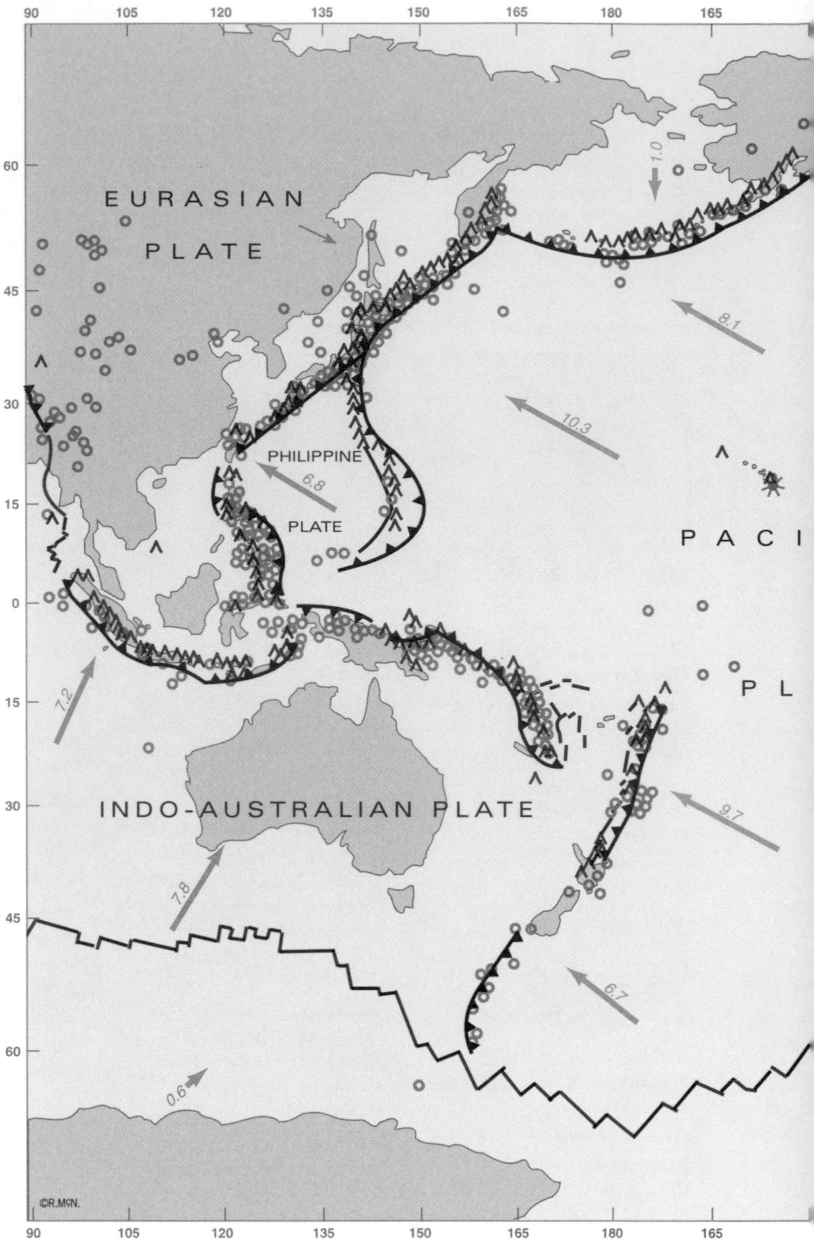

PLATE TECTONICS

Types of plate boundaries

Divergent: magma emerges from the earth's mantle at the mid-ocean ridges forming new crust and forcing the plates to spread apart at the ridges.

Convergent: plates collide at subduction zones where the denser plate is forced back into the earth's mantle forming deep ocean trenches.

Transform: plates slide past one another producing faults and fracture zones.

Other map symbols

Direction of plate movement

6.7 Length of arrow is proportional to the amount of plate movement (number indicates centimeters of movement per year)

Earthquake of magnitude 7.5 and above (from 10 A.D. to the present)

Volcano (eruption since 1900)

Selected hot spots

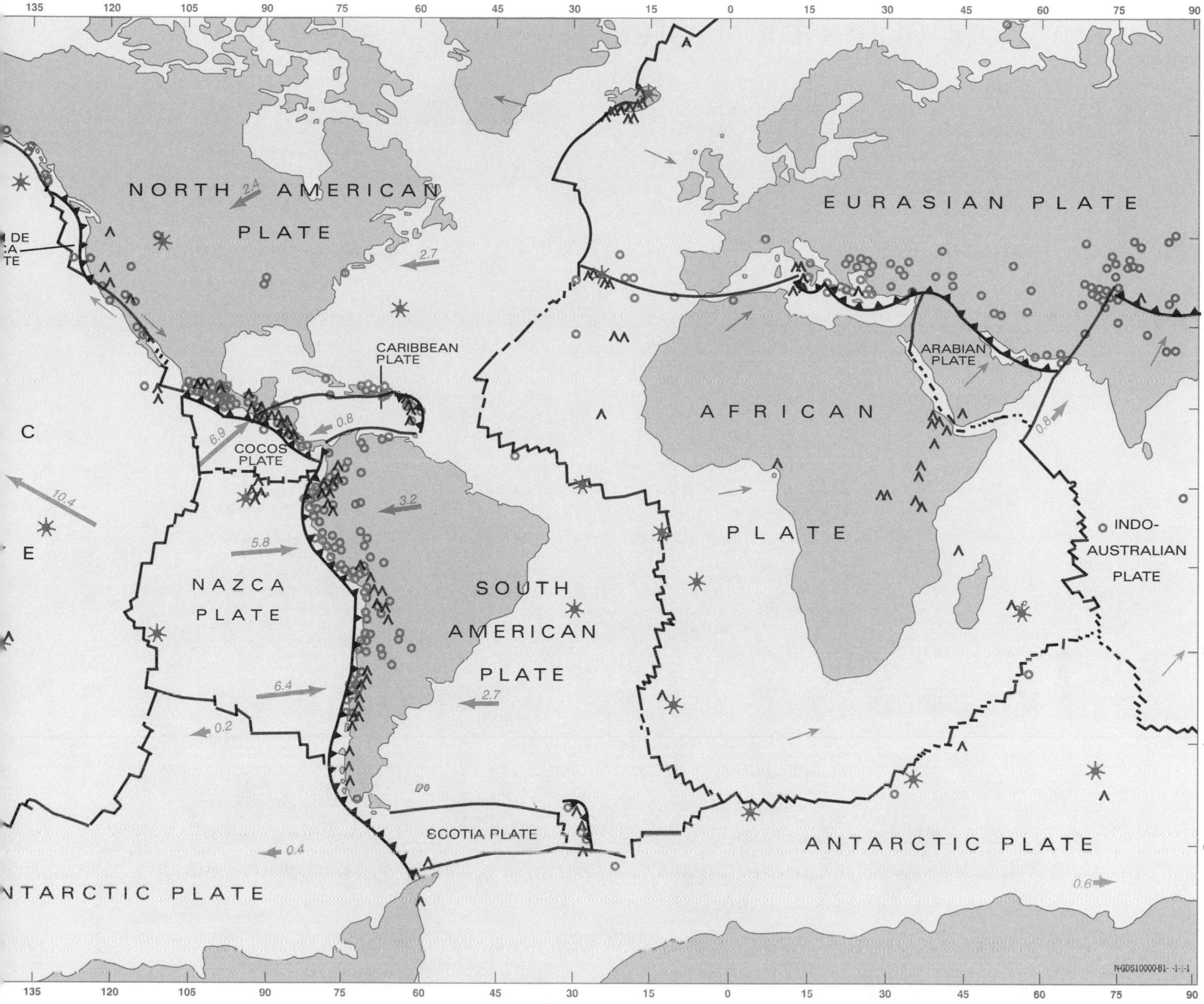

According to plate tectonic theory, Earth's lithosphere—the crust and uppermost rigid part of the mantle—is divided into plates that move relative to one another. The map above shows the locations and names of the major plates.

These rigid plates move on a molten layer of Earth's mantle called the asthenosphere. The moving plates meet at three different types of boundaries—divergent, convergent, and transform. (See map legend at the left.)

Divergent Boundaries

At divergent boundaries, plates are pushed apart by currents in the asthenosphere in a process called rifting. Most rifting occurs on the ocean floors. In ocean floor rifting, molten material from the asthenosphere wells up between the separated plates, hardens, and forms ridges. (See World Physical Map and Ocean Depths Profile, pages 54 and 55.) This process of adding to the Earth's crust is called seafloor spreading.

Convergent Boundaries

At convergent boundaries, the moving plates collide with one another. The edge of the heavier plate sinks under the crust of the lighter plate, and is consumed back into Earth's mantle in a process called subduction. Subduction can create deep ocean trenches as the crust of the lighter plate sinks into the mantle. (See World Physical Map, pages 54 and 55.) The colliding plates also create mountain chains as the lighter plate is pushed up over the heavier plate.

Transform Boundaries

When plates meet at transform boundaries or faults, they grind past each other. This movement neither increases nor destroys Earth's crust. The San Andreas Fault, north of San Francisco, is a famous example of a transform boundary.

Earthquakes and Volcanoes

Most of Earth's volcanoes and earthquakes occur along plate boundaries. The ring of volcanic and seismic activity along the west coasts of North and South America and the east coast of Asia, known as the Ring of Fire, follows plate boundaries. Volcanoes and earthquakes also occur at locations known as hot spots, where hot rock from deep in the mantle rises to the surface, creating some of Earth's tallest mountains.

Continental Drift

Plate tectonic theory assumes that the rigid plates have moved slowly through the millennia, carrying the continents with them. The history of this continental drifting is illustrated by the four maps to the left.

Continents and Islands

The word "continents" designates the largest continuous masses of land in the world.

For reasons that are mainly historical, seven continents are generally recognized: Africa, Antarctica, Asia, Australia, Europe, North America, and South America. Since Asia and Europe actually share the same land mass, they are sometimes identified as a single continent, Eurasia.

The lands of the central and south Pacific, including Australia, New Zealand, Micronesia, Melanesia, and Polynesia, are sometimes grouped together as Oceania.

The Continents

Africa

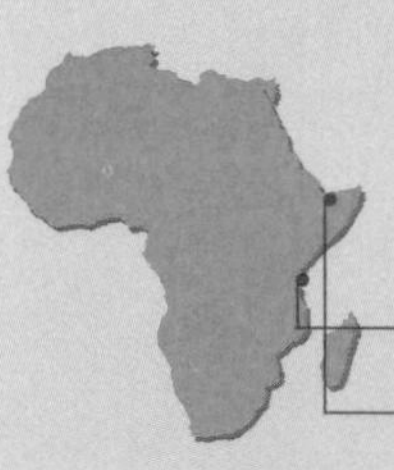

Area in square miles (sq km):
11,700,000 (30,300,000)
Estimated population:
832,590,000
Population per square mile (sq km):
71 (27)
Mean elevation in feet (meters):
1,900 (580)
Highest elevation in feet (meters):
Kilimanjaro, Tanzania, 19,340 (5,895)
Lowest elevation in feet (meters):
Lac Assal, Djibouti, 515 (157) below sea level

Antarctica

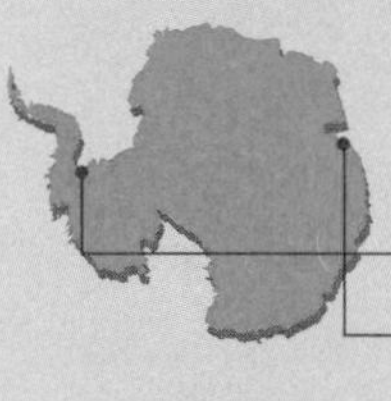

Area in square miles (sq km):
5,400,000 (14,000,000)
Estimated population:
Uninhabited
Population per square mile (sq km):
0 (0)
Mean elevation in feet (meters):
6,000 (1,830)
Highest elevation in feet (meters):
Vinson Massif, 16,066 (4,897)
Lowest elevation in feet (meters):
Deep Lake, 184 (56) below sea level

Asia

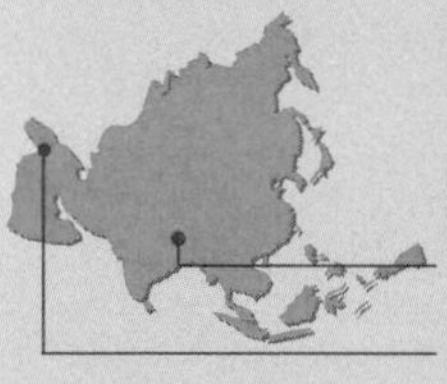

Area in square miles (sq km):
17,300,000 (44,900,000)
Estimated population:
3,761,165,000
Population per square mile (sq km):
217 (84)
Mean elevation in feet (meters):
3,000 (910)
Highest elevation in feet (meters):
Mt. Everest, China (Tibet)–Nepal, 29,028 (8,848)
Lowest elevation in feet (meters):
Dead Sea, Israel–Jordan, 1,339 (408) below sea level

Australia

Area in square miles (sq km):
2,966,155 (7,682,300)
Estimated population:
19,455,000
Population per square mile (sq km):
6.6 (2.5)
Mean elevation in feet (meters):
1,000 (305)
Highest elevation in feet (meters):
Mt. Kosciuszko, New South Wales, 7,313 (2,229)
Lake Eyre, South Australia, 52 (16) below sea level

Europe

Area in square miles (sq km):
3,800,000 (9,900,000)
Estimated population:
728,975,000
Population per square mile (sq km):
192 (74)
Mean elevation in feet (meters):
980 (300)
Highest elevation in feet (meters):
Gora El'brus, Russia, 18,510 (5,642)
Lowest elevation in feet (meters):
Caspian Sea, Asia-Europe, 92 (28) below sea level

North America

Area in square miles (sq km):
9,500,000 (24,700,000)
Estimated population:
488,780,000
Population per square mile (sq km):
51 (20)
Mean elevation in feet (meters):
2,000 (610)
Highest elevation in feet (meters):
Mt. McKinley, Alaska, U.S., 20,320 (6,194)
Lowest elevation in feet (meters):
Death Valley, California, U.S.,
282 (86) below sea level

Oceania *(incl. Australia)*

Area in square miles (sq km):
3,300,000 (8,500,000)
Estimated population:
31,415,000
Population per square mile (sq km):
9.5 (3.7)
Mean elevation in feet (meters):
0 (0)
Highest elevation in feet (meters):
Mt. Wilhelm, Papua New Guinea, 14,793 (4,509)
Lowest elevation in feet (meters):
Lake Eyre, South Australia, 52 (16) below sea level

South America

Area in square miles (sq km):
6,900,000 (17,800,000)
Estimated population:
352,960,000
Population per square mile (sq km):
51 (20)
Mean elevation in feet (meters):
1,800 (550)
Highest elevation in feet (meters):
Cerro Aconcagua, Argentina, 22,831 (6,959)
Lowest elevation in feet (meters):
Salinas Chicas, Argentina, 138 (42) below sea level

World

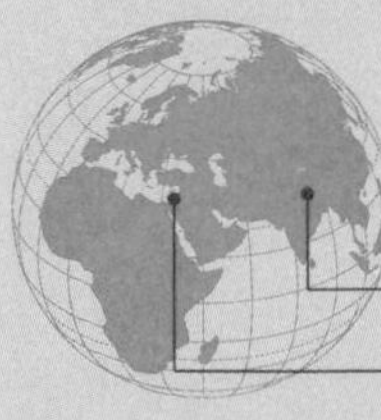

Area in square miles (sq km):
57,900,000 (150,100,000)
Estimated population:
6,195,885,000
Population per square mile (sq km):
107 (41)
Mean elevation in feet (meters):
0 (0)
Highest elevation in feet (meters):
Mt. Everest, China (Tibet)–Nepal, 29,028 (8,848)
Lowest elevation in feet (meters):
Dead Sea, Israel–Jordan,
1,339 (408) below sea level

Largest Islands

Rank	Name	Area square miles	Area square km
1	Greenland, North America	840,000	2,175,600
2	New Guinea, Asia-Oceania	309,000	800,000
3	Borneo (Kalimantan), Asia	287,300	744,100
4	Madagascar, Africa	226,500	587,000
5	Baffin Island, Canada	195,928	507,451
6	Sumatra (Sumatera), Indonesia	182,860	473,606
7	Honshū, Japan	89,176	230,966
8	Great Britain, United Kingdom	88,795	229,978
9	Victoria Island, Canada	83,897	217,291
10	Ellesmere Island, Canada	75,767	196,236
11	Celebes (Sulawesi), Indonesia	73,057	189,216
12	South Island, New Zealand	57,708	149,463
13	Java (Jawa), Indonesia	51,038	132,187
14	North Island, New Zealand	44,332	114,821
15	Cuba, North America	42,800	110,800
16	Newfoundland, Canada	42,031	108,860
17	Luzon, Philippines	40,420	104,688
18	Iceland, Europe	39,800	103,000
19	Mindanao, Philippines	36,537	94,630
20	Ireland, Europe	32,600	84,400
21	Hokkaidō, Japan	32,245	83,515
22	Sakhalin, Russia	29,500	76,400
23	Hispaniola, North America	29,400	76,200
24	Banks Island, Canada	27,038	70,028
25	Tasmania, Australia	26,200	67,800
26	Sri Lanka, Asia	24,900	64,600
27	Devon Island, Canada	21,331	55,247
28	Berkner Island, Antarctica	20,005	51,829
29	Alexander Island, Antarctica	19,165	49,652
30	Tierra del Fuego, South America	18,600	48,200
31	Novaya Zemlya, north island, Russia	18,436	47,764
32	Kyūshū, Japan	17,129	44,363
33	Melville Island, Canada	16,274	42,149
34	Southampton Island, Canada	15,913	41,214
35	Axel Heiberg, Canada	15,498	40,151
36	Spitsbergen, Norway	15,260	39,523
37	New Britain, Papua New Guinea	14,093	36,500
38	Taiwan, Asia	13,900	36,000
39	Hainan Dao, China	13,100	34,000
40	Prince of Wales Island, Canada	12,872	33,339
41	Novaya Zemlya, south island, Russia	12,633	32,730
42	Vancouver Island, Canada	12,079	31,285
43	Sicily, Italy	9,926	25,700
44	Somerset Island, Canada	9,570	24,786
45	Sardinia, Italy	9,301	24,090
46	Bathurst Island, Canada	7,600	19,684
47	Shikoku, Japan	7,258	18,799
48	Ceram (Seram), Indonesia	7,191	18,625
49	North East Land, Norway	6,350	16,446
50	New Caledonia, Oceania	6,252	16,192
51	Prince Patrick Island, Canada	5,986	15,509
52	Timor, Asia	5,743	14,874
53	Sumbawa, Indonesia	5,549	14,377
54	Ostrov Oktyabr'skoy Revolyutsii, Russia	5,511	14,279
55	Flores, Indonesia	5,502	14,250
56	Samar, Philippines	5,100	13,080
57	King William Island, Canada	4,961	12,853
58	Negros, Philippines	4,907	12,710
59	Thurston Island, Antarctica	4,854	12,576
60	Palawan, Philippines	4,550	11,785

Islands, Islands, Everywhere

Four islands—Hokkaidō, Honshū, Kyūshū, and Shikoku—constitute 98% of Japan's total land area, but the country is actually comprised of more than 3,000 islands. Similarly, two islands—Great Britain and Ireland—make up 93% of the total land area of the British Isles, but the island group also includes more than 5,000 smaller islands.

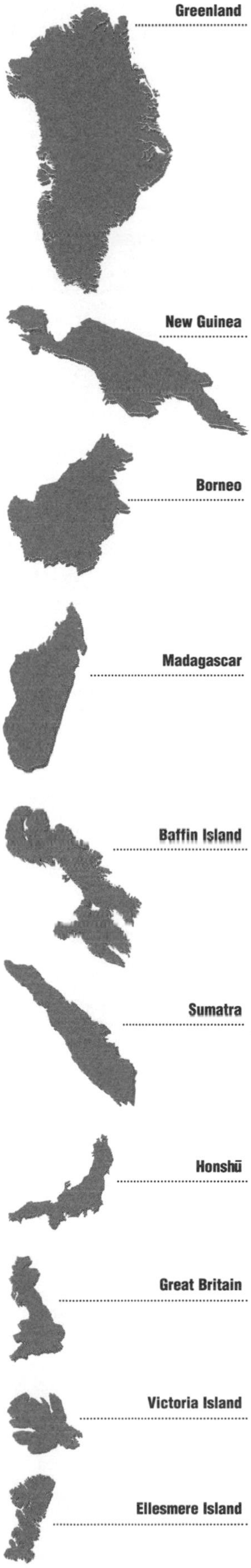

Major World Island Groups

- Aleutian Islands (Pacific Ocean)
- Alexander Archipelago (Pacific Ocean)
- Azores (Atlantic Ocean)
- Bahamas (Atlantic Ocean)
- Balearic Islands (Mediterranean Sea)
- Bismarck Archipelago (Pacific Ocean)
- British Isles (Atlantic Ocean)
- Cape Verde Islands (Atlantic Ocean)
- Dodecanese (Mediterranean Sea)
- Faroe Islands (Atlantic Ocean)
- Falkland Islands (Atlantic Ocean)
- Fiji Islands (Pacific Ocean)
- Galapagos Islands (Pacific Ocean)
- Greater Sunda Islands (Indian/Pacific Oceans)
- Hawai'ian Islands (Pacific Ocean)
- Ionian Islands (Mediterranean Sea)
- Islas Canarias (Atlantic Ocean)
- Japan (Pacific Ocean)
- Kikládhes (Mediterranean Sea)
- Kuril Islands (Pacific Ocean)
- Lesser Sunda Islands (Indian Ocean)
- Moluccas (Pacific Ocean)
- Nansei Shotō (Pacific Ocean)
- New Hebrides (Atlantic Ocean)
- New Siberian Islands (Arctic Ocean)
- Novaya Zemlya (Arctic Ocean)
- Philippine Islands (Pacific Ocean)
- Severnaya Zemlya (Arctic Ocean)
- Solomon Islands (Pacific Ocean)
- Spitsbergen (Arctic Ocean)
- West Indies (Atlantic Ocean)

Contrasting Population Densities

Some islands are among the most densely populated places on Earth, while others are among the least densely populated. This fact is dramatically illustrated by the following comparison of five islands:

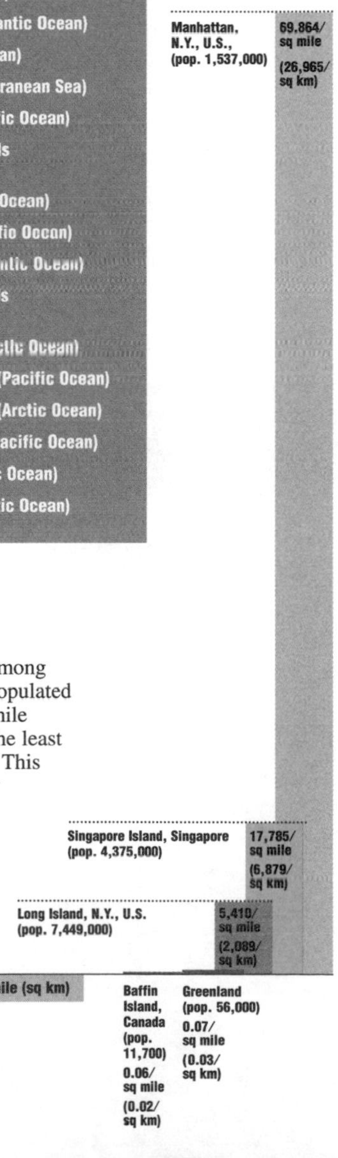

Mountains, Volcanoes, and Earthquakes

The Tallest Mountain in the World

With its peak reaching 29,028 feet (8,848 m) above sea level, Mt. Everest ranks as the *highest* mountain in the world, but not the *tallest.* That title goes to Mauna Kea, one of the five volcanic mountains that make up the island of Hawai'i. From its base on the floor of the Pacific Ocean, Mauna Kea rises 33,476 feet (10,210 m)—more than six miles—although only the top 13,796 feet (4,205 m) are above sea level.

Seafloor Atop Mt. Everest

When Sir Edmund Percival Hillary and Tenzing Norgay reached the summit of Mt. Everest in 1953, they probably did not realize they were standing on the seafloor.

The Himalayan mountain system was formed through the process of plate tectonics. Ocean once separated India and Asia, but 180 million years ago the Indo-Australian crustal plate, on which India sits, began a northward migration and eventually collided with the Eurasian plate. The seafloor between the two landmasses crumpled and was slowly thrust upward. Rock layers that once lay at the bottom of the ocean now crown the peaks of the highest mountains in the world.

Principal Mountain Systems and Ranges of the World

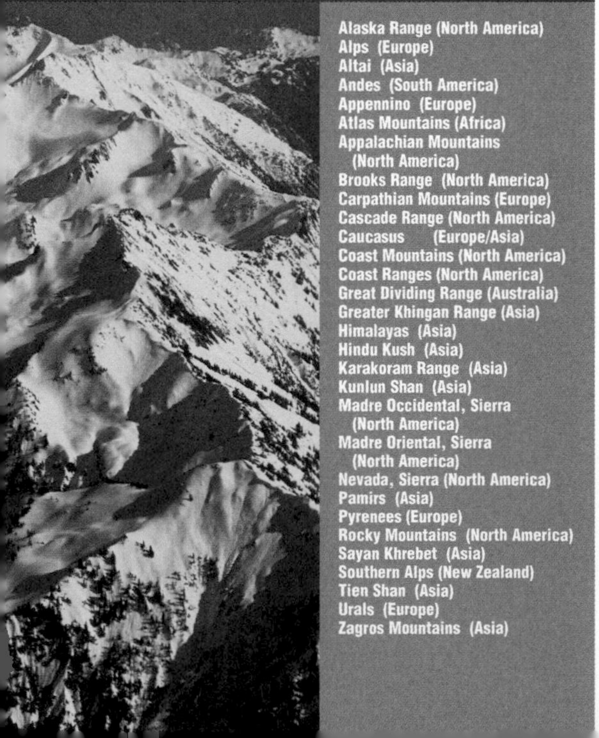

- Alaska Range (North America)
- Alps (Europe)
- Altai (Asia)
- Andes (South America)
- Appennino (Europe)
- Atlas Mountains (Africa)
- Appalachian Mountains (North America)
- Brooks Range (North America)
- Carpathian Mountains (Europe)
- Cascade Range (North America)
- Caucasus (Europe/Asia)
- Coast Mountains (North America)
- Coast Ranges (North America)
- Great Dividing Range (Australia)
- Greater Khingan Range (Asia)
- Himalayas (Asia)
- Hindu Kush (Asia)
- Karakoram Range (Asia)
- Kunlun Shan (Asia)
- Madre Occidental, Sierra (North America)
- Madre Oriental, Sierra (North America)
- Nevada, Sierra (North America)
- Pamirs (Asia)
- Pyrenees (Europe)
- Rocky Mountains (North America)
- Sayan Khrebet (Asia)
- Southern Alps (New Zealand)
- Tien Shan (Asia)
- Urals (Europe)
- Zagros Mountains (Asia)

Principal Mountains of the World

Δ = *Highest mountain in range, region, country, or state named*

Location	Height: Feet	Height: Meters
Africa		
Kilimanjaro, Δ Tanzania (Δ Africa)	19,340	5,895
Kirinyaga (Mount Kenya), Δ Kenya	17,058	5,199
Margherita Peak, Δ Uganda-Δ Dem. Rep. of the Congo	16,763	5,109
Ras Dashen Terara, Δ Ethiopia	15,158	4,620
Meru, Mount, Tanzania	14,978	4,565
Karisimbi, Volcan, Δ Rwanda-Dem. Rep. of the Congo	14,787	4,507
Elgon, Mount, Kenya-Uganda	14,178	4,321
Toubkal, Jebel, Δ Morocco (Δ Atlas Mts.)	13,665	4,165
Cameroon Mountain, Δ Cameroon	13,451	4,100
Antarctica		
Vinson Massif, Δ Antarctica	16,066	4,897
Kirkpatrick, Mount	14,856	4,528
Markham, Mount	14,049	4,282
Jackson, Mount	13,747	4,190
Sidley, Mount	13,717	4,181
Wade, Mount	13,396	4,083
Asia		
Everest, Mount, Δ China-Δ Nepal (Δ Tibet; Δ Himalayas; Δ Asia; Δ World)	29,028	8,848
K2 (Qogir Feng), China-Δ Pakistan (Δ Kashmir; Δ Karakoram Range)	28,250	8,611
Kanchenjunga, Δ India-Nepal	28,208	8,598
Makalu, China-Nepal	27,825	8,481
Dhawalāgiri, Nepal	26,810	8,172
Nanga Parbat, Pakistan	26,660	8,126
Annapurna, Nepal	26,504	8,078
Gasherbrum, China-Pakistan	26,470	8,068
Xixabangma Feng, China	26,286	8,012
Nanda Devi, India	25,645	7,817
Kamet, China-India	25,447	7,756
Namjagbarwa Feng, China	25,446	7,756
Muztag, China (Δ Kunlun Shan)	25,338	7,723
Tirich Mir, Pakistan (Δ Hindu Kush)	25,230	7,690
Gongga Shan, China	24,790	7,556
Kula Kangri, Δ Bhutan	24,784	7,554
Ismail Samani, pik, Δ Tajikistan (Δ Pamir)	24,590	7,495
Nowshak, Δ Afghanistan-Pakistan	24,557	7,485
Pobedy, Pik, China-Russia	24,406	7,439
Chomo Lhari, Bhutan-China	23,997	7,314
Muztag, China	23,891	7,282
Lenina, Pik, Δ Kyrgyzstan-Tajikistan	23,406	7,134
Api, Nepal	23,399	7,132
Kangrinboqê Feng, China	22,028	6,714
Hkakabo Razi, Δ Myanmar	19,296	5,881
Damavand, Qolleh-ye, Δ Iran	18,386	5,604
Agri Dagi (Mount Ararat), Δ Turkey	16,854	5,137
Fuladi, Kuh-e, Afghanistan	16,847	5,135
Jaya, Puncak, Δ Indonesia (Δ New Guinea)	16,503	5,030
Klyuchevskaya, Vulkan, Russia (Δ Poluostrov Kamchatka)	15,584	4,750
Trikora, Puncak, Indonesia	15,584	4,750
Belukha, Gora, Kazakhstan-Russia	14,783	4,506
Turgen, Mount, Mongolia	14,311	4,362
Kinabalu, Gunong, Δ Malaysia (Δ Borneo)	13,455	4,101
Yü Shan, Δ Taiwan	13,114	3,997
Erciyes Dagı, Turkey	12,851	3,917
Kerinci, Gunung, Indonesia (Δ Sumatra)	12,467	3,800
Fuji San, Δ Japan (Δ Honshu)	12,388	3,776
Rinjani, Gunung, Indonesia (Δ Lombok)	12,224	3,726
Semeru, Gunung, Indonesia (Δ Java)	12,060	3,676
Hadūr Shu'ayb, Jabal an-, Δ Yemen (Δ Arabian Peninsula)	12,008	3,660
Australia / Oceania		
Wilhelm, Mt., Δ Papua New Guinea	14,793	4,509
Giluwe, Mt., Papua New Guinea	14,330	4,368
Bangeta, Mt., Papua New Guinea	13,520	4,121
Victoria, Mt., Papua New Guinea (Δ Owen Stanley Range)	13,238	4,035
Aoraki (Mt. Cook), Δ New Zealand (Δ South Island)	12,316	3,754
Europe		
El'brus, Gora, Δ Russia (Δ Caucasus; Δ Europe)	18,510	5,642
Dykhtau, Mt., Russia	17,073	5,204
Blanc, Mont (Monte Bianco) Δ France-Δ Italy (Δ Alps)	15,771	4,807
Dufourspitze, Italy-Δ Switzerland	15,203	4,634
Weisshorn, Switzerland	14,783	4,506
Matterhorn, Italy-Switzerland	14,692	4,478
Finsteraarhorn, Switzerland	14,022	4,274
Jungfrau, Switzerland	13,642	4,158
Écrins, Barre des, France	13,458	4,102
Viso, Monte, Italy (Δ Cottian Alps)	12,602	3,841
Grossglockner, Δ Austria	12,461	3,798
Teide, Pico de, Δ Spain (Δ Canary Is.)	12,188	3,715
North America		
McKinley, Mt., Δ Alaska (Δ United States; Δ North America)	20,320	6,194
Logan, Mt., Δ Canada (Δ Yukon; Δ St. Elias Mts.)	19,551	5,959
Orizaba, Pico de, Δ Mexico	18,406	5,610
St. Elias, Mt., Alaska-Canada	18,008	5,489
Popocatépetl, Volcán, Mexico	17,930	5,465
Foraker, Mt., Alaska	17,400	5,304
Iztaccíhuatl, Mexico	17,159	5,230
Lucania, Mt., Canada	17,147	5,226
Fairweather, Mt., Alaska-Canada (Δ British Columbia)	15,300	4,663
Whitney, Mt., Δ California	14,494	4,418
Elbert, Mt., Δ Colorado (Δ Rocky Mts.)	14,433	4,399
Massive, Mt., Colorado	14,421	4,396
Harvard, Mt., Colorado	14,420	4,395
Rainier, Mt., Δ Washington (Δ Cascade Range)	14,410	4,392
Williamson, Mt., California	14,370	4,380
La Plata Pk., Colorado	14,361	4,377
Blanca Pk., Colorado (Δ Sangre de Cristo Mts.)	14,345	4,372
Uncompahgre Pk., Colorado (Δ San Juan Mts.)	14,309	4,361
Grays Pk., Colorado (Δ Front Range)	14,270	4,349
Evans, Mt., Colorado	14,264	4,348
Longs Pk., Colorado	14,255	4,345
Wrangell, Mt., Alaska	14,163	4,317
Shasta, Mt., California	14,162	4,317
Pikes Pk., Colorado	14,110	4,301
Colima, Nevado de, Mexico	13,991	4,240
Tajumulco, Volcán, Δ Guatemala (Δ Central America)	13,845	4,220
Gannett Pk., Δ Wyoming	13,804	4,207
Mauna Kea, Δ Hawaii	13,796	4,205
Grand Teton, Wyoming	13,770	4,197
Mauna Loa, Hawaii	13,679	4,169
Kings Pk., Δ Utah	13,528	4,123
Cloud Pk., Wyoming (Δ Bighorn Mts.)	13,167	4,013
Waddington, Mt., Canada (Δ Coast Mts.)	13,163	4,012
Wheeler Pk., Δ New Mexico	13,161	4,011
Boundary Pk., Δ Nevada	13,140	4,005
Robson, Mt., Canada (Δ Canadian Rockies)	12,972	3,954
Granite Pk., Δ Montana	12,799	3,901
Borah Pk., Δ Idaho	12,662	3,859
Humphreys Pk., Δ Arizona	12,633	3,851
Chirripó, Volcán, Δ Costa Rica	12,530	3,819
Columbia, Mt., Canada (Δ Alberta)	12,294	3,747
Adams, Mt., Washington	12,276	3,742
Gunnbjørn Fjeld, Δ Greenland	12,139	3,700
South America		
Aconcagua, Cerro, Δ Argentina (Δ Andes; Δ South America)	22,831	6,959
Ojos del Salado, Nevado, Argentina-Δ Chile	22,615	6,893
Bonete, Cerro, Argentina	22,546	6,872
Huascarán, Nevado, Δ Peru	22,133	6,746
Llullaillaco, Volcán, Argentina-Chile	22,110	6,739
Yerupaja, Nevado, Peru	21,765	6,634
Tupungato, Cerro, Argentina-Chile	21,555	6,570
Sajama, Nevado, Bolivia	21,463	6,542
Illampu, Nevado, Bolivia	21,066	6,421
Illimani, Nevado, Bolivia	20,741	6,322
Chimborazo, Δ Ecuador	20,702	6,310
Antofalla, Volcán, Argentina	20,013	6,100
Cotopaxi, Ecuador	19,347	5,897
Misti, Volcán, Peru	19,101	5,822
Huila, Nevado de, Colombia (Δ Cordillera Central)	18,865	5,750
Bolívar, Pico, Δ Venezuela	16,427	5,007

Notable Volcanic Eruptions

Year	Volcano Name, Location	Comments
ca. 4895 B.C.	Crater Lake, Oregon, U.S.	Collapse forms caldera that now contains Crater Lake.
ca. 4350 B.C.	Kikai, Ryukyu Islands, Japan	Japan's largest known eruption.
ca. 1628 B.C.	Santorini (Thira), Greece	Eruption devastates late Minoan civilization.
79 A.D.	Vesuvius (Vesuvio), Italy	Roman towns of Pompeii and Herculaneum are buried.
ca. 180	Taupo, New Zealand	Area measuring 6,200 square miles (16,000 sq km) is devastated.
ca. 260	Ilopango, El Salvador	Thousands killed, with major impact on Mayan civilization.
915	Towada, Honshu, Japan	Japan's largest historic eruption.
ca. 1000	Baitoushan, China/Korea	Largest known eruption on Asian mainland.
1259	Unknown	Evidence from polar ice cores suggests that a huge eruption, possibly the largest of the millennium, occurred in this year.
1586	Kelut, Java	Explosions in crater lake; mudflows kill 10,000.
1631	Vesuvius (Vesuvio), Italy	Eruption kills 4,000.
ca. 1660	Long Island, Papua New Guinea	"The time of darkness" in tribal legends on Papua New Guinea.
1672	Merapi, Java	Pyroclastic flows and mudflows kill 3,000.
1711	Awu, Sangihe Islands, Indonesia	Pyroclastic flows kill 3,000.
1760	Makian, Halmahera, Indonesia	Eruption kills 2,000; island evacuated for seven years.
1772	Papandayan, Java	Debris avalanche causes 2,957 fatalities.
1783	Lakagigar, Iceland	Largest historic lava flows; 9,350 deaths.
1790	Kīlauea, Hawai'i	Hawai'i's last large explosive eruption.
1792	Unzen, Kyushu, Japan	Tsunami and debris avalanche kill 14,500.
1815	Tambora, Indonesia	History's most explosive eruption; 92,000 deaths.
1822	Galunggung, Java	Pyroclastic flows and mudflows kill 4,011.
1856	Awu, Sangihe Islands, Indonesia	Pyroclastic flows kill 2,806.
1883	Krakatau, Indonesia	Caldera collapse; 36,417 people killed, most by tsunami.
1888	Ritter Island, Papua New Guinea	3,000 killed, most by tsunami created by debris avalanche.
1902	Mont Pelee, West Indies	Town of St. Pierre destroyed; 28,000 people killed.
1902	Santa Maria, Guatemala	5,000 killed as 10 villages are buried by volcanic debris.
1912	Novarupta (Katmai), Alaska	Largest 20th-century eruption.
1914	Lassen, California, U.S.	California's last historic eruption.
1919	Kelut, Java	Mudflows devastate 104 villages and kill 5,110 people.
1930	Merapi, Java	1,369 people are killed as 42 villages are totally or partially destroyed.
1943	Parícutin, Mexico	Fissure in cornfield erupts, building cinder cone 1,500 feet (460 m) high within two years. One of the few volcano births ever witnessed.
1951	Lamington, Papua New Guinea	Pyroclastic flows kill 2,942.
1963	Surtsey, Iceland	Submarine eruption builds new island.
1977	Nyiragongo, Dem. Rep. of the Congo	One of the shortest major eruptions and fastest lava flows ever recorded.
1980	St. Helens, Washington, U.S.	Lateral blast; 230-square-mile (600 sq km) area devastated.
1982	El Chichón, Mexico	Pyroclastic surges kill 1,877.
1985	Ruiz, Colombia	Mudflows kill 23,080.
1991	Pinatubo, Luzon, Philippines	Major eruption in densely populated area prompts evacuation of 250,000 people; fatalities number fewer than 800. Enormous amount of gas released into stratosphere lowers global temperatures for more than a year.
1995	Soufriere Hills Volcano, Montserrat Island	Forced evacuation of the southern half of the island, destroyed capital city of Plymouth.

Sources: Smithsonian Institution Global Volcanism Program; Volcanoes of the World, Second Edition, *by Tom Simkin and Lee Siebert, Geoscience Press and Smithsonian Institution, 1994. USGS National Earthquake Information Center.*

Eruption of Mt. St. Helens in 1980

Significant Earthquakes through History

Year	Estimated Magnitude	Number of Deaths	Place
365		50,000	Knossos, Crete
844		50,000	Damascus, Syria; Antioch, Turkey
856		150,000	Dāmghān, Kashan, Qumis, Iran
893		150,000	Caucasus region
894		180,000	western India
1042		50,000	Palmyra, Baalbek, Syria
1138		230,000	Aleppo, Gansana, Syria
1139	6.8	300,000	Gāncā, Kiapas, Azerbaijan
1201		50,000	upper Egypt to Syria
1290	6.7	100,000	eastern China
1556		820,000	Shanxi Province, China
1662		300,000	China
1667	6.9	80,000	Caucusus region, northern Iran
1668		50,000	Shandong Province, China
1693		93,000	Sicily, Italy
1727		77,000	Tabrīz, Iran
1731		100,000	Beijing, China
1739		50,000	China
1755		62,000	Morocco, Portugal, Spain
1780	6.7	100,000	Tabrīz, Iran
1868	7.7	70,000	Ecuador, Colombia
1908	7.5	83,000	Calabria, Messina, Italy
1920	8.5	200,000	Gansu and Shanxi provinces, China
1923	8.2	142,807	Tokyo, Yokohama, Japan
1927	8.3	200,000	Gansu and Qinghai provinces, China
1932	7.6	70,000	Gansu Province, China
1970	7.8	66,794	northern Peru
1976	7.8	242,000	Tangshan, China
1990	7.7	50,000	northwestern Iran

Some Significant U.S. Earthquakes

Year	Estimated Magnitude	Number of Deaths	Place
1811–12	8.6, 8.4, 8.7	<10	New Madrid, Missouri (series)
1886	7.0	60	Charleston, South Carolina
1906	8.3	3,000	San Francisco, California
1933	6.3	115	Long Beach, California
1946	7.4	5‡	Alaska
1964	8.4	125	Anchorage, Alaska
1971	6.8	65	San Fernando, California
1989	7.1	62	San Francisco Bay Area, California
1994	6.8	58	Northridge, California

‡ A tsunami generated by this earthquake struck Hilo, Hawaii, killing 159 people.

Oceans and Lakes

Oceans, Seas, Gulfs, and Bays

	Area		Volume of water		Mean depth		Greatest known depth		
	sq. miles	sq. km.	cubic miles	cubic km.	feet	meters	feet	meters	
Pacific Ocean	63,800,000	165,200,000	169,650,000	707,100,000	12,987	3,957	35,810	10,922	Mariana Trench
Atlantic Ocean	31,800,000	82,400,000	79,199,000	330,100,000	11,821	3,602	28,232	8,611	Puerto Rico Trench
Indian Ocean	28,900,000	74,900,000	68,282,000	284,600,000	12,261	3,736	23,812	7,258	Weber Basin
Arctic Ocean	5,400,000	14,000,000	4,007,000	16,700,000	3,712	1,131	17,897	5,453	Lat. 77° 45'N, long. 175°W
Coral Sea	1,850,000	4,791,000	2,752,000	11,470,000	7,857	2,394	30,079	9,165	
Arabian Sea	1,492,000	3,864,000	2,416,000	10,070,000	8,973	2,734	19,029	5,803	
South China Sea	1,331,000	3,447,000	943,000	3,929,000	3,741	1,140	18,241	5,563	
Caribbean Sea	1,063,000	2,753,000	1,646,000	6,860,000	8,175	2,491	25,197	7,685	Off Cayman Islands
Mediterranean Sea	967,000	2,505,000	901,000	3,754,000	4,916	1,498	16,470	5,023	Off Cape Matapan, Greece
Bering Sea	876,000	2,269,000	911,000	3,796,000	5,382	1,640	25,194	7,684	Off Buldir Island
Bengal, Bay of	839,000	2,173,000	1,357,000	5,616,000	8,484	2,585	17,251	5,261	
Okhotsk, Sea of	619,000	1,603,000	316,000	1,317,000	2,694	821	1,029	3,374	Lat. 146° 10'E, long. 46° 50'N
Norwegian Sea	597,000	1,546,000	578,000	2,408,000	5,717	1,742	13,189	4,022	
Mexico, Gulf of	596,000	1,544,000	560,000	2,332,000	8,205	2,500	14,370	4,382	Sigsbee Deep
Hudson Bay	475,000	1,230,000	22,000	92,000	328	100	850	259	Near entrance
Greenland Sea	465,000	1,204,000	417,000	1,740,000	4,739	1,444	15,899	4,849	
Japan, Sea of	413,000	1,070,000	391,000	1,630,000	5,037	1,535	12,041	3,669	
Arafura Sea	400,000	1,037,000	49,000	204,000	646	197	12,077	3,680	
East Siberian Sea	357,000	926,000	14,000	61,000	216	66	508	155	
Kara Sea	349,000	903,000	24,000	101,000	371	113	2,034	620	
East China Sea	290,000	752,000	63,000	263,000	1,145	349	7,778	2,370	
Banda Sea	268,000	695,000	511,000	2,129,000	10,056	3,064	24,418	7,440	
Baffin Bay	263,000	681,000	142,000	593,000	2,825	861	7,010	2,136	
Laptev Sea	262,000	678,000	87,000	363,000	1,772	540	9,780	2,980	
Timor Sea	237,000	615,000	60,000	250,000	1,332	406	10,863	3,310	
Andaman Sea	232,000	602,000	158,000	660,000	3,597	1,096	13,777	4,198	
Chukchi Sea	228,000	590,000	11,000	45,000	252	77	525	160	
North Sea	214,000	554,000	12,000	52,000	315	96	2,655	809	
Java Sea	185,000	480,000	5,000	22,000	147	45	292	89	
Beaufort Sea	184,000	476,000	115,000	478,000	3,295	1,004	12,245	3,731	
Red Sea	174,000	450,000	60,000	251,000	1,831	558	8,648	2,635	
Baltic Sea	173,000	448,000	5,000	20,000	157	48	1,506	459	
Celebes Sea	168,000	435,000	380,000	1,586,000	11,962	3,645	19,173	5,842	
Black Sea	166,000	431,000	133,000	555,000	3,839	1,170	7,256	2,211	
Yellow Sea	161,000	417,000	4,000	17,000	131	40	344	105	
Sulu Sea	134,000	348,000	133,000	553,000	5,221	1,591	18,300	5,576	
Molucca Sea	112,000	291,000	133,000	554,000	6,242	1,902	16,311	4,970	
Ceram Sea	72,000	187,000	54,000	227,000	3,968	1,209	17,456	5,319	
Flores Sea	47,000	121,000	53,000	222,000	6,003	1,829	16,813	5,123	
Bali Sea	46,000	119,000	12,000	49,000	1,349	411	4,253	1,296	
Savu Sea	41,000	105,000	43,000	178,000	5,582	1,701	11,060	3,370	
White Sea	35,000	91,000	1,000	4,400	161	49	1,083	330	
Azov, Sea of	15,000	40,000	100	400	29	9	46	14	
Marmara, Sea of	4,000	11,000	1,000	4,000	1,171	357	4,138	1,261	

Source: Atlas of World Water Balance, *USSR National Committee for the International Water Decade and UNESCO, 1977.*

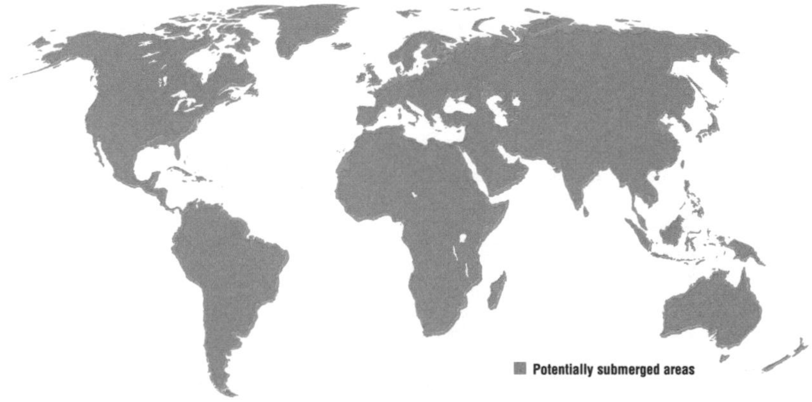

Fluctuating Sea Level

Changes in the Earth's climate have a dramatic effect on the sea level. Only 20,000 years ago, at the height of the most recent ice age, a vast amount of the Earth's water was locked up in ice sheets and glaciers, and the sea level was 330 feet (100 meters) lower than it is today. As the climate warmed slowly, the ice began to melt and the oceans began to rise.

Today there is still a tremendous amount of ice on the Earth. More than nine-tenths of it resides in the enormous ice cap which covers Antarctica. Measuring about 5.4 million square miles (14 million sq km) in surface area, the ice cap is on average one mile (1.6 km) thick but in some places is nearly three miles (4.8 km) thick. If it were to melt, the oceans would rise another 200 feet (60 m), and more than half of the world's population would have to relocate.

Ocean Depths in Profile

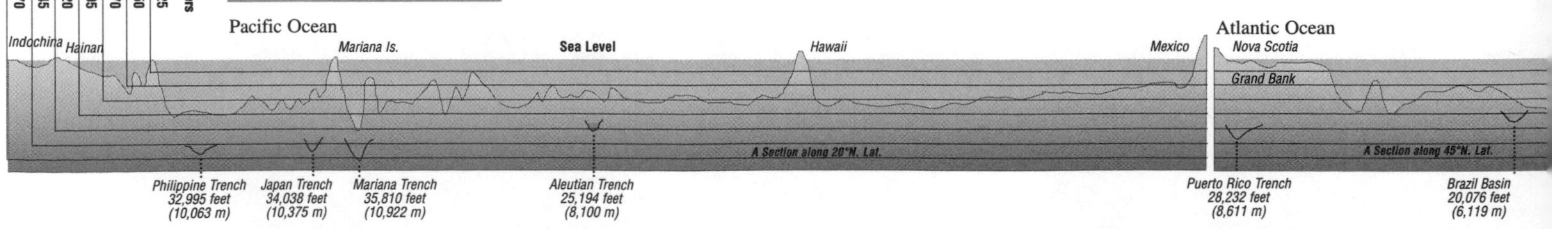

Deepest Lakes

	Lake	Greatest depth feet	meters
1	Baikal, Lake, Russia	5,315	1,621
2	Tanganyika, Lake, Africa	4,800	1,464
3	Caspian Sea, Asia-Europe	3,363	1,025
4	Nyasa, Lake (Lake Malawi), Malawi-Mozambique-Tanzania	2,317	706
5	Issyk-Kul', Lake, Kyrgyzstan	2,303	702
6	Great Slave Lake, NWT, Canada	2,015	614
7	Matana, Lake, Indonesia	1,936	590
8	Crater Lake, Oregon, U.S.	1,932	589
9	Toba, Lake (Danau Toba), Indonesia	1,736	529
10	Sarez, Lake, Tajikistan	1,657	505
11	Tahoe, Lake, California-Nevada, U.S.	1,645	502
12	Kivu, Lake, Rwanda-Dem. Rep. of the Congo	1,628	496
13	Chelan, Lake, Washington, U.S.	1,605	489
14	Quesnel Lake, BC, Canada	1,560	476
15	Adams Lake, BC, Canada	1,500	457

Lakes with the Greatest Volume of Water

	Lake	Volume of water cubic mi	cubic km
1	Caspian Sea, Asia-Europe	18,900	78,200
2	Baikal, Lake, Russia	5,500	23,000
3	Tanganyika, Lake, Africa	4,500	18,900
4	Superior, Lake, Canada-U.S.	2,900	12,200
5	Nyasa, Lake (Lake Malawi), Malawi-Mozambique-Tanzania	1,900	7,725
6	Michigan, Lake, U.S.	1,200	4,910
7	Huron, Lake, Canada-U.S.	860	3,580
8	Victoria, Lake, Kenya-Tanzania-Uganda	650	2,700
9	Issyk-Kul', Lake, Kyrgyzstan	415	1,730
10	Ontario, Lake, Canada-U.S.	410	1,710
11	Great Slave Lake, Canada	260	1,070
12	Great Bear Lake, Canada	240	1,010
13	Ladozhskoye, Ozero, Russia	220	908
14	Titicaca, Lago, Bolivia-Peru	170	710

Sources for volume and depth information: Atlas of World Water Balance, *USSR National Committee for the International Water Decade and UNESCO, 1977;* Principal Rivers and Lakes of the World, *National Oceanic and Atmospheric Administration, 1982.*

Principal Lakes

		Area sq mi	sq km
1	Caspian Sea, Asia-Europe	143,240	370,990
2	Superior, Lake, Canada-U.S.	31,700	82,100
3	Victoria, Lake, Kenya-Tanzania-Uganda	26,820	69,463
4	Huron, Lake, Canada-U.S.	23,000	60,000
5	Michigan, Lake, U.S.	22,300	57,800
6	Tanganyika, Lake, Africa	12,350	31,986
7	Baikal, Lake, Russia	12,200	31,500
8	Great Bear Lake, Canada	12,095	31,326
9	Nyasa, Lake (Lake Malawi), Malawi-Mozambique-Tanzania	11,150	28,878
10	Aral Sea, Kazakhstan-Uzbekistan	11,100	28,700
11	Great Slave Lake, Canada	11,030	28,568
12	Erie, Lake, Canada-U.S.	9,910	25,667
13	Winnipeg, Lake, Canada	9,416	24,387
14	Ontario, Lake, Canada-U.S.	7,540	19,529
15	Balqash koli (Lake Balkhash), Kazakhstan	7,100	18,300
16	Ladozhskoye, Ozero, Russia	6,833	17,700
17	Chad, Lake (Lac Tchad), Cameroon-Chad-Nigeria	6,300	16,300
18	Onezhskoye, Ozero, Russia	3,753	9,720
19	Eyre, Lake, Australia	3,700	9,500
20	Titicaca, Lago, Bolivia-Peru	3,200	8,300
21	Nicaragua, Lago de, Nicaragua	3,150	8,158
22	Mai-Ndombe, Lac, Dem. Rep. of the Congo	3,100	8,000
23	Athabasca, Lake, Canada	3,064	7,935
24	Reindeer Lake, Canada	2,568	6,650
25	Tônlé Sap, Cambodia	2,500	6,500
26	Rudolf, Lake, Ethiopia-Kenya	2,473	6,405
27	Issyk-Kul', Ozero, Kyrgyzstan	2,425	6,280
28	Torrens, Lake, Australia	2,300	5,900
29	Albert, Lake, Uganda-Dem. Rep. of the Congo	2,160	5,594
30	Vänern, Sweden	2,156	5,584
31	Nettilling Lake, Canada	2,140	5,542
32	Winnipegosis, Lake, Canada	2,075	5,374
33	Bangweulu, Lake, Zambia	1,930	4,999
34	Nipigon, Lake, Canada	1,872	4,848
35	Orumiyeh, Daryacheh-ye, Iran	1,815	4,701
36	Manitoba, Lake, Canada	1,785	4,624
37	Woods, Lake of the, Canada-U.S.	1,727	4,472
38	Kyoga, Lake, Uganda	1,710	4,429

Lake Baikal

Russia's Great Lake

On a map of the world, Lake Baikal is easy to overlook — a thin blue crescent adrift in the vastness of Siberia. But its inconspicuousness is deceptive, for Baikal is one of the greatest bodies of fresh water on Earth.

Although lakes generally have a life span of less than one million years, Baikal has existed for perhaps as long as 25 million years, which makes it the world's oldest body of fresh water. It formed in a rift that tectonic forces had begun to tear open in the Earth's crust. As the rift grew, so did Baikal. Today the lake is 395 miles (636 km) long and an average of 30 miles (48 km) wide. Only seven lakes in the world have a greater surface area.

Baikal is the world's deepest lake. Its maximum depth is 5,315 feet (1,621 m) — slightly over a mile, and roughly equal to the greatest depth of the Grand Canyon. The lake bottom lies 4,250 feet (1,295 m) below sea level and two-and-a-third miles (3.75 km) below the peaks of the surounding mountains. The crustal rift which Baikal occupies is the planet's deepest land depression, extending to a depth of more than five-and-a-half miles (9 km). The lake sits atop at least four miles (6.4 km) of sediment, the accumulation of 25 million years.

More than 300 rivers empty into Baikal, but only one, the Angara, flows out of it. Despite having only 38% of the surface area of North America's Lake Superior, Baikal contains more water than all five of the Great Lakes combined. Its volume of 5,500 cubic miles (23,000 cubic km) is greater than that of any other freshwater lake in the world and represents approximately one-fifth of all of the Earth's unfrozen fresh water.

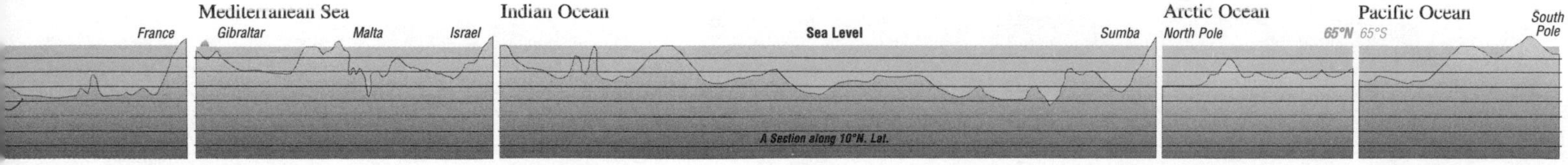

Rivers

World's Longest Rivers

Rank	River	Length Miles	Length Kilometers	Rank	River	Length Miles	Length Kilometers
1	Nile, Africa	4,145	6,671	36	Murray, Australia	1,566	2,520
2	Amazon (Amazonas)-Ucayali, South America	4,000	6,400	37	Ganges, Asia	1,560	2,511
3	Yangtze (Chang), Asia	3,900	6,300	38	Pilcomayo, South America	1,550	2,494
4	Mississippi-Missouri, North America	3,740	6,019	39	Euphrates, Asia	1,510	2,430
5	Huang (Yellow), Asia	3,395	5,464	40	Ural, Asia	1,509	2,428
6	Ob'-Irtysh, Asia	3,362	5,410	41	Arkansas, North America	1,459	2,348
7	Río de la Plata-Paraná, South America	3,030	4,876	42	Colorado, North America (U.S.-Mexico)	1,450	2,334
8	Congo, Africa	2,900	4,700	43	Aldan, Asia	1,412	2,273
9	Paraná, South America	2,800	4,500	44	Syr Darya, Asia	1,370	2,205
10	Amur-Argun, Asia	2,761	4,444	45	Dnieper, Europe	1,350	2,200
11	Lena, Asia	2,700	4,400	46	Araguaia, South America	1,350	2,200
12	Mackenzie, North America	2,635	4,241	47	Cassai (Kasai), Africa	1,338	2,153
13	Mekong, Asia	2,600	4,200	48	Tarim, Asia	1,328	2,137
14	Niger, Africa	2,600	4,200	49	Kolyma, Asia	1,323	2,129
15	Yenisey, Asia	2,543	4,092	50	Orange, Africa	1,300	2,100
16	Missouri-Red Rock, North America	2,533	4,076	51	Negro, South America	1,300	2,100
17	Mississippi, North America	2,348	3,779	52	Ayeyarwady (Irrawaddy), Asia	1,300	2,100
18	Murray-Darling, Australia	2,330	3,750	53	Red, North America	1,270	2,044
19	Missouri, North America	2,315	3,726	54	Juruá, South America	1,250	2,012
20	Volga, Europe	2,194	3,531	55	Columbia, North America	1,240	2,000
21	Madeira, South America	2,013	3,240	56	Xingu, South America	1,230	1,979
22	São Francisco, South America	1,988	3,199	57	Ucayali, South America	1,220	1,963
23	Grande, Rio (Río Bravo), North America	1,885	3,034	58	Saskatchewan-Bow, North America	1,205	1,939
24	Purús, South America	1,860	2,993	59	Peace, North America	1,195	1,923
25	Indus, Asia	1,800	2,900	60	Tigris, Asia	1,180	1,899
26	Danube, Europe	1,776	2,858	61	Don, Europe	1,162	1,870
27	Brahmaputra, Asia	1,770	2,849	62	Songhua, Asia	1,140	1,835
28	Yukon, North America	1,770	2,849	63	Pechora, Europe	1,124	1,809
29	Salween (Nu), Asia	1,750	2,816	64	Kama, Europe	1,122	1,805
30	Zambezi, Africa	1,700	2,700	65	Limpopo, Africa	1,120	1,800
31	Vilyuy, Asia	1,647	2,650	66	Angara, Asia	1,105	1,779
32	Tocantins, South America	1,640	2,639	67	Snake, North America	1,038	1,670
33	Orinoco, South America	1,615	2,600	68	Uruguay, South America	1,025	1,650
34	Paraguay, South America	1,610	2,591	69	Churchill, North America	1,000	1,600
35	Amu Darya, Asia	1,578	2,540	70	Marañón, South America	995	1,592

The World's Greatest River

Although the Nile is slightly longer, the Amazon surpasses all other rivers in volume, size of drainage basin, and in nearly every other important category. If any river is to be called the greatest in the world, surely it is the Amazon.

It has been estimated that one-fifth of all of the flowing water on Earth is carried by the Amazon. From its 150-mile (240-km)-wide mouth, the river discharges 6,180,000 cubic feet (174,900 cubic m) of water per second — four-and-a-half times as much as the Congo, ten times as much as the Mississippi, and fifty-six times as much as the Nile. The Amazon's tremendous outflow turns the waters of the Atlantic from salty to brackish for more than 100 miles (160 km) offshore.

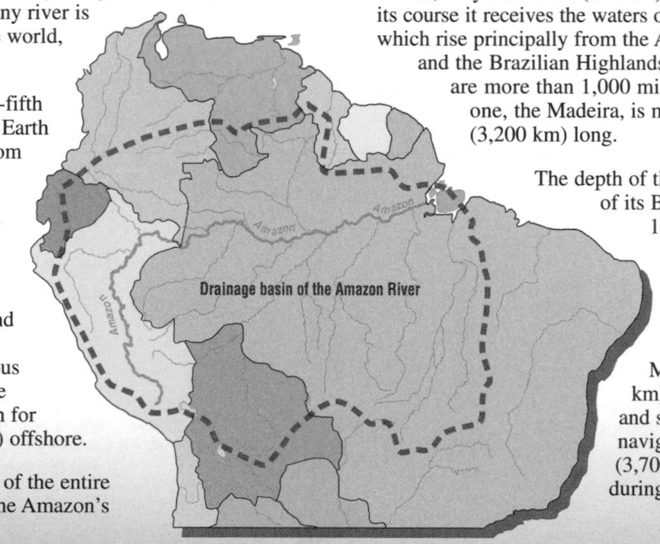

Covering more than one-third of the entire continent of South America, the Amazon's vast drainage basin measures 2,669,000 square miles (6,915,000 sq km) and is nearly twice as large as that of the second-ranked Congo. The Amazon begins its 4,000-mile (6,400-km) journey to the Atlantic from high up in the Andes, only 100 miles (160 km) from the Pacific. Along its course it receives the waters of more than 1,000 tributaries, which rise principally from the Andes, the Guiana Highlands, and the Brazilian Highlands. Seven of the tributaries are more than 1,000 miles (1,600 km) long, and one, the Madeira, is more than 2,000 miles (3,200 km) long.

The depth of the Amazon throughout most of its Brazilian segment exceeds 150 feet (45 m). Depths of more than 300 feet (90 m) have been recorded at points near the mouth. The largest ocean-going vessels can sail as far inland as Manaus, 1,000 miles (1,600 km) from the mouth. Freighters and small passenger vessels can navigate to Iquitos, 2,300 miles (3,700 km) from the mouth, even during times of low water.

Rivers with the Greatest Volume of Water

Rank	River Name	Flow of water per second at mouth: cubic feet	cubic meters
1	Amazon (Amazonas), South America	6,180,000	174,900
2	Congo, Africa	1,377,000	39,000
3	Negro, South America (tributary of Amazon)	1,236,000	35,000
4	Orinoco, South America	890,000	25,200
5	Río de la Plata-Paraná, South America	809,000	22,900
6	Yangtze (Chang), Asia;	770,000	21,800
	Madeira, South America (trib. of Amazon)	770,000	21,800
7	Missouri, North America (trib. of Mississippi)	763,000	21,600
8	Mississippi, North America*	640,300	18,100
9	Yenisey, Asia	636,000	18,000
10	Brahmaputra, Asia	575,000	16,300
11	Lena, Asia	569,000	16,100
12	Zambezi, Africa	565,000	16,000
13	Mekong, Asia	500,000	14,100
14	Saint Lawrence, North America	460,000	13,000
15	Ayeyarwady (Irrawaddy), Asia	447,000	12,600
16	Ob'-Irtysh, Asia; Ganges, Asia	441,000	12,500
17	Amur, Asia	390,000	11,000
18	Para-Tocantins, South America (joins Amazon at mouth)	360,000	10,200
19	Salween, Asia	353,000	10,000
20	Cassai (Kasai), Africa (trib. of Congo)	351,000	9,900
21	Mackenzie, North America	343,000	9,700
22	Volga, Europe	271,000	7,700
23	Ohio, North America (trib. of Mississippi)	257,000	7,300
24	Yukon, North America	240,000	6,800
25	Indus, Asia	235,000	6,600
26	Danube, Europe	227,000	6,400
27	Niger, Africa	215,000	6,100
28	Atchafalaya, North America	181,000	5,100
29	Paraguay, South America	155,000	4,400
30	Ob'-Katun, Asia	147,000	4,200
31	São Francisco, South America	120,000	3,400
32	Tunguska, Asia	118,000	3,350
33	Huang (Yellow), Asia	116,000	3,300
34	Nile, Africa	110,000	3,100

*Approximately one-third of the Mississippi's water is diverted above Baton Rouge, Louisiana, and reaches the Gulf of Mexico via the Atchafalaya River.

Principal Rivers of the Continents

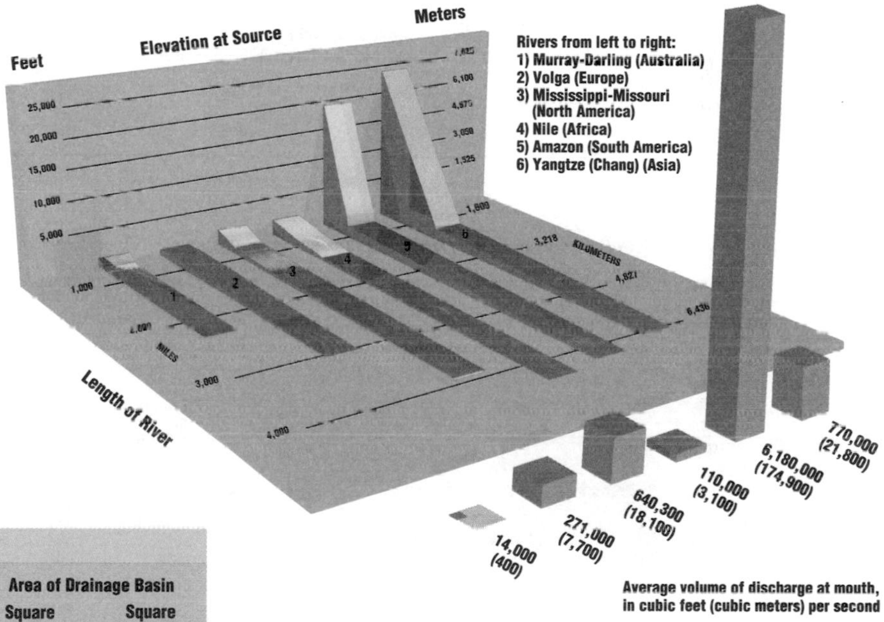

Rivers with the Largest Drainage Basins

Rank	River	Area of Drainage Basin: Square Miles	Square Kilometers
1	Amazon (Amazonas), South America	2,669,000	6,915,000
2	Congo, Africa	1,474,500	3,820,000
3	Mississippi-Missouri, North America	1,243,000	3,220,000
4	Río de la Plata-Paraná, South America	1,197,000	3,100,000
5	Ob'-Irtysh, Asia	1,154,000	2,990,000
6	Nile, Africa	1,108,000	2,870,000
7	Yenisey-Angara, Asia	1,011,000	2,618,500
8	Lena, Asia	961,000	2,490,000
9	Niger, Africa	807,000	2,090,000
10	Amur-Argun, Asia	792,000	2,051,300
11	Yangtze (Chang), Asia	705,000	1,826,000
12	Volga, Europe	525,000	1,360,000
13	Zambezi, Africa	513,500	1,330,000
14	St. Lawrence, North America	503,000	1,302,800
15	Huang (Yellow), Asia	486,000	1,258,700

Sources for volume and drainage basin information: Atlas of World Water Balance, *USSR National Committee for the International Hydrological Decade and UNESCO, 1977;* Principal Rivers and Lakes of the World, *National Oceanic and Atmospheric Administration, 1982.*

Climate and Weather

Temperature Extremes by Continent

Africa

Highest recorded temperature
Al 'Azīzīyah, Libya, September 13, 1922:
136° F (58° C),
Lowest recorded temperature
Ifrane, Morocco, February 11, 1935:
-11° F (-24° C)

Antarctica

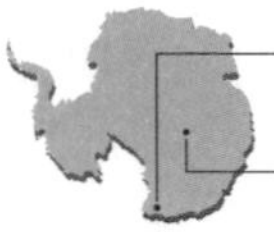

Highest recorded temperature
Vanda Station, January 5, 1974:
59° F (15° C)
Lowest recorded temperature
Vostok, July 21, 1983:
-129° F (-89° C)

Asia

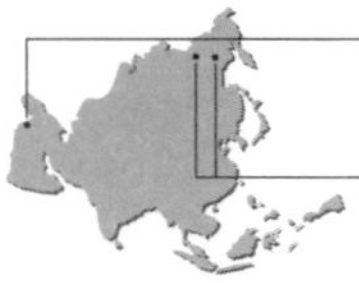

Highest recorded temperature
Tirat Zevi, Israel, June 21, 1942:
129° F (54° C)
Lowest recorded temperature
Oymyakon and Verkhoyansk,
Russia, February 5 and 7, 1892,
and February 6, 1933: -90° F (-68° C)

Australia / Oceania

Highest recorded temperature
Cloncurry, Queensland, January 16, 1889:
128° F (53° C)
Lowest recorded temperature
Charlottes Pass, New South Wales,
June 14, 1945, and July 22, 1947: -8° F (-22° C)

Europe

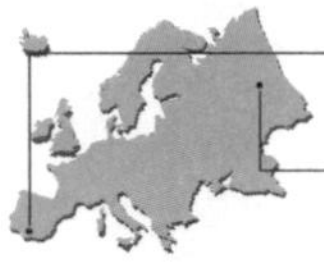

Highest recorded temperature
Sevilla, Spain, August 4, 1881:
122° F (50° C)
Lowest recorded temperature
Ust' Ščugor, Russia, (date not known):
-67° F (-55° C)

North America

Highest recorded temperature
Death Valley, California, United States,
July 10, 1913: 134° F (57° C)
Lowest recorded temperature
Northice, Greenland, January 9, 1954:
-87° F (-66° C)

South America

Highest recorded temperature
Rivadavia, Argentina, December 11, 1905:
120° F (49° C)
Lowest recorded temperature
Sarmiento, Argentina, June 1, 1907:
-27° F (-33° C)

World

Highest recorded temperature
Al 'Azīzīyah, Libya, September 13, 1922:
136° F (58° C)
Lowest recorded temperature
Vostok, Antarctica, July 21, 1983:
-129° F (-89° C)

World Temperature Extremes

Highest mean annual temperature Dalol, Ethiopia, 94° F (34° C)
Lowest mean annual temperature Plateau Station, Antarctica: -70° F (-57° C)

Greatest difference between highest and lowest recorded temperatures
Verkhoyansk, Russia. The highest temperature ever recorded there is 93.5° F (34.2° C); the lowest is -89.7° F (–67.6° C) — a difference of 183° F (102° C).

Highest temperature ever recorded at the South Pole 7.5° F (-14° C) on December 27, 1978

Most consecutive days with temperatures of 100° F (38° C) or above Marble Bar, Australia, 162 days: October 30, 1923 to April 7, 1924

Greatest rise in temperature within a 12-hour period
Granville, North Dakota, on February 21, 1918. The temperature rose 83° F (46° C), from -33° F (-36° C) in early morning to +50° F (10° C) in late afternoon

Greatest drop in temperature within a 12-hour period
Fairfield, Montana, on December 24, 1924. The temperature dropped 84° F (46° C), from 63° F (17° C) at noon to -21° F (-29° C) by midnight

Temperature Ranges for 14 Major Cities around the World

City	Mean Temperature: Coldest Winter Month	Mean Temperature: Hottest Summer Month
Buenos Aires, Argentina	Aug: 51.3° F (10.7° C)	Jan: 75.0° F (23.9° C)
Kolkata (Calcutta), India	Jan: 67.5° F (19.7° C)	May: 88.5° F (31.4° C)
London, England	Feb: 39.4° F (4.1° C)	Jul: 63.9° F (17.7° C)
Los Angeles, U.S.	Jan: 56.3° F (13.5° C)	Jul: 74.1° F (23.4° C)
Manila, Philippines	Jan: 77.7° F (25.4° C)	May: 84.9° F (29.4° C)
Mexico City, Mexico	Jan: 54.1° F (12.3° C)	May: 64.9° F (18.3° C)
Moscow, Russia	Feb: 14.5° F (-9.7° C)	Jul: 65.8° F (18.8° C)
Mumbai (Bombay), India	Jan: 74.3° F (23.5° C)	May: 85.5° F (29.7° C)
New York City, U.S.	Jan: 32.9° F (0.5° C)	Jul: 77.0° F (25.0° C)
Osaka, Japan	Jan: 40.6° F (4.8° C)	Aug: 82.2° F (27.9° C)
Rio de Janeiro, Brazil	Jul: 70.2 ° F (21.2° C)	Jan: 79.9° F (26.6° C)
São Paulo, Brazil	Jul: 58.8° F (14.9° C)	Jan: 71.1° F (21.7° C)
Seoul, South Korea	Jan: 23.2° F (-4.9° C)	Aug: 77.7° F (25.4° C)
Tokyo, Japan	Jan: 39.6° F (4.2° C)	Aug: 79.3° F (26.3° C)

Precipitation

Greatest local average annual rainfall
Mt. Waialeale, Kaua'i, Hawaii,
460 inches (1,168 cm)

Lowest local average annual rainfall
Arica, Chile, .03 inches (.08 cm)

Greatest rainfall in 12 months
Cherrapunji, India, August 1860 to August 1861:
1,042 inches (2,647 cm)

Greatest rainfall in one month
Cherrapunji, India, July 1861: 366 inches (930 cm)

Greatest rainfall in 24 hours
Cilaos, Reunion, March 15 and 16, 1952:
74 inches (188 cm)

Greatest rainfall in 12 hours
Belouve, Reunion, February 28 and 29, 1964:
53 inches (135 cm)

Most thunderstorms annually
Kampala, Uganda, averages 242 days per
year with thunderstorms

Between 1916 and 1920, Bogor, Indonesia,
averaged 322 days per year with thunderstorms

Longest dry period
Arica, Chile, October, 1903
to January, 1918 — over 14 years

Largest hailstone ever recorded
Coffeyville, Kansas, U.S., September 3, 1970:
circumference 17.5 inches (44.5 cm)
diameter 5.6 inches (14 cm),
weight 1.67 pounds (758 grams)

Heaviest hailstone ever recorded
Kazakhstan, 1959: 4.18 pounds (1.9 kilograms)

North America's greatest snowfall in one season
Rainier Paradise Ranger Station, Washington,
U.S., 1971–1972: 1,122 inches (2,850 cm)

North America's greatest snowfall in one storm
Mt. Shasta Ski Bowl, California, U.S.,
February 13 to 19, 1959: 189 inches (480 cm)

North America's greatest snowfall in 24 hours
Silver Lake, Colorado, U.S., April 14 and 15, 1921:
76 inches (1 92.5 cm)

N. America's greatest depth of snowfall on the ground
Tamarack, California, U.S., March 11, 1911:
451 inches (1,145.5 cm)

Foggiest place on the U.S. West Coast
Cape Disappointment, Washington,
averages 2,552 hours of fog per year

Foggiest place on the U.S. East Coast
Mistake Island, Maine, averages
1,580 hours of fog per year

Wind

Highest 24-hour mean surface wind speed
Mt. Washington, New Hampshire, U.S.,
April 11 and 12, 1934: 128 mph (206 kph)

Highest 5-minute mean surface wind speed
Mt. Washington, New Hampshire, U.S.,
April 12, 1934: 188 mph (303 kph)

Highest surface wind peak gust:
Mt. Washington, New Hampshire, U.S.,
April 12, 1934: 231 mph (372 kph)

Windiest U.S. Cities

Chicago is sometimes called The Windy City.
It earned this nickname because of long-winded politicians,
not because it has the strongest gales.

The windiest cities in the U.S. are as follows:

Cities	Average wind speed mph	kph
Great Falls, Montana	13.1	21.0
Oklahoma City, Oklahoma	13.0	20.9
Boston, Massachusetts	12.9	20.7
Cheyenne, Wyoming	12.8	20.6
Wichita, Kansas	12.7	20.4

Chicago ranks 16th, with a 10.4 mph (16.7 kph) average.

Deadliest Hurricanes in the U.S. since 1890

Rank	Place	Year	Number of Deaths
1	Texas (Galveston)	1900	8,000
2	Louisiana	1893	2,000
3	Florida (Lake Okeechobee)	1928	1,836
4	South Carolina, Georgia	1893	>1,000
5	Florida (Keys)	1919	>600
6	New England	1938	600
7	Florida (Keys)	1935	408
8	Southwest Louisiana, north Texas—"Hurricane Audrey"	1957	390
	Northeast U.S.	1944	390
9	Louisiana (Grand Isle)	1909	350
10	Louisana (New Orleans)	1915	275

Tornadoes in the U.S., 1950—1993

Rank	State	Total Number of Tornadoes	Yearly Average	Total Number of Deaths
1	Texas	5,303	120	471
2	Oklahoma	2,259	51	217
3	Kansas	2,068	47	199
4	Florida	1,932	44	81
5	Nebraska	1,618	37	51
U.S. Total		33,120	753	4,045

Deadliest Floods in the U.S. since 1900

Rank	Place	Year	Number of Deaths
1	Ohio River and tributaries	1913	467
2	Mississippi Valley	1927	313
3	Black Hills, South Dakota	1972	237
4	Willow Creek, Oregon	1903	225
5	Texas rivers	1921	215
6	Northeastern U.S., following Hurricane Dianne	1955	187
7	Texas rivers	1913	177
8	James River basin, Virginia	1969	153
9	New England	1936	150+
10	Big Thompson Canyon, Colorado	1976	139
11	Ohio and Lower Mississippi river basins	1937	137
12	Buffalo Creek, West Virginia	1972	125

Population

During the first two million years of our species' existence, human population grew at a very slow rate, and probably never exceeded 10 million. With the development of agriculture circa 8000 B.C., the growth rate began to rise sharply: by the year A.D. 1, the world population stood at approximately 250 million.

By 1650 the population had doubled to 550 million, and within only 200 years it doubled again, reaching almost 1.2 billion by 1850. Each subsequent doubling has taken only about half as long as the previous one: 100 years to reach 2.5 billion, and 40 years to reach 5.2 billion.

World Population

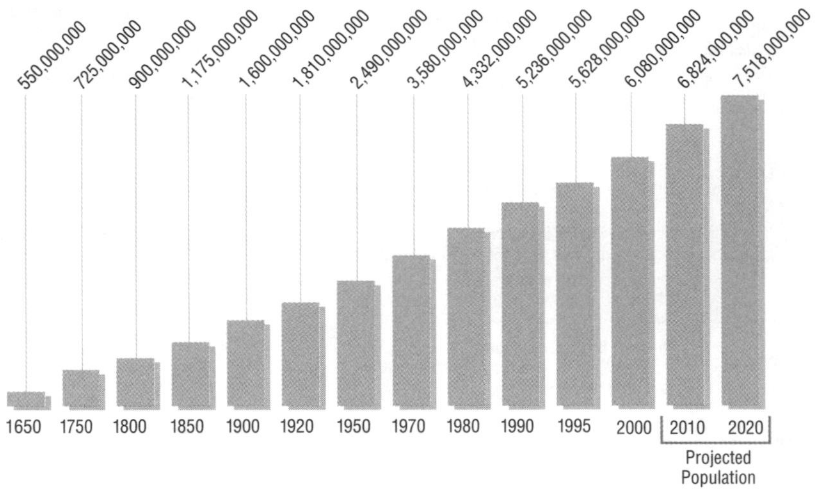

Historical Populations of the Continents and the World

Year	Africa	Asia	Australia	Europe	North America	Oceania, incl. Australia	South America	World
1650	*100,000,000*	335,000,000	*<1,000,000*	*100,000,000*	*5,000,000*	*2,000,000*	*8,000,000*	*550,000,000*
1750	*95,000,000*	476,000,000	*<1,000,000*	*140,000,000*	*5,000,000*	*2,000,000*	*7,000,000*	*725,000,000*
1800	*90,000,000*	593,000,000	*<1,000,000*	*190,000,000*	*13,000,000*	*2,000,000*	*12,000,000*	*900,000,000*
1850	*95,000,000*	754,000,000	*<1,000,000*	265,000,000	*39,000,000*	*2,000,000*	*20,000,000*	*1,175,000,000*
1900	*118,000,000*	932,000,000	4,000,000	400,000,000	106,000,000	6,000,000	38,000,000	*1,600,000,000*
1920	*140,000,000*	1,000,000,000	6,000,000	453,000,000	147,000,000	9,000,000	61,000,000	*1,810,000,000*
1950	199,000,000	1,418,000,000	8,000,000	530,000,000	219,000,000	13,000,000	111,000,000	*2,490,000,000*
1970	346,900,000	2,086,200,000	12,460,000	623,700,000	316,600,000	19,200,000	187,400,000	3,580,000,000
1980	463,800,000	2,581,000,000	14,510,000	660,000,000	365,000,000	22,700,000	239,000,000	4,332,000,000
1990	648,300,000	3,156,100,000	16,950,000	688,000,000	423,600,000	26,300,000	293,700,000	5,236,000,000

Figures for years prior to 1970 are rounded to the nearest million. Figures in italics represent rough estimates.

The Most Populous City in the World, through History

With more than 30 million people, Japan's Tokyo-Yokohama agglomeration ranks as the most populous metropolitan area in the world today. New York City held this title from the mid-1920's through the mid-1960's. But what city was the most populous in the world five hundred years ago? Five *thousand* years ago?

The following time line represents one expert's attempt to name the cities that have reigned as the most populous in the world since 3200 B.C. The time line begins with Memphis, the capital of ancient Egypt, which was possibly the first city in the world to attain a population of 20,000.

Listed after each city name is the name of the political entity to which the city belonged during the time that it was the most populous city in the world. The name of the modern political entity in which the city, its ruins, or its site is located, where this entity differs from the historic political entity, is listed in parentheses.

For the purpose of this time line, the word "city" is used in the general sense to denote a city, metropolitan area, or urban agglomeration.

It is important to note that reliable census figures are not available for most of the 5,200 years covered by this time line. Therefore the time line is somewhat subjective and conjectural.

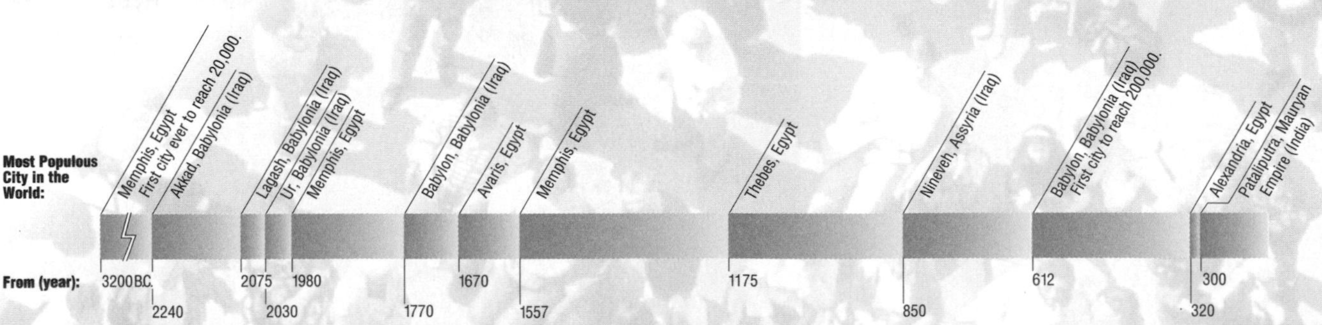

Most Densely Populated Countries

Rank	Country (Population)	Population per Square Mile	Population per Square Kilometer
1	Monaco (32,000)	45,489	16,759
2	Singapore (4,375,000)	17,481	6,762
3	Vatican City (1,000)	5,000	2,500
4	Malta (395,000)	3,234	1,249
5	Maldives (315,000)	2,702	1,043
6	Bahrain (650,000)	2,417	934
7	Bangladesh (132,315,000)	2,361	912
8	Guernsey (64,000)	2,144	825
9	Jersey (89,000)	1,986	770
10	Barbados (275,000)	1,659	640
11	Taiwan (22,460,000)	1,609	621
12	Mauritius (1,195,000)	1,510	583
13	Nauru (12,000)	1,492	576
14	Korea, South (48,120,000)	1,253	484
15	San Marino (28,000)	1,136	448

Least Densely Populated Countries

Rank	Country (Population)	Population per Square Mile	Population per Square Kilometer
1	Greenland (56,000)	0.07	0.03
2	Mongolia (2,675,000)	4.4	1.7
3	Namibia (1,810,000)	5.6	2.2
4	Australia (19,455,000)	6.5	2.5
5	Mauritania (2,790,000)	6.9	2.6
6	Suriname (435,000)	6.9	2.6
7	Iceland (280,000)	7.0	2.7
8	Botswana (1,590,000)	7.1	2.7
9	Libya (5,305,000)	7.7	3.0
10	Canada (31,750,000)	8.2	3.2
11	Guyana (695,000)	8.4	3.2
12	Gabon (1,225,000)	11.8	4.6
13	Central African Republic (3,610,000)	14.9	5.7
14	Kazakhstan (16,735,000)	15.9	6.2
15	Chad (8,850,000)	17.6	6.8

Most Highly Urbanized Countries

Country	Urban pop. as a % of total pop.
Vatican City	100%
Singapore	100%
Monaco	100%
Belgium	96%
Kuwait	96%
Iceland	92%
Uruguay	91%
Israel (excl. Occupied Areas)	90%
Qatar	90%
Andorra	89%
Argentina	89%
San Marino	89%
United Kingdom	89%
Bahrain	88%
Malta	87%

Least Urbanized Countries

Country	Urban pop. as a % of total pop.
Bhutan	5%
Burundi	5%
Rwanda	5%
Nepal	9%
Oman	11%
Cambodia (Kampuchea)	14%
Bangladesh	14%
Uganda	15%
Burkina Faso	15%
Eritrea	15%
Grenada	15%
Solomon Islands	15%
Niger	15%
Ethiopia	16%
Nigeria	16%

World's Largest Metropolitan Areas

Rank	Name	Population
1	Tōkyō-Yokohama, Japan	31,915,000
2	Seoul, South Korea	21,450,000
3	Mexico City, Mexico	20,150,000
4	New York City, U.S.	19,500,000
5	Jakarta, Indonesia	17,600,000
6	São Paulo, Brazil	17,480,000
7	Ōsaka-Kobe-Kyoto, Japan	17,350,000
8	Mumbai (Bombay), India	16,600,000
9	Delhi-New Delhi, India	16,000,000
10	Los Angeles, U.S.	15,200,000
11	Kolkata (Calcutta), India	14,000,000
12	Buenos Aires, Argentina	13,900,000
13	Cairo, Egypt	13,300,000
14	Moscow, Russia	12,800,000
15	London, England	12,700,000

The 50 Most Populous Countries

Rank	Country	Population
1	China	1,278,720,000
2	India	1,037,955,000
3	United States	279,310,000
4	Indonesia	230,260,000
5	Brazil	175,260,000
6	Pakistan	146,145,000
7	Russia	145,215,000
8	Bangladesh	132,315,000
9	Nigeria	128,285,000
10	Japan	126,880,000
11	Mexico	102,640,000
12	Philippines	83,685,000
13	Germany	83,145,000
14	Vietnam	80,520,000
15	Egypt	70,125,000
16	Turkey	66,905,000
17	Ethiopia	66,780,000
18	Iran	66,365,000
19	Thailand	62,080,000
20	United Kingdom	59,715,000
21	France	59,660,000
22	Italy	57,700,000
23	Dem. Rep. of the Congo	54,455,000
24	Ukraine	48,570,000
25	Korea, South	48,120,000
26	South Africa	43,645,000
27	Myanmar	42,120,000
28	Colombia	40,680,000
29	Spain	40,060,000
30	Poland	38,630,000
31	Argentina	37,600,000
32	Tanzania	36,705,000
33	Sudan	36,585,000
34	Algeria	32,005,000
35	Canada	31,750,000
36	Kenya	30,960,000
37	Morocco	30,905,000
38	Peru	27,720,000
39	Afghanistan	27,280,000
40	Nepal	25,580,000
41	Uzbekistan	25,355,000
42	Uganda	24,335,000
43	Venezuela	24,105,000
44	Iraq	23,665,000
45	Saudi Arabia	23,130,000
46	Taiwan	22,460,000
47	Malaysia	22,445,000
48	Romania	22,340,000
49	Korea, North	22,100,000
50	Ghana	20,070,000

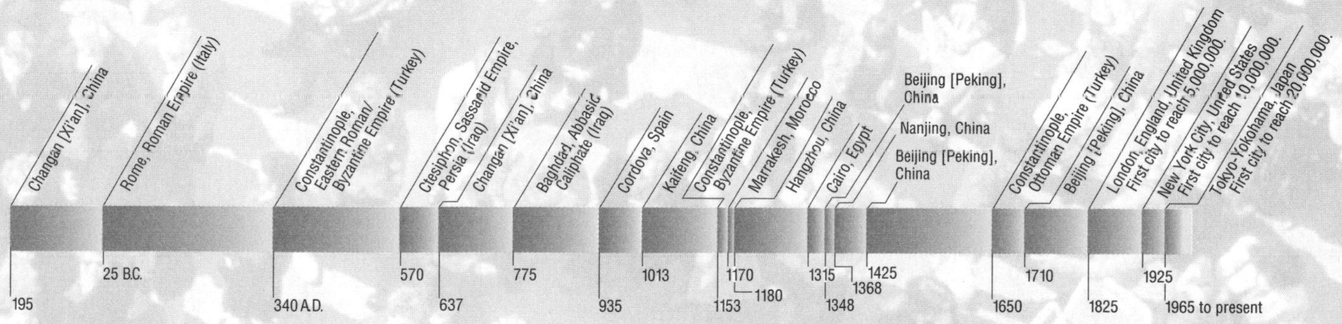

Source: Four Thousand Years of Urban Growth *by Tertius Chandler, Edwin Mellen Press, 1987.*

Economics and Energy

Annual World Production

Cattle

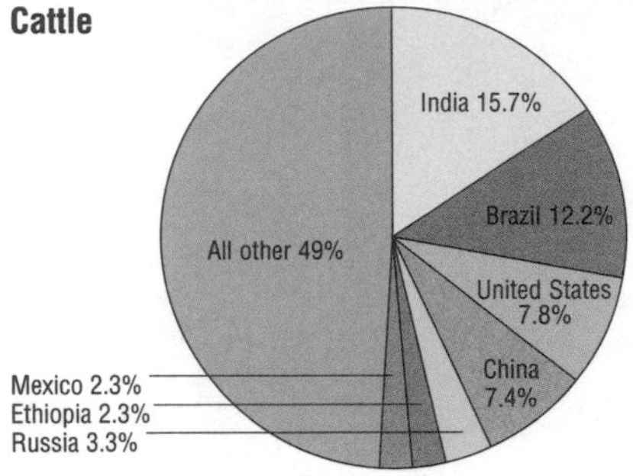

Total annual world production: 1,318,408,000 head

Hogs

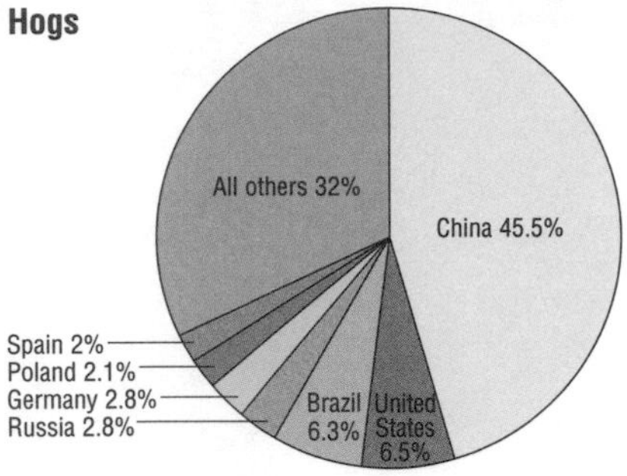

Total annual world production: 902,866,000 head

Corn

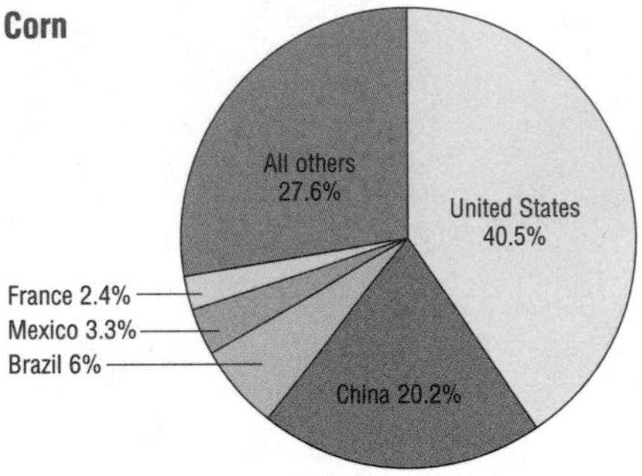

Total annual world production: 559,077,000 metric tons

Crude Steel

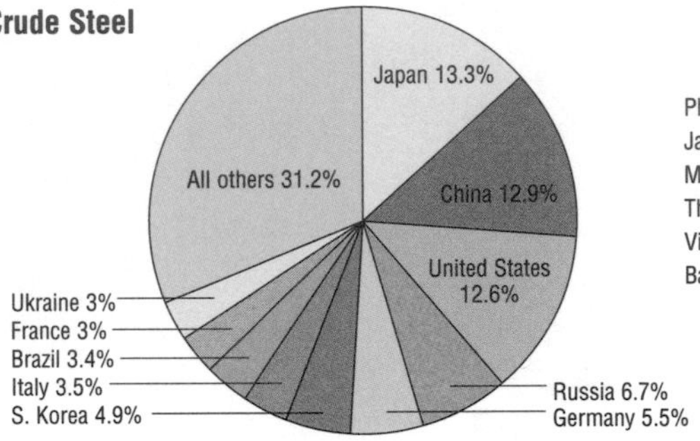

Total annual world production: 747,333,000 metric tons

Rice

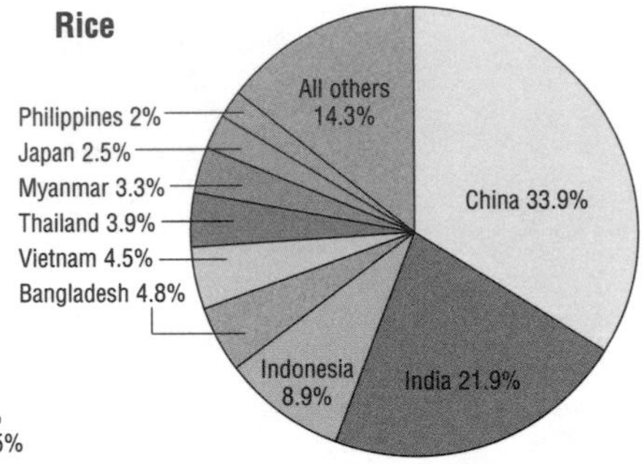

Total annual world production: 553,032,000 metric tons

Gross Domestic Product

Annual gross domestic product is the total market value of all the goods and services produced by a nation in a year. Annual per capita gross domestic product is the total value of the goods and services divided by the nation's population.

The United States, Canada, Chile, the countries of western Europe, Australia, Japan, South Korea, Malaysia, and Taiwan have annual per capita GDP's of more than $10,000 U.S. dollars. Most of the countries of South America have annual per capita GDP's between $5,000 and $10,000. Most of the countries of Asia and eastern Europe have annual per capita GDP's between $1,000 and $5,000. Most African countries have annual per capita GDP's under $2,500.

Percentage of World Population in each Per Capita GDP Category

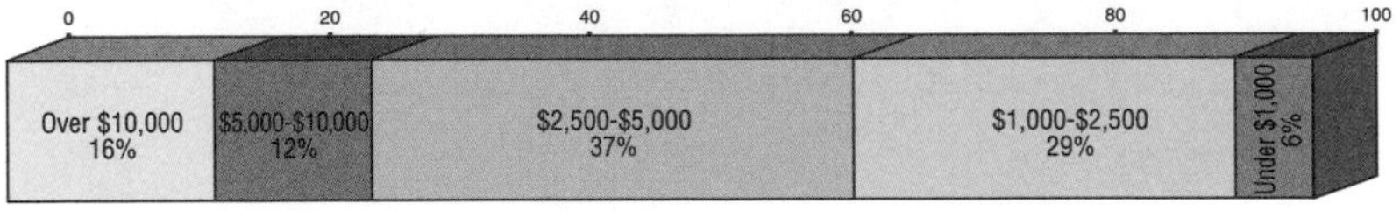

Electricity

Hydroelectricity

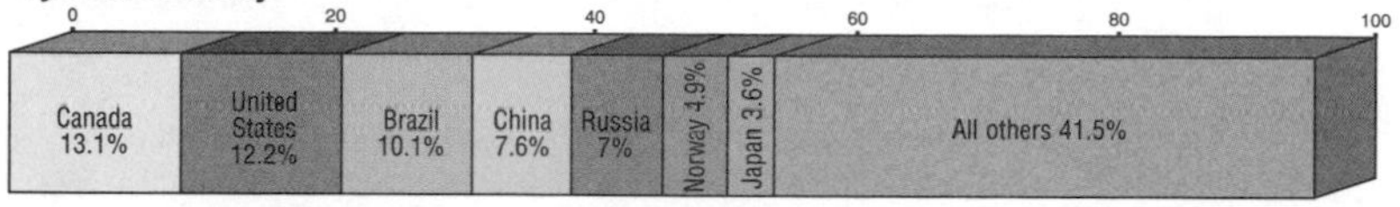

Total annual world production: 2,533,000 gigawatt hours

Nuclear Energy

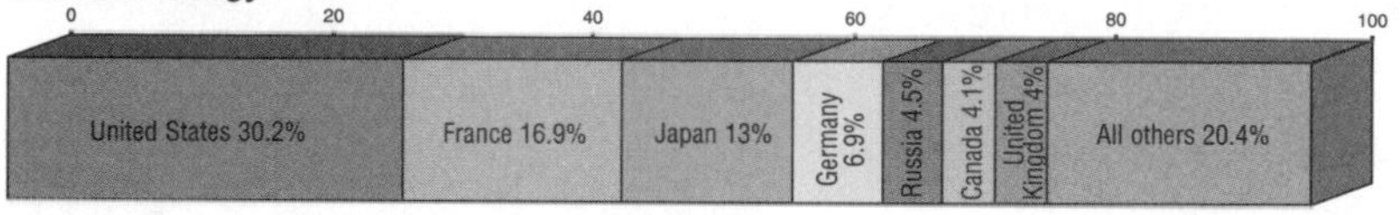

Total annual world production: 2,268,000 gigawatt hours

World Electricity Production

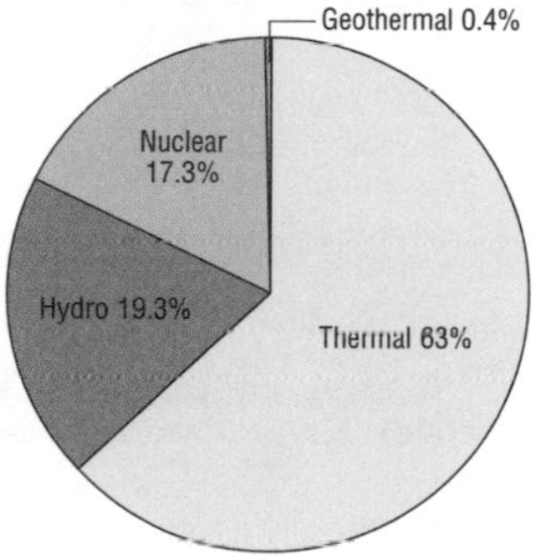

Total annual world electricity production: 13,098,000 gigawatt hours

Petroleum

Petroleum Production

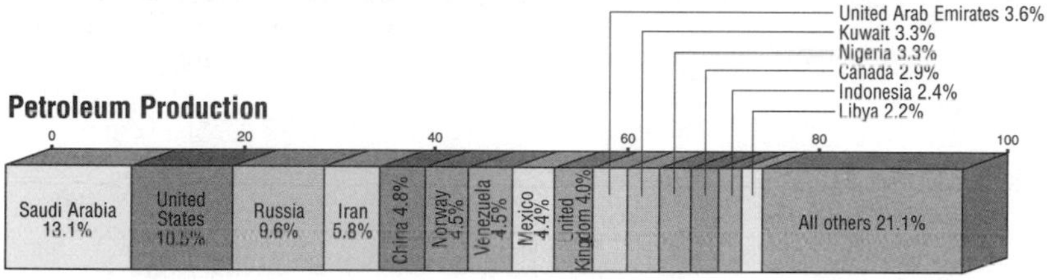

Total annual world production: 22,797,544,000 barrels

Petroleum Reserves

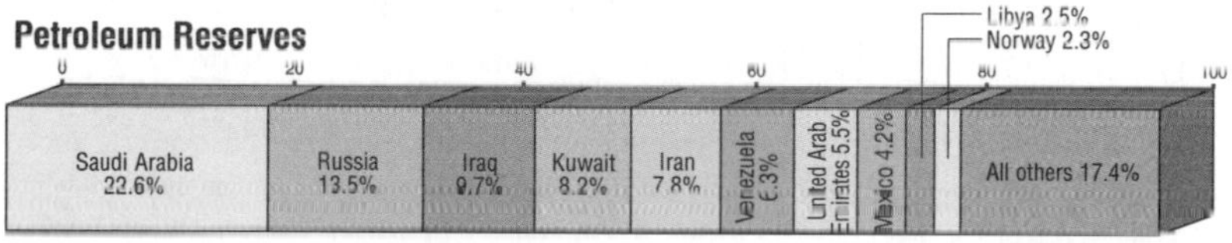

Total world reserves: 1,160,069,500,000 barrels

Commercial Energy

Commercial Energy Production

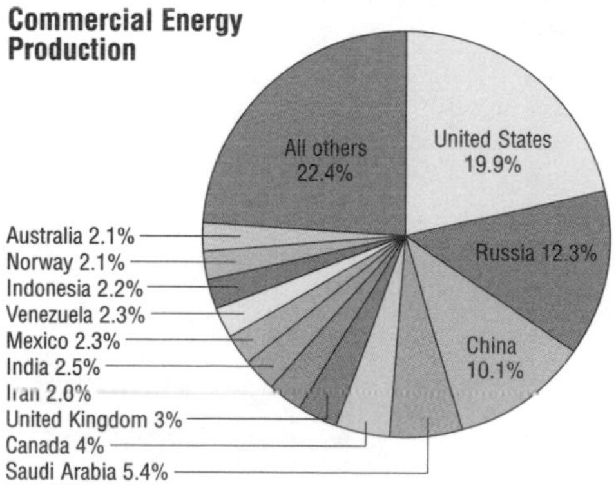

Total annual world production: equivalent of 12,321,830,000 metric tons of coal

Commercial Energy Consumption

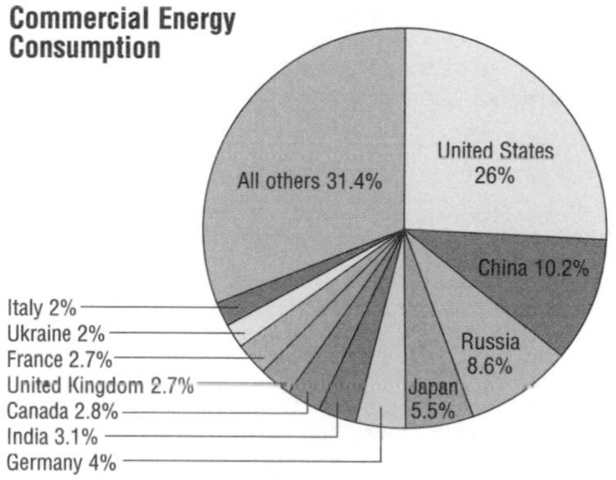

Total annual world consumption: equivalent of 11,720,193,000 metric tons of coal

Questions and Answers

North America

Q What is the difference between "Central America" and "Middle America"?

A The term "Central America" refers to the North American countries which lie south of Mexico and north of Colombia: Belize, Guatemala, Honduras, El Salvador, Nicaragua, Costa Rica, and Panama. The Caribbean islands are not considered part of Central America. "Middle America" is comprised of Central America as well as Mexico and all of the Caribbean islands.

Q What is the largest U.S. city east of Reno, Nevada and west of Chicago?

Los Angeles, California

A Surprisingly, the answer is Los Angeles. Although Los Angeles is located on the Pacific Coast, it actually lies slightly farther east than Reno. The coast, which forms the western edge of the U.S., curves dramatically eastward below Cape Mendocino in northern California. San Diego, at the southern end of California's coast, is approximately as far east as the eastern borders of Washington and Oregon. *(Refer to map on pages 74-75.)*

Q Which is the southernmost U.S. state? The northernmost? The westernmost? The easternmost?

A Hawaii is the southernmost state; Alaska is both the westernmost and the northernmost. The question of which state is the easternmost is a bit problematic. Generally, Maine is considered to be the easternmost, since it extends farther east than any other state along the Atlantic seaboard. However, Alaska is technically the easternmost state, since the Aleutian Islands cross the 180° longitude line which divides the globe into eastern and western hemispheres. These islands sit at the eastern edge of the eastern hemisphere.

Q How many national flags have flown over Texas?

A Six. Spain (1682-1821), France (1685-1686), Mexico (1821-1836), the Republic of Texas (1836-1845), the United States (1845-1861), the Confederate States of America (from 1861 until the state was re-admitted to the Union in 1870), and the United States again (1870 through the present). Texas is the only U.S. state to have existed as an independent country.

Q What is the oldest city in the United States to be founded by Europeans?

A St. Augustine, Florida. Spanish explorer Juan Ponce de León, searching for the Fountain of Youth, landed nearby and claimed the area for Spain in 1513. The French established a colony on the site in 1564, but it was destroyed in 1565 by the Spanish, who then founded the present city. The oldest U.S. state capital is Santa Fe, New Mexico, which was founded in 1609, also by the Spanish.

Q What is Papiamento?

A Papiamento is a language which blends Dutch, Spanish, Portuguese, English, and Indian words. It is the principal language of Aruba and other islands in the Dutch Caribbean, and is spoken by an estimated 200,000 people.

Q If you were on a ship sailing from the Atlantic Ocean to the Pacific Ocean, in which direction would you be traveling as you passed through the Panama Canal?

A Southeast. The Pacific lies west of the Atlantic, and it would seem that a ship passing through the canal from the Atlantic would be sailing west. However, because of the twisting shape of the Isthmus of Panama, the canal's Pacific end lies south and east of its Atlantic end. *(Refer to inset map on page 96.)*

Q Into what body of water does the Colorado River empty?

A Currently, it doesn't empty into any body of water. Until recently, the river flowed into the Gulf of California. As the populations of water-poor Arizona and California have soared, more and more water has been drawn from the river for farms, industry, and homes. Today the Colorado is barely a trickle when it crosses the border into Mexico, and it disappears in the desert before it reaches the Gulf of California.

Q What is Canada's smallest province? Its largest?

A Prince Edward Island is Canada's smallest province, at 2,185 square miles (5,660 sq km). Canada's largest province is Quebec, which covers 594,860 square miles (1,540,680 sq km). The newly created territory of Nunavut represents the country's largest administrative division: It spreads over an area of 733,594 square miles (1,900,000 sq km), much of which lies within the Arctic Circle. If Nuvavut were an independent country, it would be larger than all but 15 of the world's countries.

Q What is the Continental Divide?

A An imaginary line running down the backbone of North America. Except for those which empty into the Great Basin and other basins, rivers to the west of this line flow into the Pacific Ocean, including its bays and gulfs; rivers to the east flow into the Atlantic or Arctic oceans, including their bays and gulfs. From northwest Canada south to New Mexico, the Divide runs along the crest of the Rocky Mountains, and in northern Mexico it follows the ridge of the Sierra Madre Occidental. All continents except frozen Antarctica have "divides."

Q Is Niagara Falls the highest waterfall in the world?

A Not even close. Niagara Falls' maximum drop of 167 feet (51 m) is surpassed by at least 22 waterfalls in North America alone. The highest waterfall in the world is Angel Falls in Venezuela, which spills 3,212 feet (979 m) from a flat mountain plateau. However, Niagara Falls ranks first in a different category: more than 210,000 cubic feet of water cascade over its edge each second, an amount nearly double that of any other waterfall.

Niagara Falls actually consists of two separate waterfalls: American Falls, at left, and Canadian (Horseshoe) Falls.

Q What did ships do before the Panama Canal was built?

A Before the canal opened, ships traveling between New York and San Francisco would sail 13,000 miles (21,000 km) around the entire continent of South America. When the canal opened in 1914, this journey was shortened to 5,200 miles (8,400 km). However, the canal is now too narrow for many of today's largest ocean-going vessels, so they must once again sail around South America to reach their destination. A project to widen the canal began in 1992.

Gatun Lake, Panama Canal

Q What is the largest inland body of water in Central America?

A Lake Nicaragua, which has a surface area of 3,150 square miles (8,158 sq km). Its only outlet is the San Juan River, which flows into the Caribbean Sea. Lying in a lowland region called the Nicaragua Depression, the lake was once part of the sea but became separated when the land began to rise. The freshwater lake is home to many species of fish usually found only in salt water, including sharks, tuna, and swordfish.

Q Why does Minnesota have so many lakes?

A During the height of the most recent Ice Age, glaciers moved southward from the Arctic regions to cover Canada and much of the northern U.S., including Minnesota. As they advanced, the glaciers scoured the landscape, gouging out countless depressions. When the Earth's climate grew warmer, the glaciers began to melt and retreat, and the depressions filled with meltwater to become lakes. Although Minnesota bills itself as the "Land of 10,000 Lakes," it actually has more than 15,000 lakes. Other areas of the world which experienced extreme glaciation, including parts of Europe and Siberia, also contain many lakes.

Q What is the most popular U.S. national park?

A Great Smoky Mountains National Park. Covering over 521,500 acres (211,200 hectares) in eastern Tennessee, the park receives approximately 9.1 million visitors each year. Arizona's Grand Canyon National Park has the second-highest visitor count: it receives around 4.6 million people annually.

Q What two U.S. states share borders with the most other states?

A Missouri and Tennessee, which each border eight other states. Missouri borders Iowa, Illinois, Kentucky, Tennessee, Arkansas, Oklahoma, Kansas, and Nebraska. Tennessee borders Kentucky, Virginia, North Carolina, Georgia, Alabama, Mississippi, Arkansas, and Missouri.

Q How many U.S. states border only one other state?

A One: Maine, which borders only New Hampshire. Two states, Alaska and Hawaii, border no others.

Q What is the one place in North America where you can see both the Atlantic Ocean and the Pacific Ocean?

A Irazú, a volcano in central Costa Rica. From its summit, both the Atlantic and Pacific oceans can be seen on a clear day.

Q Where is the Yucatan Peninsula?

A This thumb of land juts off of southeastern Mexico, separating the Gulf of Mexico from the Caribbean Sea. Yucatan was the center of the Maya civilization from about the first century B.C. through the tenth century A.D. Extensive Mayan ruins can be found at Chichén Itzá, Kabah, Mayapán, Tulum, and Uxmal. Near the town of Chicxulub at the northern tip of the peninsula, there is evidence of an enormous crater which is thought to be the point of impact of a meteorite 65 million years ago. The impact would have sent so much dust into the atmosphere that the sun's rays would have been blocked for months or perhaps years, lowering temperatures globally and possibly causing the extinction of the dinosaurs.

Q What is the oldest capital city in the Americas?

A Mexico City. The city originated as Tenochtitlán, the capital of the Aztecs, founded in the mid-1300s. By the early 1500s, the city had a population of perhaps 150,000, which was not only greater than any other city in the Americas but also greater than any European city at the time. In 1521, after a three-month siege, Spanish invaders under Hernán Cortés captured Tenochtitlán, razed the entire city, and founded Mexico City upon its ruins.

Q What is the most densely populated country in North America?

A El Salvador, which has a density of 775 people per square mile (299 per sq km). The U.S. ranks eighth, with 75 people per square mile (29 per sq km). Canada, the continent's largest country, is by far the least densely populated: it averages only 8.2 people per square mile (3.2 per sq km).

Q What is the largest island in Caribbean Sea?

A Cuba, the world's 15th-largest island. It has a land area of 42,800 square miles (110,800 sq km). The second-largest Caribbean island is Hispaniola, which covers 29,400 square miles (76,200 sq km) and contains the countries of Haiti and the Dominican Republic. Jamaica, measuring 4,200 square miles (11,000 sq km), is the third-largest Caribbean island.

Q How many U.S. states have volcanoes that were active in the 20th century?

A Four. Alaska has the most: 34 of its volcanoes, most of which are located on the Alaska Peninsula and the Aleutian Islands, have erupted since 1900. The other states with documented eruptions in the 20th century are: Hawaii (3), Washington (1), and California (1).

Caldera and lava lake of Kīlauea, on the island of Hawai'i

Q What is the only Caribbean island with large oil reserves?

A Trinidad. The island's economy is based on oil, which accounts for about 80% of its exports. As a result of oil wealth, Trinidadians enjoy a higher standard of living than the people of most other Caribbean countries.

Q Which U.S. state has the highest average elevation?

A Colorado, with an average elevation of 6,800 feet (2,074 m) above sea level. However, the four highest peaks in the U.S. are found not in Colorado but in Alaska.

Questions and Answers

South America

Q What is Latin America?

A The term "Latin America" designates the parts of North and South America which were settled by Spanish and Portuguese colonists and still retain a Hispanic character. These include Mexico, Cuba, Puerto Rico, the Dominican Republic, some of the smaller islands in the West Indies, all of Central America except for Belize, and all of South America except for Guyana, Suriname, and French Guiana.

Q If you flew due south from Chicago, which South American country would you fly over first?

A You wouldn't fly over any South American countries. A straight line drawn south from Chicago passes through the Gulf of Mexico, Central America, and the Pacific Ocean. Point Parinas, Peru, the westernmost point of mainland South America, is about 500 miles (800 km) east of this line. The Galapagos Islands, which belong to Ecuador, lie about 75 miles (120 km) west of the line.

Q What percentage of the world's coffee beans come from South America?

A South America currently produces approximately 45% of the world's coffee beans. Brazil leads the continent, producing just under one-quarter of the world total. Another 16% are grown in Colombia. Coffee plants require hot, moist climates, and they yield the most flavorful beans when cultivated at elevations between 3,000 and 6,000 feet (900 and 1800 m). South America's principal coffee-growing regions are found in the Brazilian and Guiana Highlands, and in the valleys and foothills of the Andes.

Giant Galapagos turtle

Q What scientist made the Galapagos Islands famous?

A Charles Darwin, who visited the islands during his 1831-1836 expedition on the H.M.S. *Beagle*. Darwin's observations of how various animal species had adapted to life on the islands contributed to his ground-breaking theory of evolution, which he presented in the 1859 book *On the Origin of Species*.

Q Where are the Falkland Islands?

A In the Atlantic Ocean, about 275 miles (440 km) off the east coast of Argentina. The Falklands are a dependency of the United Kingdom, and nearly all of the residents are English-speakers of British descent. Argentina, which has asserted claims to the Falklands since 1816, invaded and occupied the islands in 1982. The U.K. sent a large task force that defeated the Argentineans in a war lasting less than a month.

Q What South American country is the longest when measured from north to south?

A Brazil. The country measures 2,725 miles (4,395 km) north to south, which is the approximate distance from New York City to Reno, Nevada. The second-longest country is Chile, with a length of 2,647 miles (4,270 km). In contrast to its great length, Chile measures only 235 miles (380 km) east to west at its widest point.

Q What was discovered in Venezuela's Lake Maracaibo in 1914?

A Oil. Maracaibo sits above one of the world's largest oil fields, and today the lake's surface is a thicket of oil derricks. Wealth from oil exportation has helped to make Venezuela one of the richest countries in Latin America.

Q What is Patagonia?

A Patagonia is a wind-swept plateau region occupying the southern third of South America, east of the Andes. The plateau receives little precipitation, and its only vegetation is scrubby grasses and thorny desert shrubs. The name "Patagonia" probably comes from the Grand Patagon, a dog-headed monster in a European romance called *Primaleon of Greece*. In 1592, the crew members of the ship *Desire* were attacked by a war-party of Tehuelche Indians wearing dog masks.

Q What South American city is the world's highest national capital?

A La Paz, Bolivia. The city sprawls across the floor of a deep canyon high in the Andes, at an elevation of 12,000 feet (19,350 km)—approximately the same height as the summit of Japan's Mt. Fuji. The canyon walls protect the city from the bitterly cold winds that whip across the surrounding plateau. Visitors from lower elevations often suffer from altitude sickness for several days until their bodies adjust to the thin, oxygen-poor air.

Q What is the southernmost city in the world?

A Ushuaia, Argentina, on the island of Tierra del Fuego. This city of 29,452 people lies at 54°48' south latitude, less than 700 miles (1,100 km) from Antarctica. The world's southernmost city with a population greater than 100,000 is Punta Arenas, Chile, located 150 miles (240 km) northwest of Ushuaia.

Q How many South American countries are named for famous people or cities?

A Three. Bolivia was named for Simón Bolívar, the revolutionary who helped to liberate much of northern South America from Spanish rule. Colombia takes its name from the explorer Christopher Columbus, who "discovered" South America in 1498 and sailed along the coast of present-day Colombia in 1502. The name "Venezuela" is Spanish for "Little Venice." When European explorers reached Lake Maracaibo in 1499, they found villages built on pilings over the shallow waters, which reminded them of Venice, Italy.

Q Why is South America sometimes referred to as "the hollow continent"?

A South America earned this nickname because most of its people live on or near the coasts; the interior is sparsely populated. Sixteen of the 20 largest metropolitan areas lie within 200 miles (320 km) of the coast. The continent's uneven population distribution has both a historical and a geographical explanation. Beginning in the 16th century, European colonists settled in the coastal regions from which raw materials were shipped back to Europe. The Amazon rain forest—hot, humid, and nearly impenetrable in places—has discouraged settlement of the northern half of the continent, and the Andes present a formidable barrier to eastward expansion from the Pacific coast. *(Refer to population map on page 99.)*

Q How many of South America's 20 longest rivers empty into the Pacific Ocean?

A None. South America's continental divide runs along the crest of the Andes at the continent's western edge. In most places the divide lies within 200 miles (320 km) of the Pacific coast. Rivers originating west of the divide have only a short distance to travel before reaching the Pacific. Rivers flowing east from the divide have nearly the whole expanse of the continent to cross before emptying into the Atlantic.

Q What South American city was the capital of the Inca empire?

Cathedral and rooftops in Cusco

A Cusco, Peru. The city was built by the Incas in the fourteenth century and served as their capital for 200 years until it was destroyed by Francisco Pizarro in 1533. Today, Cusco thrives as a major tourist attraction. Many of its houses and buildings are constructed on foundations of stone first cut by the Incas. Lying about 50 miles (80 km) northwest of Cusco is Machu Picchu, a well-preserved mountaintop Inca city, which was rediscovered in 1911.

Q What stretch of ocean off the South American coast is considered one of the most treacherous to ships?

A The Drake Passage. Approximately 500 miles (1,800 km) wide, this strait separates Cape Horn—at the southern tip of South America—from the South Shetland Islands which lie just north of Antarctica. First traversed in 1615, the passage was part of a major trade route between the Atlantic and Pacific oceans until 1914, when the Panama Canal opened. Frigid temperatures, rough waters, and high winds make the passage treacherous for all vessels but especially for the sailing ships of centuries past. Because the passage is so perilous, many ships avoid it by cutting through the Strait of Magellan to the north. However, this strait has its own dangers: it is narrow and twisting, and has been the site of numerous major shipwrecks.

Q Where is the Land of Fire?

A At the southern tip of South America. Tierra del Fuego, Spanish for "Land of Fire," is a group of islands lying south of the Strait of Magellan. When Portuguese explorer Ferdinand Magellan arrived in 1520, he named the islands after observing the native inhabitants carrying torches. The largest island, also called Tierra del Fuego, accounts for two-thirds of the land area of the island group. The eastern third of the islands belong to Argentina, and the rest belong to Chile.

Q What are the Nazca Lines?

A The Nazca Lines are gigantic drawings that were etched into Peru's desert floor by the Nazca people between 500 B.C. and A.D. 500. Scattered across 200 square miles (520 sq km), they form the world's largest display of art. The drawings fall into two categories: animal motifs and geometric patterns of crisscrossing straight lines. They were made by scraping away the top layer of red gravel to reveal the yellow sand below it. Archaeologists still disagree about the purpose of the Nazca Lines, but some theories hold that the lines formed ancient highways or were used as a giant calendar.

Q What is "El Niño"?

A El Niño is a seasonal ocean current that flows south along the Pacific coast of South America. The current takes its name—which is Spanish for "the Child"—from its usual arrival during the Christmas season. In normal years, when El Niño reaches northern Peru, southeasterly trade winds push its warm surface waters westward across the Pacific, away from the coast. Every four or five years, these trade winds weaken, allowing El Niño to travel farther south along the coast, raising local water temperatures by several degrees. This warmer water kills plankton and fish, crippling the fishing industry. Increased evaporation leads to excessive rainfall over parts of South America. The change in El Niño's normal flow pattern affects other ocean currents which often leads to dramatic climatic changes around the world.

Q How many of the Earth's species are found in the Amazon rain forest?

A Most of the Amazon basin has not been fully explored, and therefore most of its plant and animal species have not yet been catalogued. However, scientists estimate that the Amazon rain forest, which covers less than 5% of the Earth's total land area, contains almost one-half of the planet's animal and plant species. One in ten of the most common medicines we use today comes from rain forest plants, and scientists believe that cures for many diseases, such as cancer, might be derived from plant species not yet discovered.

Q Where in South America could you find places in which no rainfall has ever been recorded?

A The Atacama Desert in northern Chile. This barren land of sand, rocks, borax lakes and saline deposits is one of the driest regions in the world. In parts of the desert, no rainfall has ever been recorded, and the city of Arica, at the northern edge, endured more than 14 consecutive years of drought from October 1903 through January 1918.

Q What South American possession lies farthest from the mainland?

A Easter Island, situated 2,300 miles (3,700 km) west of Chile in the Pacific Ocean. This small volcanic island was discovered on Easter Sunday in 1722, and was annexed by Chile in 1888. Although it belongs to Chile, geographically Easter Island is considered to be part of Oceania, not South America. It is best known for its strange monuments: scattered over the island are more than 600 huge stone faces, the earliest dating back more than 1,500 years.

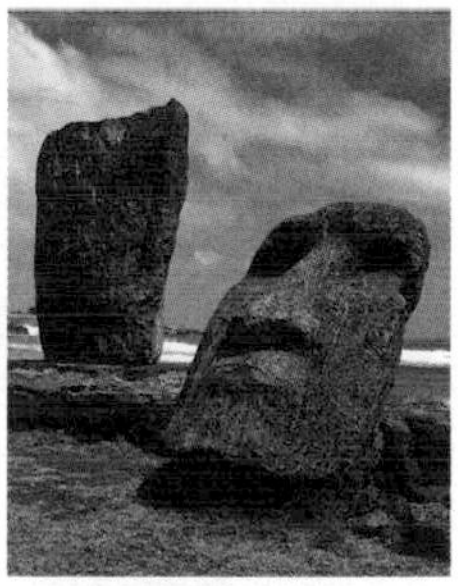

Ancient statues, Easter Island

Q Where are the pampas?

A These flat, grassy plains—which are much like the prairies of North America—are found in the temperate regions of southern South America, east of the Andes. The largest such plain, known simply as the Pampa, covers much of central and northern Argentina, and extends into Uruguay. Since the 1550s, when European colonists introduced cattle to the Pampa, livestock raising has been a thriving industry. For many people, gauchos, or Argentinean cowboys, are the enduring symbol of the Pampa, although in the last century farming has superseded cattle ranching in economic importance.

Questions and Answers

Europe

Q Where is the Black Forest?

A In southwestern Germany, between the Rhine and Neckar rivers. The Black Forest, or *Schwarzwald* in German, is a mountainous region that takes its name from the dark coniferous trees that cover its slopes. Its fertile valleys provide good pastureland and produce grapes for wine, and its trees supply the lumber and woodworking industries, as well as toy and cuckoo clock manufacturers. The region's scenic beauty, winter sports facilities, and mineral springs attract many tourists each year.

Q How many national capitals are located on the Danube River?

A Four. The capital cities of Bratislava (Slovakia), Budapest (Hungary), Belgrade (Serbia and Montenegro), and Vienna (Austria) are all found along the banks of the Danube. Five other capitals are located on tributaries of the Danube: Bucharest (Romania), Sofia (Bulgaria), Ljubljana (Slovenia), Zagreb (Croatia), and Sarajevo (Bosnia and Herzegovina).

Old Town of Zagreb, Croatia

Q What is killing the forests of Northern Europe?

A Acid rain. In the atmosphere, airborne pollutants—especially sulfur and nitrogen dioxides from automobile and industrial emissions—adhere to water droplets, and then fall back to Earth as acidified rain, snow, or hail. This precipitation poisons plant and animal life, erodes buildings, and contaminates soil and drinking water. As a result of acid rain, as many as one-half of the trees in Germany's Black Forest and Switzerland's central alpine region are dead or dying. At least 4,000 lakes in Sweden are so acidic that no fish survive in them. To combat acid rain, the countries of the European Union recently agreed to significantly reduce nitrogen oxide and sulfur dioxide emissions.

Q What independent countries were once part of the U.S.S.R.?

A When the Union of Soviet Socialist Republics (U.S.S.R.) broke up in 1991, its 15 republics all became independent countries: Armenia, Azerbaijan, Belarus, Estonia, Georgia, Kazakhstan, Krygyzstan, Latvia, Lithuania, Moldova, Russia, Tajikistan, Turkmenistan, Ukraine, and Uzbekistan.

Q How many times did the name of St. Petersburg, Russia, change in the 20th century?

A Three times. St. Petersburg was founded in 1703 by Peter the Great. In 1914, its name was changed to Petrograd, Russian for "Peter's City," and then in 1924 it was changed again, this time to Leningrad, in honor of Vladimir Lenin, the founder of Russian Communism. In 1991, following the collapse of Communist rule, the city name was changed back to St. Petersburg. Older citizens joke about being born in St. Petersburg, attending school in Petrograd, working in Leningrad, and growing old in St. Petersburg—all while living in the same place.

Q What independent countries were once part of Yugoslavia?

A Prior to 1991, Yugoslavia was comprised of six republics: Bosnia and Herzegovina, Croatia, Macedonia, Montenegro, Serbia, and Slovenia. In 1991-92, four of the six republics—Croatia, Slovenia, Macedonia, and Bosnia and Herzegovina—declared their independence. In 2003, the remaining republics agreed to change the name from Yugoslavia to Serbia and Montenegro.

Q What is the Chunnel?

A "Chunnel" is a nickname for the English Channel Tunnel, which connects England and France via rail under the English Channel. There are actually three separate tunnels: two for trains and a parallel service tunnel. The tunnels run for 31 miles between Coquelles, France, and Folkestone, England, at an average depth of 150 feet (46 m) below the seafloor. Work on the tunnels began in 1987, and the first trains crossed under the Channel in 1994.

Q Where is "Europe's Grand Canyon"?

A Along the Verdon River in the Provence region of southeastern France. The Verdon has carved a deep, narrow gorge, known as the Grand Cañon du Verdon, through the limestone plateau between the town of Castellane and the artificial Lac de Ste-Croix. The gorge stretches for 13 miles (21 km) and reaches a depth of 3,170 feet (965 m). It is considered one of the natural wonders of Europe.

Q What is the only volcano on the European mainland that erupted in the 20th century?

A Mt. Vesuvius (Vesuvio), located in southern Italy nine miles (15 km) east of Naples. It was active through much of the century, with significant eruptions in 1906, 1929, and 1944. Two thousand years ago, most Romans did not recognize Vesuvius as a volcano, and numerous farming communities thrived on the fertile land around its base. Then, in August of A.D. 79, the volcano exploded in a mighty eruption, burying the cities of Pompeii, Herculaneum, and Stabiae under cinders, ash, and mud, and killing more than 3,500 people.

Q How many European countries fall partially within the Arctic Circle?

A Four: Finland, Norway, Russia, and Sweden. Technically, a fifth country could be added to this list: Iceland's mainland ends just short of the Arctic Circle, but one of the country's islands, Grimsey, straddles the line, its northern half sitting within the Circle.

The historic Henningsvaer Port in the Lofoten Islands of Norway, north of the Arctic Circle

Q Where is Waterloo, site of Napoleon's famous defeat?

A Today, Waterloo is a suburb of Brussels, Belgium, although at the time of the battle—June 18, 1815—it lay 12 miles (19 km) away from the city, which was then much smaller. At Waterloo, the troops of French emperor Napoleon I were defeated by British forces under the command of the Duke of Wellington and Prussian forces led by Gebhard Blücher. The French defeat ended the Napoleonic Wars, which had begun in 1803.

Is Venice, Italy, really sinking?

Yes, although at a much slower rate than previously. The city, which dates back to the 4th century A.D., is built on 118 small islands in a lagoon at the top of the Adriatic Sea. Its buildings sit on foundations of wooden pilings driven deep into the underlying sand, silt and clay. Originally the buildings were safely above high tide level, but over the course of 15 centuries, natural compaction of the subsoil caused the city to sink more than 30 inches (76 cm). Earlier this century, groundwater was pumped out of the subsoil to satisfy water needs on the mainland. This proved disastrous for Venice: the city quickly sank another five inches (13 cm) at a time when the sea level was rising by four inches (10 cm). The pumping was stopped, and Venice's sinking has slowed to its earlier "natural" rate. Unfortunately, the foundations of many buildings have been severely damaged by high water.

Gondola and canal, Venice

Which independent European countries are smaller than Rhode Island, the smallest U.S. state?

Seven independent European countries cover a smaller area than Rhode Island's 1,545 square miles (4,002 sq km): Vatican City, Monaco, San Marino, Liechtenstein, Malta, Andorra, and Luxembourg.

How many official languages are recognized in Switzerland?

Four: German, French, Italian, and Romansch. German is the most widely spoken language: 65% of the Swiss speak a dialect known as *Schwyzerdutsch*, or Swiss German. French is spoken by 18% of the population, Italian by 10%, and Romansch by only 1%.

Why is Ukraine called "the breadbasket of Europe"?

Ukraine's topography—flat plains, or "steppes," cover most of the country—and extremely fertile soils combine to make it one of the world's most outstanding agricultural areas. In 1994, the country produced almost 36 million tons (33 metric tons) of grain. Major crops include wheat, rye, barley, corn, potatoes, sunflower seeds, sugar beets, and cotton. Ukraine also has thriving dairy and livestock industries, as well as many food-processing plants.

If the Caspian Sea is a *sea*, then how can it be the world's largest *lake*?

Actually, it is both a sea *and* a lake. The word "sea" is used most often to designate specific regions of the oceans that are more or less surrounded by land; however, it can also apply to inland bodies of water, especially if they are large and/or salty. The Caspian Sea is both large and salty, so it is called a sea. "Lake" is a general term for inland bodies of water of substantial size. The Caspian Sea lies inland and has a surface area of 143,240 square miles (370,990 sq km), so it is also considered to be a lake. Other "sea-lakes" in the world include the Aral Sea, the Dead Sea, the Sea of Galilee, and California's Salton Sea.

Where is Transylvania?

In northwestern Romania. The region is bounded by the Carpathian Mountains in the north and east, the Transylvanian Alps in the south, and by Romania's borders with Hungary and Yugoslavia in the west. A high plateau, averaging 1,000 to 1,600 feet (300 to 500 m) in elevation, covers much of Transylvania. In Bram Stoker's 1897 novel *Dracula*, Transylvania is the home of the blood-sucking Count. Stoker based the story on local vampire legends, many of which persist today: in some parts of eastern Europe, peasants still wear garlic necklaces and hang garlic wreaths from their doors to ward off vampire spirits.

What countries contain parts of the Carpathian Mountains?

Five: the Czech Republic, Slovakia, Poland, Ukraine, and Romania. Curving for more than 900 miles (1,450 km) along the north and east sides of the Danube plain in central and eastern Europe, the Carpathians roughly form a half-circle connecting the Alps and the Balkans. The mountain system consists of two main parts: the Northern Carpathians, which include the Beskid and the Tatra ranges, and the Southern Carpathians, also called the Transylvanian Alps. The Carpathians' highest peak is Gerlachovský štít in Slovakia, which rises to 8,711 feet (2,655 m).

Where is Lapland?

In northern Scandinavia. Lapland is home to the Lapps, a nomadic people who have traditionally engaged in hunting, fishing, and reindeer-herding. When the Finns arrived in the southern part of present-day Finland 2,000 years ago, they found the Lapps already settled there. Over the years, the Lapps have been pushed north, and their territory has expanded to cover parts of northern Norway, Sweden, Finland, and northwestern Russia. Today, there are approximately 42,000 Lapps, most of whom work in a variety of farming, construction, and service fields. The Finnish government has made many efforts to protect the Lapps' language, called Sami, and culture.

What European country has a shorter coastline than any other maritime country in the world?

Monaco, whose Mediterranean coastline is a mere three-and-a-half miles (5.6 km) long. Another European country, Bosnia and Herzegovina, ranks second in this category: its coast on the Adriatic Sea between Croatia and Serbia and Montenegro is only 13 miles (21 km) long. In third place is Slovenia, whose Adriatic coast is 29 miles (47 km) long.

Harbor and coastline, Monaco

What European city is the largest city in the world north of the Arctic Circle?

Murmansk, Russia, a city of 472,900 people located on the Kola Gulf of the Barents Sea. Although Murmansk lies approximately 150 miles north of the Arctic Circle, its harbor remains ice-free throughout the year due to the moderating effect of a warm ocean current called the North Atlantic Drift. While there are thousands of cities and towns north of the Arctic Circle, there are none at all south of the Antarctic Circle at the opposite end of the world.

Questions and Answers

Africa

Q What is the East African Rift System?

A This term refers to a series of rift valleys running through East Africa from Mozambique to the southern end of the Red Sea. These valleys are part of the Great Rift Valley, a 4,000-mile (6,430-km)-long depression that also includes the Red Sea, the Dead Sea, and the rest of the Jordan Valley. The East African Rift System marks the line along which geological forces are splitting East Africa off from the rest of the continent. Eventually, everything east of the Rift System—including all or part of present-day Mozambique, Tanzania, Rwanda, Burundi, Uganda, Kenya, Ethiopia, Djibouti, and Somalia—will be a huge island off of Africa's eastern coast. Madagascar was attached to the African mainland before similar forces split it off into an island 175 million years ago.

Q What is the Serengeti?

A Located in northern Tanzania, east of Lake Victoria and west of Kilimanjaro, the Serengeti is a vast plain of grassland, acacia bushes, forest, and rocky outcrops. Serengeti National Park, established in 1951, covers an area of the plain about the size of Connecticut. The park is home to one of the last great concentrations of African wildlife, including antelope, buffalo, cheetahs, elephants, gazelles, giraffes, hyenas, leopards, lions, black rhinoceroses, wildebeests and zebras. Tourists from all over the world visit the park to observe the wildlife and to witness the large-scale animal migrations that occur in May and June.

Giraffes on the Serengeti

Q How has the Aswan High Dam affected the Nile Valley ?

A Before the dam was built in 1971, floodwaters inundated the Nile Valley each fall, depositing fresh, fertile silt across the valley floor. This annual replenishment of the soil helped agriculture to thrive in the valley for thousands of years. The dam ended the annual floods, and now much of the Nile's water-borne silt settles to the bottom of Lake Nassar, the enormous artificial lake behind the dam. Water evaporating from the lake's surface has increased the regional humidity, which has accelerated the decay of many of the valley's great tombs and monuments. On the positive side, the dam supplies more than 25% of Egypt's hydro-electric power, and desert irrigation projects using water from Lake Nassar have created 900,000 new acres of arable land.

Q What is remarkable about the delta of the Okavango River?

A It is the largest inland delta in the world. The Okavango originates in the mountains of central Angola and flows 1,000 miles (1,600 km) to the northwest corner of Botswana, where it spills over the Gomare fault and fans out into a swampy delta covering 4,000 square miles (10,350 sq km). Meandering through a myriad of shallow channels, the waters of the Okavango quickly evaporate. The small amount that eventually emerges from the southeastern end of the delta represents less than 5% of the river's pre-delta flow.

Q What African country was previously known as Upper Volta?

A Burkina Faso. The Volta River's three upper branches —the Volta Blanche (White Volta), Volta Rouge (Red Volta), and Volta Noire (Black Volta)—all originate within the country, hence the earlier name. Burkina Faso, the Mossi-dialect name adopted in 1984, translates roughly as "Country of Honest Men."

Q What are the most important crops grown in Africa?

A Africa is the world's leading producer of cocoa beans (55% of the world total) and cassava roots (45% of the world total). It is also a major producer of grain and millet sorghum (27%), coffee (20%), peanuts (20%), palm oil (14%), tea (12%), and olive oil (12%).

Woman in sorghum fields, Bema

Q What object found along the banks of the Orange River in 1867 changed the course of South African history?

A A 21-carat diamond. The discovery of this gem near Hopetown precipitated a huge diamond rush, and thousands of people from all over the continent and the world raced to southern Africa. The town of Kimberley, site of the famous open mine known as the Big Hole, became the diamond capital of the world. Between 1871 and 1914, more than 14 million carats of diamonds were removed from the mine, which eventually reached a depth of 4,000 feet (1,220 m) and a width of one mile (1.6 km).

Q What is Cabinda?

A A coastal province of Angola that lies north of the Congo River and is separated from the rest of the country by a 19-mile (31-km)-wide corridor belonging to the Democratic Republic of the Congo. Most of Cabinda is covered by tropical forest. Offshore lie rich oil fields which produce one million barrels annually.

Q What African country was founded in 1847 by freed American slaves?

A Liberia, whose name comes from the Latin word *liber*, meaning "free." It is the only country in sub-Saharan Africa that has never been ruled by a colonial power. Liberia's capital city, Monrovia, was named for James Monroe, the fifth U.S. president.

Q What two African countries border only a single other country?

A Lesotho and The Gambia. South Africa surrounds Lesotho, and The Gambia is bordered in the north, east, and south by Senegal; to its west lies the Atlantic Ocean.

Q What is the Ngorongoro Crater?

A Located in northern Tanzania, Ngorongoro is the crater of a volcano that has been extinct for several million years. It has a diameter of 9 miles (14.5 km) and its walls rise about 2,000 feet (610 m) above its floor. The crater supports an abundance of wildlife, including wildebeests, elephants, rhinoceroses, hippopotamuses, lions, leopards, and flamingoes. In 1956 Ngorongoro was established as a conservation area, but its ecological balance is threatened by growing numbers of tourists and the large cattle herds of the nomadic Masai people.

Q Why is it difficult to say how large Lake Chad is?

A The lake's size fluctuates dramatically throughout the year. Numerous rivers and streams flow into Lake Chad, but it has no outlet. During the summer rainy season, floodwaters swell the lake to 10,000 square miles (25,900 sq km) and occasionally to twice that size. Even at its maximum size the lake is extremely shallow; its greatest depth is only 25 feet (8 m). By the end of the following spring, evaporation has shrunk the lake by 60%, to about 4,000 square miles (10,360 sq km). In recent decades, Lake Chad's cyclical fluctuations have been greatly affected by recurring droughts, which have reduced the flow of water into the lake and accelerated evaporation. Its volume has dropped by 80% since 1970.

Q What is significant about the location of Khartoum, Sudan?

A Khartoum, the capital of Sudan, is located at the point where the White Nile and Blue Nile rivers meet to form the Nile. Capitalizing on its strategic location, the city has become Sudan's commercial center and transportation hub. It is built on a curving strip of land that resembles the trunk of an elephant: the name "Khartoum" comes from the Arabic *Ras-al-hartum*, which means "end of the elephant's trunk."

Q What is Africa's newest country?

A Eritrea, which officially became independent in 1993. An Italian colony from 1890 to 1941, Eritrea was captured by the British during World War II. In 1952, the United Nations awarded Eritrea to Ethiopia under the condition that it be ruled as a self-governing territory. Ethiopia violated this agreement by annexing Eritrea in 1962, touching off a civil war which lasted more than 30 years. Eritrea formally declared its independence in May 1993, two years after defeating Ethiopia's Marxist regime.

Q What is the Sahel?

A The Sahel (Sudan) is a semiarid region that separates the Sahara Desert from the tropical savanna and rain forests of central Africa. It stretches halfway across the continent, from Mauritania in the west to Chad in the east, in a band averaging more than 1,000 miles (1,600 km) in width. Most of the Sahel is semiarid savanna, with low grasses in the north and tall grasses in the south. Annual precipitation varies from 4 inches to 24 inches (100 to 600 mm). The 8-month dry season makes farming difficult, and the region has experienced several severe droughts in recent decades.

Woman returning from well in the Sahel

Q In what country would you find Africa's northernmost point?

A Tunisia. The northernmost point is Cape Ben Sekka, which lies just north of the continent's northernmost town, Bechater. Parts of five European countries—Greece, Italy, Malta, Portugal, and Spain—lie farther south than Cape Ben Sekka. From the tip of the cape, Africa stretches southward approximately 5,000 miles (8,000 km) to its southernmost point, Cape Agulhas in South Africa.

Q How has the Sahara Desert changed in the last 5,000 years?

A Scientists believe that 5,000 years ago the climate of the Sahara was more temperate and far less arid than it is today. Much of the region was grassland. Around 3000 B.C. global climate patterns began to shift, and the region entered an arid period which continues today. The desert currently covers 3,500,000 square miles (9,100,000 sq km), an area nearly as large as the United States, and its size is increasing. In recent decades, recurring droughts and overgrazing in the Sahel region have contributed to the Sahara's southward expansion.

Q What is the traditional mode of transportation in the Sahara Desert?

A The camel, or more specifically, the one-humped dromedary, which was domesticated at least 3,000 years ago. Dromedaries are extremely well-suited to desert conditions. They have the ability to store water in their hump, and can tolerate water losses equal to one-fourth of their body weight. Their heavy-lidded eyes and closeable nostrils offer protection in sandstorms. Today, as the Saharan road system expands, truck convoys are replacing camel caravans, although trucks require frequent refueling, often overheat in the desert sun, and grind to a halt when sand clogs their engines.

Camel eating leaves

Q Which African country can boast the greatest known deposits, variety, and output of minerals in the world?

A South Africa. It has the world's largest known deposits of chromite, gold, manganese, platinum, and vanadium. The country leads the world in production of gold, chromite, vanadium, and the platinum group metals: platinum, palladium, iridium, rhodium, and ruthenium. It is also one of the leading producers of manganese, antimony, and gem and industrial diamonds.

Q Where is the Horn of Africa?

A This term refers to the horn-shaped area of eastern Africa that juts into the Indian Ocean. Somalia and Ethiopia occupy most of the horn. The cape of Gees Gwardafuy and the city of Caluula sit at the northeastern tip of the horn, marking the entrance to the Gulf of Aden, which connects the Arabian Sea and the Red Sea.

Q What is the Valley of the Kings?

A This narrow valley, across the Nile River from the city of Luxor, contains the tombs of the pharaohs who ruled Egypt during the New Kingdom period, 1550 B.C. to 1200 B.C. The tombs are carved deep into the sandstone walls of the valley; most have five to fifteen rooms. Among the pharaohs buried in the valley are Ramses II, Ramses VI, and Seti I. Upon their death, the pharaohs were mummified and then entombed with all of the material things that they might need in the afterlife, including gold, jeweled ornaments, furniture, clothing, and food. Most of the tombs were soon looted by robbers, who removed all items of value. However, in 1922 the tomb of Tutankhamen—"King Tut"—was discovered with most of its riches untouched.

Questions and Answers

Asia

Q What natural features form the physical boundary between Europe and Asia?

A Europe and Asia share the same huge landmass, which is known as Eurasia. The imaginary line dividing this landmass into two continents runs through the Ural Mountains, the Ural River, the Caspian Sea, the Caucasus mountains, the Black Sea, the Bosporus strait, the Sea of Marmara, and the Dardanelles strait.

Q How many countries lie partially within Europe and partially within Asia?

A Four: Azerbaijan, which is traversed by the Caucasus Mountains; Kazakhstan, whose far western lands lie west of the Ural River; Russia, which is split by the Ural Mountains, and Turkey, which includes a small area on the northwestern side of the Sea of Marmara.

Q Why was the Great Wall of China built?

A To defend China against invasion by the Huns and other enemies. Defensive walls were built in China as early as the 6th century B.C. In 214 B.C., under Emperor Shih Huang-ti, the existing walls were connected to form a single continuous wall with watchtowers. This wall was extended during the Han Dynasty (202 B.C. – A.D. 220) and the Sui Dynasty (A.D. 581 – 618). Seven hundred years later the wall had mostly crumbled, and in the late 1400s, under the Ming Emperors, it was completely rebuilt. The portions of the wall that remain today are those that were constructed during this most recent period.

The Great Wall winding through a hilly region in northern China

Q How has the Aral Sea changed in recent decades?

A It has shrunk by about 55% since 1960. The sea once covered nearly 25,000 square miles (64,720 sq km) and was the fourth-largest inland body of water in the world. Today it covers only about 11,100 square miles (28,700 sq km), and the former port city of Muynak lies 30 miles (48 km) inland. The sea's shrinkage can be blamed on cotton farming in the surrounding desert. Soviet-era efforts to establish a profitable cotton industry led to the creation of an extensive network of irrigation canals. These huge canals drain large amounts of water from the Syr Darya and Amu Darya, the only two rivers that empty into the sea.

Q What is the Ring of Fire?

A "Ring of Fire" designates the narrow band of active volcanoes encircling the Pacific Ocean basin. Of the approximately 1,500 volcanoes in the world that have been active within the last 10,000 years, more than two-thirds are part of the Ring. Over half of the Ring's active volcanoes are found in its Asian portion, which passes through Russia's Kamchatka Peninsula, the Kuril Islands, Japan, and the Philippines. The Ring of Fire's most recent major volcanic event was the 1991 eruption of Pinatubo on the Philippine island of Luzon, which prompted the evacuation of 250,000 people.

Q What part of Asia is called Indochina?

A "Indochina" refers to the southeastern Asian peninsula situated south of China and east of India. Countries located on the peninsula are Cambodia, Laos, Myanmar (Burma), Thailand, Vietnam, and the western portion of Malaysia. The eastern part of the Indochinese peninsula, including Cambodia, Laos, and Vietnam, was formerly known as French Indochina because of France's strong colonial presence there.

Q The Khyber Pass links which two countries?

A Afghanistan and Pakistan. Approximately 33 miles (53 km) long and reaching a maximum elevation of about 3,500 feet (1,067 m), the pass cuts through the Safed Koh mountains just south of the Kabul River, connecting the high plateau of Afghanistan with the Indus Valley. It has been used for centuries as a caravan route and as an invasion route into India. Today it is also traversed by a paved highway and, in Pakistan, by a railroad. In the 1980s several million refugees fleeing Afghanistan's civil war crossed into Pakistan via the pass.

Q What Persian Gulf country is a federation of seven Arab sheikdoms?

A United Arab Emirates, formed in 1971 through the unification of the sheikdoms of Abu Dhabi, Ajman, Dubai, Fujeirah, Sharjah, and Umm al-Qawain. Ras al-Khaimah joined the federation in 1972. Underdeveloped a few decades ago, the U.A.E. has been transformed by oil wealth into a modern and affluent country.

Q What Asian country contains, or is bordered by, six of the world's ten highest mountains?

A Nepal. Within Nepal or along its borders with China and India are found the following peaks: Mt. Everest (highest in the world), Kanchenjunga (3rd), Makalu (4th), Dhawalāgiri (5th), Annapurna (7th), and Xixabangma Feng (9th). Nanda Devi (10th) lies only 50 miles (80 km) northwest of Nepal's western border.

Q Where is the Empty Quarter?

A This hostile desert is found in the southern third of the Arabian Peninsula. Called *Ar Rub' Al-Khālī*, or "the Empty Quarter" in Arabic, it covers 250,000 square miles (647,000 sq km) and is the world's largest continuous sand body. Few people live in the Empty Quarter, and much of the region has never been explored.

Q What Asian volcanic eruption has been called the loudest natural explosion in recorded history?

A The 1883 eruption of Krakatau (Krakatoa), an island volcano between Sumatra and Java. Krakatau exploded three times on August 26 and 27, 1883, shooting tremendous amounts of gas and ash 50 miles (80 km) into the atmosphere. The explosions were so violent that they were heard nearly 3,000 miles (4,653 km) away on Rodrigues Island in the western Indian Ocean. Krakatau collapsed into itself, and when the explosions were over most of the island was submerged under 900 feet of water. Tsunamis up to 130 feet (40 m) high slammed the coasts of Sumatra and Java, washing away hundreds of villages and killing more than 36,000 people.

Q At their closest point, how far apart are Asia and North America?

A At the narrowest point of the Bering Strait, Asia and North America are separated by only 56 miles (90 km). Russia's Big Diomede (Ratmanov) Island and the United States' Little Diomede Island, which lie in the middle of the strait, are only 2.5 miles (4 km) apart.

Q Where is the Fertile Crescent?

A This term refers to a crescent-shaped area of fertile land in the Middle East which begins in the south with Egypt's Nile Valley, runs north along the eastern coast of the Mediterranean Sea, then turns southeast through Mesopotamia, the land between the Tigris and Euphrates rivers, and ends at the head of the Persian Gulf. The Fertile Crescent was the birthplace of some of the world's oldest civilizations, including the Sumerians, Babylonians, and Assyrians.

Q What country was Pakistan part of before it became independent?

A India. Conflicts between Hindus and Muslims in British India led to the creation of Pakistan as a separate Muslim state in 1947. Originally, Pakistan included the two main centers of Muslim population, which lay in northwest and east India. The two areas, West Pakistan and East Pakistan, were separated by 1,000 miles (1,600 km). In 1971, East Pakistan declared its independence and changed its name to Bangladesh. The name "Pakistan" comes from the Urdu words *pakh*, meaning "pure," and *stan*, meaning "land."

Q What was Sri Lanka called before 1972?

A Ceylon, which is the name the British had given to the island when they claimed it in 1796. The island became independent in 1948, and in 1972 was renamed Sri Lanka, which in the Sinhala language means "Resplendent Land."

The Taj Mahal

Q What is India's most famous tomb?

A The Taj Mahal, located in the city of Agra. Often described as one of the world's most beautiful buildings, it was built by the Mogul emperor Shah Jahan to honor the memory of his wife, Mumtaz-i-Mahal. Construction began in 1631 and was completed in 1648.

Q What two seas are linked by the Suez Canal?

A The Red Sea and the Mediterranean Sea. Before the 101-mile (163-km) canal was built in the mid-1800s, ships traveling between Europe and the Far East had to sail all the way around the southern tip of Africa. Depending on the origin and destination of the ship, the canal could shorten its trip dramatically. For example, a ship sailing from London to Bombay would have to travel almost 11,000 miles (17,700 km) around the African continent. Using the Suez Canal, the trip could be shortened to 6,300 miles (10,140 km), a distance reduction of over 40%.

Q Which independent Asian country has the highest population density?

A The tiny republic of Singapore, with 17,814 people per square mile (6,879 per sq km). Singapore's 4,375,000 people occupy an island measuring only 26 miles east-to-west and 14 miles north-to-south. Mongolia has the lowest density: 4.4 people per square mile (1.7 per sq km). Mongolia's land area is 2,458 times larger than Singapore's, but it holds only 2,675,000 people.

Q How long is Japan, from north to south?

A The islands of Japan stretch approximately 1,900 miles (3,060 km) from Hokkaido in the north to the Sakishima Archipelago in the south. This is approximately equal to the distance between New York City and Denver.

Landscape on Hokkaido, Japan's northernmost island

Q What region is known as the "Roof of the World"?

A Tibet, the high plateau region which lies north of the Himalayas. Covering 471,000 square miles (1,220,000 sq km), and with an average elevation of 15,000 feet (4,600 m), the Tibetan Plateau is the largest and highest plateau in the world. Much of Tibet is uninhabited; the region's fewer than two million people are concentrated in the valleys of the Brahmaputra (Yarlung) River and its tributaries.

Q Which Asian country leads the world in number of earthquake-related deaths since 1900?

A China, where 48 deadly earthquakes have killed an estimated 967,420 people since 1900. During the same period Iran has lost 147,293 people in 57 earthquakes, and in Japan 32 earthquakes have killed 123,462 people.

Q What cities mark the endpoints of the Trans-Siberian Railway?

A The longest railway line in the world, the Trans-Siberian Railway stretches 5,764 miles (9,297 km) between Moscow in the west and the Pacific Coast port city of Nakhodka (near Vladivostok) in the east. The eight-day journey between the two cities includes stops in 92 Russian cities and towns.

Q How many people live on the Indonesian island of Java?

A Java is home to approximately 118 million people. It is the world's most populous island, although it is only the 13th-largest in area. By contrast, the island of Cuba is four-fifths the size of Java, but its population is only one-eleventh as large.

Q What was the name of Ho Chi Minh City, Vietnam, prior to 1975?

A Saigon. When the city fell to North Vietnamese forces in 1975, it was renamed for Ho Chi Minh, founder of the Indochina Communist Party and president of North Vietnam from 1945 until his death in 1969.

Questions and Answers

Oceania (including Australia and New Zealand)

Q What is Oceania?

A The name "Oceania" refers to the scattered islands of a vast area of the Pacific Ocean, from Palau in the west to Easter Island in the east, and from the Midway Islands in the north to New Zealand in the south. The three main island groups of Oceania are Melanesia, Micronesia, and Polynesia. The continent of Australia and the islands of New Zealand are sometimes considered part of Oceania.

Eucalyptus tree in the Outback, Northern Territory

Q What is the Outback?

A This nickname refers to Australia's vast, largely uninhabited interior. Over the years, the Outback's harsh beauty and its remoteness from the rest of Australia have made it popular with adventurous explorers and travelers. Through depictions in literature, art, and film, the region has become an integral part of Australia's identity. However, it is difficult to characterize the Outback, for its boundaries are undefined and its landscape varies from hot deserts to lush wilderness.

Q Why is Australia sometimes referred to as "the Land Down Under"?

A This nickname originated with the British, who began colonizing Australia in the late 1700s. Because of its extreme southern location in relation to Britain, Australia was considered "Down." The "Under" part of the phrase refers to the continent's position "under" the Eurasian landmass. But while people from the Northern Hemisphere think of Australia as "Down Under," Australians do not.

Q How much of Australia is arid or semiarid?

A More than two-thirds of the continent is considered to be arid or semiarid. The arid areas comprise several large deserts, including the Great Victoria Desert, the Gibson Desert, the Great Sandy Desert, and the Simpson Desert.

Q What distinction does Wellington, New Zealand have among national capitals of independent countries?

A Located at 41°18' south latitude, Wellington is the world's southernmost national capital. In second place is Canberra, Australia, which lies at 35°17' south latitude.

Q What is unusual about how the island of Nauru was formed?

A Nauru, the world's smallest republic, began as a coral atoll. Over the millennia, accumulated bird droppings filled in the central lagoon and created an 8-square-mile (21-sq-km) island whose highest point rises 210 feet (64 m) above sea level. The droppings are a rich source of phosphate, which is used in making fertilizers. Phosphate mining has long been Nauru's economic mainstay, but the resource will soon be exhausted.

Q What are the principal islands of New Zealand?

A Two islands, North Island and South Island, account for more than 98% of New Zealand's total land area. The country also includes Stewart Island, the Chatham Islands, the Antipodes Islands, the Auckland Islands, and hundreds of tiny islets.

Q What is Ayers Rock?

A Ayers Rock, now called by its Aboriginal name, Uluru, is a huge, red, oval-shaped rock outcropping that rises 2,831 feet (863 m) above the plains of central Australia. One of the largest monoliths in the world, Uluru is actually the summit of a massive sandstone hill, most of which is hidden underground. Aborigines consider Uluru sacred and incorporate numerous places around it into their ceremonial life.

Q What is the ratio of sheep to humans in Australia and New Zealand?

A Because both countries are major wool, mutton, and lamb producers, Australia and New Zealand each have a high ratio of sheep to humans. In Australia, there are 132 million sheep, or seven sheep for each human in the country. In New Zealand, the ratio is even greater: the country's 50 million sheep translate into 14 sheep for each human.

Q How many of Oceania's countries have become independent since 1975?

A Eight. Papua New Guinea became independent in 1975, the Solomon Islands and Tuvalu in 1978, Kiribati in 1979, Vanuatu in 1980, the Marshall Islands and the Federated States of Micronesia in 1986, and Palau (Belau) in 1994.

Q What is the Great Barrier Reef?

A This vast coral reef system is the longest in the world, stretching 1,250 miles (2,000 km) along Australia's northeast coast. It is composed of reefs, shoals, and hundreds of islands. Popular with divers, the Great Barrier Reef is home to a myriad of aquatic creatures.

Q On what island is Robert Louis Stevenson buried?

A Stevenson, author of *Dr. Jekyll and Mr. Hyde*, *Kidnapped*, and *Treasure Island*, is buried on the island of Upolu in Western Samoa. Born in Edinburgh, Scotland in 1850, Stevenson sailed to the South Pacific in 1888 and settled permanently in Samoa in 1890. He died there in 1894.

Q Where does Sydney rank among Australia's most populous cities?

Harbor and skyline of Sydney

A Measured by actual city population, Sydney is not even ranked in the top hundred: only 13,501 people live within its tiny city limits. Brisbane is Australia's largest city, with 751,115 people. The Sydney metropolitan area, however, is by far the largest in Australia, with 3,538,749 people.

Q What is Australia's only island state?

A Tasmania, which lies about 150 miles (240 km) south of the Australian mainland. Measuring 26,200 square miles (67,800 sq km) in area, it is the smallest of Australia's six states and accounts for less than 1% of the country's area. Originally part of New South Wales, Tasmania became a separate colony in 1825 and a state in 1901. Hobart, its capital, is home to 45% of the state's population.

Countries and Flags

This 12-page section presents basic information about each of the world's countries, along with an illustration of each country's flag. A total of 198 countries are listed: the world's 191 fully independent countries, and 7 internally independent countries which are under the protection of other countries in matters of defense and foreign affairs. Colonies and other dependent political entities are not listed. The design of the East Timor flag has not been finalized.

The categories of information provided for each country are as follows.

Flag: In many countries two or more versions of the national flag exist. For example, there is often a "civil" version which the average person flies, and a "state" version which is flown only at government buildings and government functions. A common difference between the two is the inclusion of a coat of arms on the state version.

Country name: The short form of the English translation of the official country name.

Official name: The long form of the English translation of the official country name.

Population: The population figures listed are 2002 estimates based on U.S. census bureau figures and other available information.

Area: Figures provided represent total land area and all inland water. They are based on official data or U.N. data.

Population density: The number of people per square mile and square kilometer, calculated by dividing the country's population figure by its area figure.

Capital: The city that serves as the official seat of government. Population figures follow the capital name. These figures are based upon the latest official data.

AFGHANISTAN
Official Name: Islamic State of Afghanistan
Population: 27,280,000
Area: 251,826 sq mi (652,225 sq km)
Density: 108/sq mi (42/sq km)
Capital: Kābul, 1,424,400

ALBANIA
Official Name: Republic of Albania
Population: 3,525,000
Area: 11,100 sq mi (28,748 sq km)
Density: 318/sq mi (123/sq km)
Capital: Tiranë, 243,000

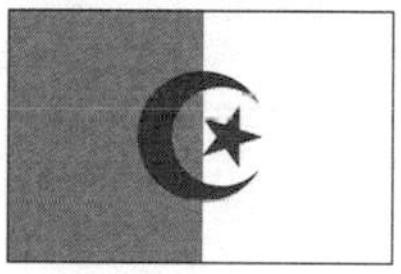

ALGERIA
Official Name: Democratic and Popular Republic of Algeria
Population: 32,005,000
Area: 919,595 sq mi (2,381,741 sq km)
Density: 35/sq mi (13/sq km)
Capital: Algiers (El Djazaïr),1,507,241

ANDORRA
Official Name: Principality of Andorra
Population: 68,000
Area: 175 sq mi (453 sq km)
Density: 389/sq mi (150/sq km)
Capital: Andorra, 20,437

ANGOLA
Official Name: Republic of Angola
Population: 10,480,000
Area: 481,354 sq mi (1,246,700 sq km)
Density: 22/sq mi (8.4/sq km)
Capital: Luanda, 1,459,900

ANGUILLA
Official Name: Anguilla
Population: 12,000
Area: 35 sq mi (91 sq km)
Density: 342/sq mi (132/sq km)
Capital: The Valley, 1,462

ANTIGUA AND BARBUDA
Official Name: Antigua and Barbuda
Population: 67,000
Area: 171 sq mi (442 sq km)
Density: 393/sq mi (152/sq km)
Capital: St. John's, 24,359

Countries and Flags *continued*

ARGENTINA
Official Name: Argentine Republic
Population: 37,600,000
Area: 1,073,519 sq mi (2,780,400 sq km)
Pop. Density: 35/sq mi (14/sq km)
Capital: Buenos Aires (de facto), 2,960,976, and Viedma (future), 40,452

ARMENIA
Official Name: Republic of Armenia
Population: 3,335,000
Area: 11,506 sq mi (29,800 sq km)
Pop. Density: 290/sq mi (112/sq km)
Capital: Yerevan, 1,199,000

AUSTRALIA
Official Name: Commonwealth of Australia
Population: 19,455,000
Area: 2,969,910 sq mi (7,692,030 sq km)
Pop. Density: 6.6/sq mi (2.5/sq km)
Capital: Canberra, 298,847

AUSTRIA
Official Name: Republic of Austria
Population: 8,160,000
Area: 32,378 sq mi (83,859 sq km)
Pop. Density: 252/sq mi (97/sq km)
Capital: Vienna (Wien), 1,539,848

AZERBAIJAN
Official Name: Azerbaijani Republic
Population: 7,785,000
Area: 33,437 sq mi (86,600 sq km)
Pop. Density: 233/sq mi (90/sq km)
Capital: Baku (Bakı), 1,080,500

BAHAMAS
Official Name: Commonwealth of the Bahamas
Population: 300,000
Area: 5,382 sq mi (13,939 sq km)
Pop. Density: 56/sq mi (22/sq km)
Capital: Nassau, 141,000

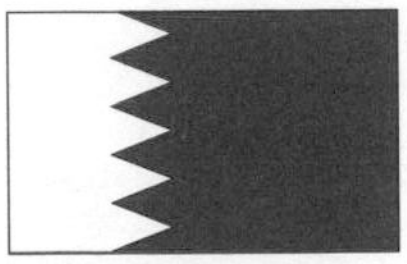

BAHRAIN
Official Name: State of Bahrain
Population: 650,000
Area: 267 sq mi (691 sq km)
Pop. Density: 2,436/sq mi (941/sq km)
Capital: Al Manāmah, 127,578

BANGLADESH
Official Name: People's Republic of Bangladesh
Population: 132,315,000
Area: 55,598 sq mi (143,998 sq km)
Pop. Density: 2,380/sq mi (919/sq km)
Capital: Dhaka (Dacca), 3,637,892

BARBADOS
Official Name: Barbados
Population: 275,000
Area: 166 sq mi (430 sq km)
Pop. Density: 1,657/sq mi (640/sq km)
Capital: Bridgetown, 5,928

BELARUS
Official Name: Republic of Belarus
Population: 10,340,000
Area: 80,155 sq mi (207,600 sq km)
Pop. Density: 129/sq mi (50/sq km)
Capital: Minsk, 1,661,000

BELGIUM
Official Name: Kingdom of Belgium
Population: 10,265,000
Area: 11,787 sq mi (30,528 sq km)
Pop. Density: 871/sq mi (336/sq km)
Capital: Brussels (Bruxelles), 136,424

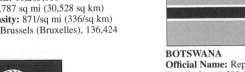

BELIZE
Official Name: Belize
Population: 260,000
Area: 8,866 sq mi (22,963 sq km)
Pop. Density: 29/sq mi (11/sq km)
Capital: Belmopan, 8,130

BENIN
Official Name: Republic of Benin
Population: 6,690,000
Area: 43,475 sq mi (112,600 sq km)
Pop. Density: 154/sq mi (59/sq km)
Capital: Porto-Novo (designated), 179,138, and Cotonou (de facto), 536,827

BHUTAN
Official Name: Kingdom of Bhutan
Population: 2,070,000
Area: 17,954 sq mi (46,500 sq km)
Pop. Density: 115/sq mi (45/sq km)
Capital: Thimphu, 12,000

BOLIVIA
Official Name: Republic of Bolivia
Population: 8,375,000
Area: 424,165 sq mi (1,098,581 sq km)
Pop. Density: 20/sq mi (7.6/sq km)
Capital: La Paz (seat of government), 792,611, and Sucre (legal capital), 194,888

BOSNIA AND HERZEGOVINA
Official Name: Republic of Bosnia and Herzegovina
Population: 3,950,000
Area: 19,741 sq mi (51,129 sq km)
Pop. Density: 200/sq mi (77/sq km)
Capital: Sarajevo, 367,703

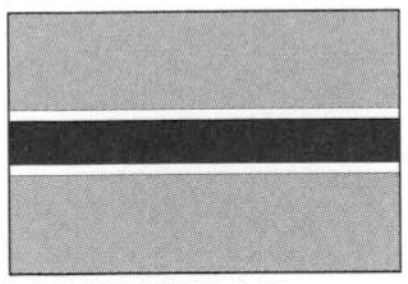

BOTSWANA
Official Name: Republic of Botswana
Population: 1,590,000
Area: 224,712 sq mi (582,000 sq km)
Pop. Density: 7.1/sq mi (2.7/sq km)
Capital: Gaborone, 133,468

BRAZIL
Official Name: Federative Republic of Brazil
Population: 175,260,000
Area: 3,300,172 sq mi (8,547,404 sq km)
Pop. Density: 53/sq mi (21/sq km)
Capital: Brasília, 1,947,133

BRUNEI
Official Name: Negara Brunei Darussalam
Population: 345,000
Area: 2,226 sq mi (5,765 sq km)
Pop. Density: 155/sq mi (60/sq km)
Capital: Bandar Seri Begawan, 45,867

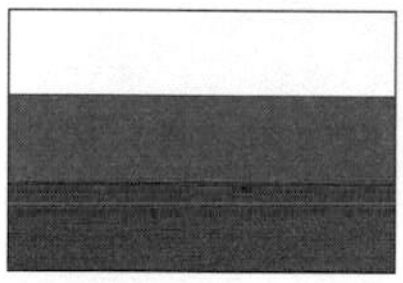

BULGARIA
Official Name: Republic of Bulgaria
Population: 7,665,000
Area: 42,855 sq mi (110,994 sq km)
Pop. Density: 179/sq mi (69/sq km)
Capital: Sofia (Sofiya), 1,190,126

BURKINA FASO
Official Name: Burkina Faso
Population: 12,435,000
Area: 105,869 sq mi (274,200 sq km)
Pop. Density: 117/sq mi (45/sq km)
Capital: Ouagadougou, 441,514

BURUNDI
Official Name: Republic of Burundi
Population: 6,300,000
Area: 10,745 sq mi (27,830 sq km)
Pop. Density: 586/sq mi (226/sq km)
Capital: Bujumbura, 226,628

CAMBODIA
Official Name: Kingdom of Cambodia
Population: 12,630,000
Area: 69,898 sq mi (181,035 sq km)
Pop. Density: 181/sq mi (70/sq km)
Capital: Phnom Penh (Phnum Pénh), 620,000

CAMEROON
Official Name: Republic of Cameroon
Population: 15,995,000
Area: 183,568 sq mi (475,440 sq km)
Pop. Density: 87/sq mi (34/sq km)
Capital: Yaoundé, 620,000

CANADA
Official Name: Canada
Population: 31,750,000
Area: 3,855,103 sq mi (9,984,670 sq km)
Pop. Density: 8.2/sq mi (3.2/sq km)
Capital: Ottawa, 323,340

CAPE VERDE
Official Name: Republic of Cape Verde
Population: 405,000
Area: 1,557 sq mi (4,033 sq km)
Pop. Density: 260/sq mi (100/sq km)
Capital: Praia, 61,644

CENTRAL AFRICAN REPUBLIC
Official Name: Central African Republic
Population: 3,610,000
Area: 240,536 sq mi (622,984 sq km)
Pop. Density: 15/sq mi (5.8/sq km)
Capital: Bangui, 451,690

CHAD
Official Name: Republic of Chad
Population: 8,850,000
Area: 495,755 sq mi (1,284,000 sq km)
Pop. Density: 18/sq mi (6.9/sq km)
Capital: N'Djamena, 546,572

CHILE
Official Name: Republic of Chile
Population: 15,415,000
Area: 292,135 sq mi (756,626 sq km)
Pop. Density: 53/sq mi (20/sq km)
Capital: Santiago, 4,295,593

CHINA
Official Name: People's Republic of China
Population: 1,278,720,000
Area: 3,690,045 sq mi (9,557,172 sq km)
Pop. Density: 347/sq mi (134/sq km)
Capital: Beijing (Peking), 6,690,000

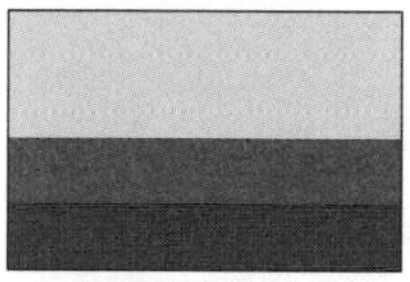

COLOMBIA
Official Name: Republic of Colombia
Population: 40,680,000
Area: 440,831 sq mi (1,141,748 sq km)
Pop. Density: 92/sq mi (36/sq km)
Capital: Bogotá, 4,931,796

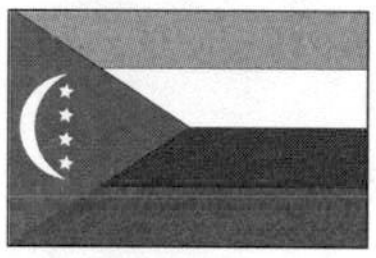

COMOROS
Official Name: Federal Islamic Republic of the Comoros
Population: 605,000
Area: 863 sq mi (2,235 sq km)
Pop. Density: 701/sq mi (271/sq km)
Capital: Moroni, 23,432

CONGO
Official Name: Republic of the Congo
Population: 2,925,000
Area: 132,047 sq mi (342,000 sq km)
Pop. Density: 22/sq mi (8.6/sq km)
Capital: Brazzaville, 693,712

CONGO, DEMOCRATIC REPUBLIC OF THE
Official Name: Democratic Republic of the Congo
Population: 54,455,000
Area: 905,446 sq mi (2,345,095 sq km)
Pop. Density: 60/sq mi (23/sq km)
Capital: Kinshasa, 3,000,000

COSTA RICA
Official Name: Republic of Costa Rica
Population: 3,805,000
Area: 19,730 sq mi (51,100 sq km)
Pop. Density: 193/sq mi (74/sq km)
Capital: San José, 309,672

Countries and Flags *continued*

COTE D'IVOIRE
Official Name: Republic of Cote d'Ivoire
Population: 16,600,000
Area: 124,518 sq mi (322,500 sq km)
Pop. Density: 133/sq mi (51/sq km)
Capital: Abidjan (de facto), 1,929,079, and Yamoussoukro (designated), 106,786

CROATIA
Official Name: Republic of Croatia
Population: 4,365,000
Area: 21,829 sq mi (56,538 sq km)
Pop. Density: 200/sq mi (77/sq km)
Capital: Zagreb, 867,865

CUBA
Official Name: Republic of Cuba
Population: 11,205,000
Area: 42,804 sq mi (110,861 sq km)
Pop. Density: 262/sq mi (101/sq km)
Capital: Havana (La Habana), 2,189,716

CYPRUS
Official Name: Republic of Cyprus
Population: 625,000
Area: 2,277 sq mi (5,896 sq km)
Pop. Density: 275/sq mi (106/sq km)
Capital: Nicosia (Levkosía), 47,036

CYPRUS, NORTH
Official Name: Turkish Republic of Northern Cyprus
Population: 140,000
Area: 1,295 sq mi (3,355 sq km)
Pop. Density: 108/sq mi (42/sq km)
Capital: Nicosia (Lefkoşa), 37,400

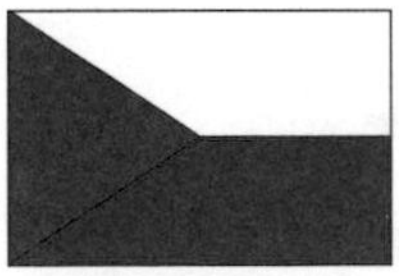

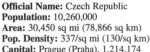

CZECH REPUBLIC
Official Name: Czech Republic
Population: 10,260,000
Area: 30,450 sq mi (78,866 sq km)
Pop. Density: 337/sq mi (130/sq km)
Capital: Prague (Praha), 1,214,174

DENMARK
Official Name: Kingdom of Denmark
Population: 5,360,000
Area: 16,639 sq mi (43,094 sq km)
Pop. Density: 322 sq mi (124/sq km)
Capital: Copenhagen (København), 487,969

DJIBOUTI
Official Name: Republic of Djibouti
Population: 465,000
Area: 8,958 sq mi (23,200 sq km)
Pop. Density: 52/sq mi (20/sq km)
Capital: Djibouti, 329,337

DOMINICA
Official Name: Commonwealth of Dominica
Population: 70,000
Area: 305 sq mi (790 sq km)
Pop. Density: 230/sq mi (89/sq km)
Capital: Roseau, 9,348

DOMINICAN REPUBLIC
Official Name: Dominican Republic
Population: 8,650,000
Area: 18,704 sq mi (48,442 sq km)
Pop. Density: 462/sq mi (179/sq km)
Capital: Santo Domingo, 1,609,966

ECUADOR
Official Name: Republic of Ecuador
Population: 13,315,000
Area: 105,037 sq mi (272,045 sq km)
Pop. Density: 127/sq mi (49/sq km)
Capital: Quito, 1,100,847

EGYPT
Official Name: Arab Republic of Egypt
Population: 70,125,000
Area: 386,662 sq mi (1,001,449 sq km)
Pop. Density: 181/sq mi (70/sq km)
Capital: Cairo (Al Qāhirah), 6,801,695

EL SALVADOR
Official Name: Republic of El Salvador
Population: 6,295,000
Area: 8,124 sq mi (21,041 sq km)
Pop. Density: 775/sq mi (299/sq km)
Capital: San Salvador, 415,346

EQUATORIAL GUINEA
Official Name: Republic of Equatorial Guinea
Population: 490,000
Area: 10,831 sq mi (28,051 sq km)
Pop. Density: 45/sq mi (17/sq km)
Capital: Malabo, 31,630

ERITREA
Official Name: State of Eritrea
Population: 4,380,000
Area: 36,170 sq mi (93,679 sq km)
Pop. Density: 121/sq mi (47/sq km)
Capital: Asmera, 358,100

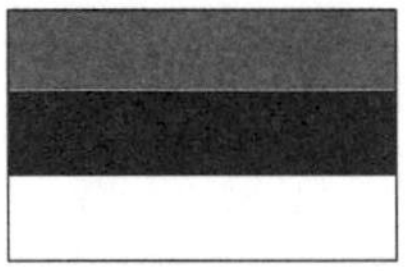

ESTONIA
Official Name: Republic of Estonia
Population: 1,420,000
Area: 17,413 sq mi (45,100 sq km)
Pop. Density: 82/sq mi (31/sq km)
Capital: Tallinn, 403,981

ETHIOPIA
Official Name: Ethiopia
Population: 66,780,000
Area: 446,953 sq mi (1,157,603 sq km)
Pop. Density: 149/sq mi (58/sq km)
Capital: Addis Ababa (Adis Abeba), 2,084,588

FIJI
Official Name: Republic of Fiji
Population: 850,000
Area: 7,056 sq mi (18,274 sq km)
Pop. Density: 120/sq mi (47/sq km)
Capital: Suva, 77,366

FINLAND
Official Name: Republic of Finland
Population: 5,180,000
Area: 130,559 sq mi (338,145 sq km)
Pop. Density: 40/sq mi (15/sq km)
Capital: Helsinki (Helsingfors), 512,686

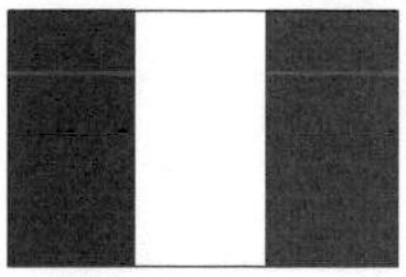

FRANCE
Official Name: French Republic
Population: 59,660,000
Area: 208,482 sq mi (539,965 sq km)
Pop. Density: 286/sq mi (110/sq km)
Capital: Paris, 2,147,857

GABON
Official Name: Gabonese Republic
Population: 1,225,000
Area: 103,347 sq mi (267,667 sq km)
Pop. Density: 12/sq mi (4.6/sq km)
Capital: Libreville, 337,700

THE GAMBIA
Official Name: Republic of the Gambia
Population: 1,435,000
Area: 4,127 sq mi (10,689 sq km)
Pop. Density: 348/sq mi (134/sq km)
Capital: Banjul, 42,407

GEORGIA
Official Name: Republic of Georgia
Population: 4,975,000
Area: 26,911 sq mi (69,700 sq km)
Pop. Density: 185/sq mi (71/sq km)
Capital: Tbilisi, 1,279,000

GERMANY
Official Name: Federal Republic of Germany
Population: 83,145,000
Area: 137,822 sq mi (356,955 sq km)
Pop. Density: 603/sq mi (233/sq km)
Capital: Berlin, 3,425,759

GHANA
Official Name: Republic of Ghana
Population: 20,070,000
Area: 92,098 sq mi (238,533 sq km)
Pop. Density: 218/sq mi (84/sq km)
Capital: Accra, 949,113

GREECE
Official Name: Hellenic Republic
Population: 10,635,000
Area: 50,949 sq mi (131,957 sq km)
Pop. Density: 209/sq mi (81/sq km)
Capital: Athens (Athínai), 772,072

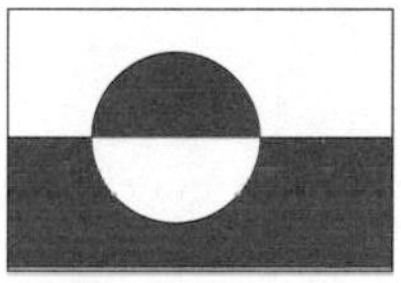

GREENLAND
Official Name: Greenland
Population: 56,000
Area: 840,004 sq mi (2,175,600 sq km)
Pop. Density: 0.07/sq mi (0.03/sq km)
Capital: Godthåb (Nuuk), 13,445

GRENADA
Official Name: Grenada
Population: 89,000
Area: 133 sq mi (344 sq km)
Pop. Density: 670/sq mi (259/sq km)
Capital: St. George's, 4,439

GUATEMALA
Official Name: Republic of Guatemala
Population: 13,145,000
Area: 42,042 sq mi (108,889 sq km)
Pop. Density: 313/sq mi (121/sq km)
Capital: Guatemala, 823,301

GUINEA
Official Name: Republic of Guinea
Population: 7,690,000
Area: 94,926 sq mi (245,857 sq km)
Pop. Density: 81/sq mi (31/sq km)
Capital: Conakry, 950,000

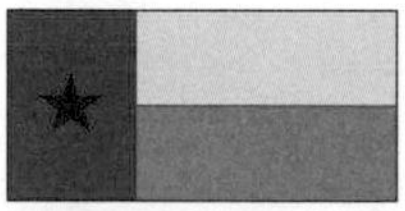

GUINEA-BISSAU
Official Name: Republic of Guinea-Bissau
Population: 1,330,000
Area: 13,948 sq mi (36,125 sq km)
Pop. Density: 95/sq mi (37/sq km)
Capital: Bissau, 125,000

GUYANA
Official Name: Co-operative Republic of Guyana
Population: 695,000
Area: 83,000 sq mi (214,969 sq km)
Pop. Density: 8.4/sq mi (3.2/sq km)
Capital: Georgetown, 78,500

HAITI
Official Name: Republic of Haiti
Population: 7,015,000
Area: 10,714 sq mi (27,750 sq km)
Pop. Density: 655/sq mi (253/sq km)
Capital: Port-au-Prince, 846,247

HONDURAS
Official Name: Republic of Honduras
Population: 6,485,000
Area: 43,277 sq mi (112,088 sq km)
Pop. Density: 150/sq mi (58/sq km)
Capital: Tegucigalpa, 576,661

HUNGARY
Official Name: Republic of Hungary
Population: 10,090,000
Area: 35,919 sq mi (93,030 sq km)
Pop. Density: 281/sq mi (108/sq km)
Capital: Budapest, 1,906,798

ICELAND
Official Name: Republic of Iceland
Population: 280,000
Area: 39,769 sq mi (103,000 sq km)
Pop. Density: 7.0/sq mi (3.0/sq km)
Capital: Reykjavik, 100,850

Countries and Flags *continued*

INDIA
Official Name: Republic of India
Population: 1,037,955,000
Area: 1,222,559 sq mi (3,166,414 sq km)
Pop. Density: 849/sq mi (328/sq km)
Capital: New Delhi, 294,783

INDONESIA
Official Name: Republic of Indonesia
Population: 230,260,000
Area: 735,310 sq mi (1,904,443 sq km)
Pop. Density: 313/sq mi (121/sq km)
Capital: Jakarta, 8,227,746

IRAN
Official Name: Islamic Republic of Iran
Population: 66,365,000
Area: 630,578 sq mi (1,633,189 sq km)
Pop. Density: 105/sq mi (41/sq km)
Capital: Tehrān, 6,758,845

IRAQ
Official Name: Republic of Iraq
Population: 23,665,000
Area: 169,235 sq mi (438,317 sq km)
Pop. Density: 140/sq mi (54/sq km)
Capital: Baghdād, 3,841,268

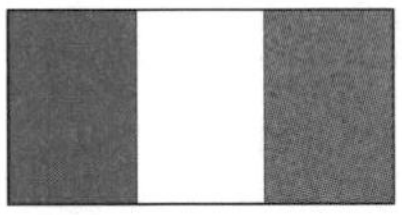

IRELAND
Official Name: Ireland
Population: 3,860,000
Area: 27,133 sq mi (70,273 sq km)
Pop. Density: 142/sq mi (55/sq km)
Capital: Dublin (Baile Átha Cliath), 481,854

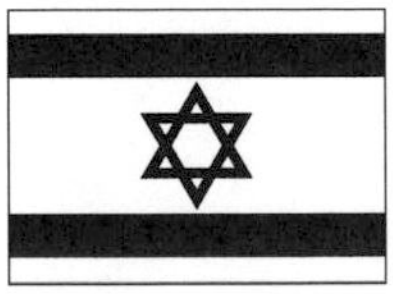

ISRAEL
Official Name: State of Israel
Population: 5,985,000
Area: 8,019 sq mi (20,770 sq km)
Pop. Density: 746/sq mi (288/sq km)
Capital: Jerusalem (Yerushalayim), 633,700

ITALY
Official Name: Italian Republic
Population: 57,700,000
Area: 116,342 sq mi (301,323 sq km)
Pop. Density: 496/sq mi (191/sq km)
Capital: Rome (Roma), 2,649,765

JAMAICA
Official Name: Jamaica
Population: 2,670,000
Area: 4,244 sq mi (10,991 sq km)
Pop. Density: 629/sq mi (243/sq km)
Capital: Kingston, 516,500

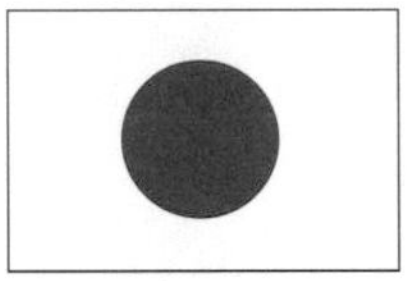

JAPAN
Official Name: Japan
Population: 126,880,000
Area: 145,850 sq mi (377,750 sq km)
Pop. Density: 870/sq mi (336/sq km)
Capital: Tōkyō, 7,967,614

JORDAN
Official Name: Hashemite Kingdom of Jordan
Population: 5,230,000
Area: 35,135 sq mi (91,000 sq km)
Pop. Density: 149/sq mi (57/sq km)
Capital: ‘Ammān, 963,490

KAZAKHSTAN
Official Name: Republic of Kazakhstan
Population: 16,735,000
Area: 1,049,156 sq mi (2,717,300 sq km)
Pop. Density: 16/sq mi (6.2/sq km)
Capital: Astana, 286,000

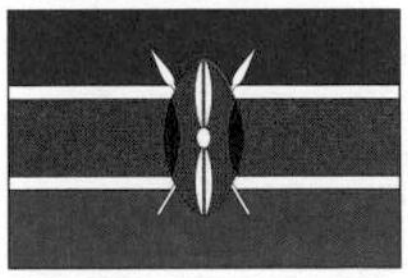

KENYA
Official Name: Republic of Kenya
Population: 30,960,000
Area: 224,961 sq mi (582,646 sq km)
Pop. Density: 138/sq mi (53/sq km)
Capital: Nairobi, 2,143,254

KIRIBATI
Official Name: Republic of Kiribati
Population: 95,000
Area: 313 sq mi (811 sq km)
Pop. Density: 303/sq mi (117/sq km)
Capital: Bairiki, 2,226

KOREA, NORTH
Official Name: Democratic People's Republic of Korea
Population: 22,100,000
Area: 46,540 sq mi (120,538 sq km)
Pop. Density: 475/sq mi (183/sq km)
Capital: P'yŏngyang, 2,355,000

KOREA, SOUTH
Official Name: Republic of Korea
Population: 48,120,000
Area: 38,230 sq mi (99,016 sq km)
Pop. Density: 1,259/sq mi (486/sq km)
Capital: Seoul (Sŏul), 10,627,790

KUWAIT
Official Name: State of Kuwait
Population: 2,075,000
Area: 6,880 sq mi (17,818 sq km)
Pop. Density: 302/sq mi (116/sq km)
Capital: Kuwait (Al Kuwayt), 28,859

KYRGYZSTAN
Official Name: Kyrgyz Republic
Population: 4,785,000
Area: 76,641 sq mi (198,500 sq km)
Pop. Density: 62/sq mi (24/sq km)
Capital: Bishkek, 631,300

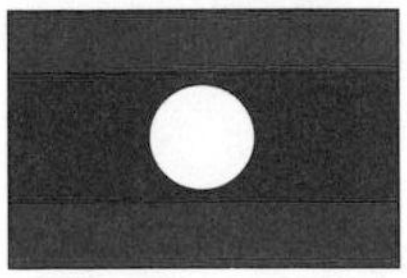

LAOS
Official Name: Lao People's Democratic Republic
Population: 5,705,000
Area: 91,429 sq mi (236,800 sq km)
Pop. Density: 62/sq mi (24/sq km)
Capital: Viangchan (Vientiane), 464,000

LATVIA
Official Name: Republic of Latvia
Population: 2,375,000
Area: 24,595 sq mi (63,700 sq km)
Pop. Density: 97/sq mi (37/sq km)
Capital: Rīga, 874,200

LEBANON
Official Name: Republic of Lebanon
Population: 3,655,000
Area: 4,016 sq mi (10,400 sq km)
Pop. Density: 910/sq mi (351/sq km)
Capital: Beirut (Bayrūt), 509,000

LESOTHO
Official Name: Kingdom of Lesotho
Population: 2,195,000
Area: 11,720 sq mi (30,355 sq km)
Pop. Density: 187/sq mi (72/sq km)
Capital: Maseru, 137,837

LIBERIA
Official Name: Republic of Liberia
Population: 3,255,000
Area: 38,250 sq mi (99,067 sq km)
Pop. Density: 85/sq mi (33/sq km)
Capital: Monrovia, 465,000

LIBYA
Official Name: Socialist People's Libyan Arab Jamahiriya
Population: 5,305,000
Area: 679,362 sq mi (1,759,540 sq km)
Pop. Density: 7.8/sq mi (3.0/sq km)
Capital: Tripoli (Tarābulus), 591,062

LIECHTENSTEIN
Official Name: Principality of Liechtenstein
Population: 33,000
Area: 62 sq mi (160 sq km)
Pop. Density: 534/sq mi (206/sq km)
Capital: Vaduz, 5,106

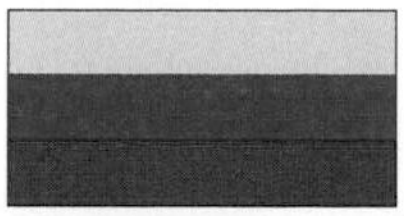

LITHUANIA
Official Name: Republic of Lithuania
Population: 3,605,000
Area: 25,213 sq mi (65,300 sq km)
Pop. Density: 143/sq mi (55/sq km)
Capital: Vilnius, 578,639

LUXEMBOURG
Official Name: Grand Duchy of Luxembourg
Population: 445,000
Area: 999 sq mi (2,586 sq km)
Pop. Density: 446/sq mi (172/sq km)
Capital: Luxembourg, 81,800

MACEDONIA
Official Name: Republic of Macedonia
Population: 2,050,000
Area: 9,928 sq mi (25,713 sq km)
Pop. Density: 206/sq mi (80/sq km)
Capital: Skopje, 440,577

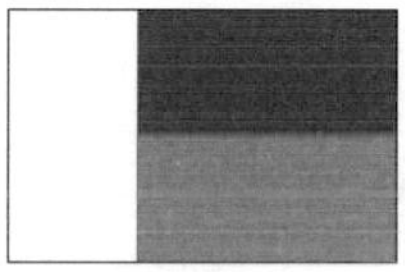

MADAGASCAR
Official Name: Republic of Madagascar
Population: 16,225,000
Area: 226,658 sq mi (587,041 sq km)
Pop. Density: 72/sq mi (28/sq km)
Capital: Antananarivo, 1,250,000

MALAWI
Official Name: Republic of Malawi
Population: 10,625,000
Area: 45,747 sq mi (118,484 sq km)
Pop. Density: 232/sq mi (90/sq km)
Capital: Lilongwe, 435,964

MALAYSIA
Official Name: Malaysia
Population: 22,445,000
Area: 127,320 sq mi (329,758 sq km)
Pop. Density: 176/sq mi (68/sq km)
Capital: Kuala Lumpur (de facto), 1,297,526 and Putrajaya (future)

MALDIVES
Official Name: Republic of Maldives
Population: 315,000
Area: 115 sq mi (298 sq km)
Pop. Density: 2,737/sq mi (1,057/sq km)
Capital: Male', 55,130

MALI
Official Name: Republic of Mali
Population: 11,170,000
Area: 482,077 sq mi (1,248,574 sq km)
Pop. Density: 23/sq mi (8.9/sq km)
Capital: Bamako, 658,275

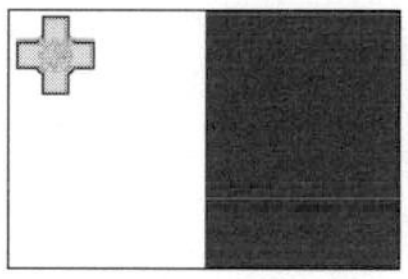

MALTA
Official Name: Republic of Malta
Population: 395,000
Area: 122 sq mi (316 sq km)
Pop. Density: 3,238/sq mi (1,250/sq km)
Capital: Valletta, 7,262

MARSHALL ISLANDS
Official Name: Republic of the Marshall Islands
Population: 72,000
Area: 70 sq mi (181 sq km)
Pop. Density: 1,029/sq mi (397/sq km)
Capital: Majuro (island)

MAURITANIA
Official Name: Islamic Republic of Mauritania
Population: 2,790,000
Area: 397,956 sq mi (1,030,700 sq km)
Pop. Density: 7.0/sq mi (2.7/sq km)
Capital: Nouakchott, 393,325

MAURITIUS
Official Name: Republic of Mauritius
Population: 1,195,000
Area: 788 sq mi (2,040 sq km)
Pop. Density: 1,517/sq mi (586/sq km)
Capital: Port Louis, 132,460

Countries and Flags *continued*

MEXICO
Official Name: United Mexican States
Population: 102,640,000
Area: 758,452 sq mi (1,964,382 sq km)
Pop. Density: 135/sq mi (52/sq km)
Capital: Mexico City (Ciudad de México), 8,489,007

MICRONESIA, FEDERATED STATES OF
Official Name: Federated States of Micronesia
Population: 135,000
Area: 271 sq mi (702 sq km)
Pop. Density: 498/sq mi (192/sq km)
Capital: Palikir, 5,047

MOLDOVA
Official Name: Republic of Moldova
Population: 4,435,000
Area: 13,012 sq mi (33,700 sq km)
Pop. Density: 341/sq mi (132/sq km)
Capital: Chişinău (Kishinev), 676,700

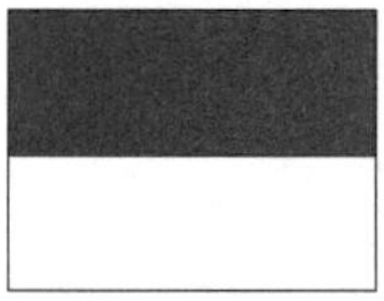

MONACO
Official Name: Principality of Monaco
Population: 32,000
Area: 0.8 sq mi (2.0 sq km)
Pop. Density: 40,000/sq mi (16,000/sq km)
Capital: Monaco, 32,000

MONGOLIA
Official Name: Mongolia
Population: 2,675,000
Area: 604,829 sq mi (1,566,500 sq km)
Pop. Density: 4.4/sq mi (1.7/sq km)
Capital: Ulan Bator (Ulaanbaatar), 616,900

MOROCCO
Official Name: Kingdom of Morocco
Population: 30,905,000
Area: 172,414 sq mi (446,550 sq km)
Pop. Density: 179/sq mi (69/sq km)
Capital: Rabat, 717,000

MOZAMBIQUE
Official Name: Republic of Mozambique
Population: 19,495,000
Area: 308,642 sq mi (799,380 sq km)
Pop. Density: 63/sq mi (24/sq km)
Capital: Maputo, 966,837

MYANMAR
Official Name: Union of Myanmar
Population: 42,120,000
Area: 261,228 sq mi (676,577 sq km)
Pop. Density: 161/sq mi (62/sq km)
Capital: Rangoon (Yangon), 2,705,053

NAMIBIA
Official Name: Republic of Namibia
Population: 1,810,000
Area: 317,818 sq mi (823,144 sq km)
Pop. Density: 5.7/sq mi (2.2/sq km)
Capital: Windhoek, 147,056

NAURU
Official Name: Republic of Nauru
Population: 12,000
Area: 8.0 sq mi (21 sq km)
Pop. Density: 1,481/sq mi (571/sq km)
Capital: Yaren District

NEPAL
Official Name: Kingdom of Nepal
Population: 25,580,000
Area: 56,827 sq mi (147,181 sq km)
Pop. Density: 450/sq mi (174/sq km)
Capital: Kathmandu, 421,258

NETHERLANDS
Official Name: Kingdom of the Netherlands
Population: 16,025,000
Area: 16,164 sq mi (41,864 sq km)
Pop. Density: 991/sq mi (383/sq km)
Capital: Amsterdam (designated), 727,053, and The Hague ('s-Gravenhage) (seat of government), 440,743

NEW ZEALAND
Official Name: New Zealand
Population: 3,885,000
Area: 104,454 sq mi (270,534 sq km)
Pop. Density: 37/sq mi (14/sq km)
Capital: Wellington, 150,301

NICARAGUA
Official Name: Republic of Nicaragua
Population: 4,970,000
Area: 50,054 sq mi (129,640 sq km)
Pop. Density: 99/sq mi (38/sq km)
Capital: Managua, 864,201

NIGER
Official Name: Republic of Niger
Population: 10,495,000
Area: 489,192 sq mi (1,267,000 sq km)
Pop. Density: 21/sq mi (8.3/sq km)
Capital: Niamey, 392,165

NIGERIA
Official Name: Federal Republic of Nigeria
Population: 128,285,000
Area: 356,669 sq mi (923,768 sq km)
Pop. Density: 360/sq mi (139/sq km)
Capital: Abuja, 250,000

NIUE
Official Name: Niue
Population: 2,000
Area: 100 sq mi (259 sq km)
Pop. Density: 20/sq mi (7.7/sq km)
Capital: Alofi, 682

NORTHERN MARIANA ISLANDS
Official Name: Commonwealth of the Northern Mariana Islands
Population: 76,000
Area: 184 sq mi (477 sq km)
Pop. Density: 413/sq mi (159/sq km)
Capital: Saipan (island)

NORWAY
Official Name: Kingdom of Norway
Population: 4,515,000
Area: 149,405 sq mi (386,958 sq km)
Pop. Density: 30/sq mi (12/sq km)
Capital: Oslo, 504,040

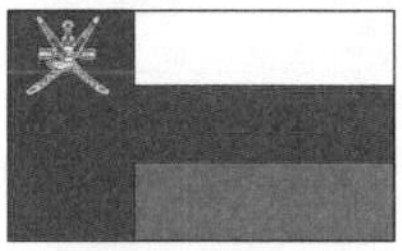

OMAN
Official Name: Sultanate of Oman
Population: 2,665,000
Area: 82,030 sq mi (212,457 sq km)
Pop. Density: 32/sq mi (13/sq km)
Capital: Muscat (Masqat), 34,683

PAKISTAN
Official Name: Islamic Republic of Pakistan
Population: 146,145,000
Area: 339,732 sq mi (879,902 sq km)
Pop. Density: 430/sq mi (166/sq km)
Capital: Islāmābād, 204,364

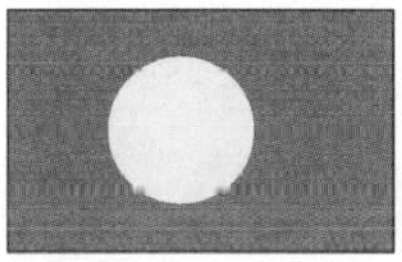

PALAU
Official Name: Republic of Palau
Population: 19,000
Area: 196 sq mi (508 sq km)
Pop. Density: 97/sq mi (37/sq km)
Capital: Koror (de facto), 9,018, and Melekeok (future), 42

PANAMA
Official Name: Republic of Panama
Population: 2,865,000
Area: 29,157 sq mi (75,517 sq km)
Pop. Density: 98/sq mi (38/sq km)
Capital: Panamá, 415,964

PAPUA NEW GUINEA
Official Name: Independent State of Papua New Guinea
Population: 5,110,000
Area: 178,704 sq mi (462,840 sq km)
Pop. Density: 29/sq mi (11/sq km)
Capital: Port Moresby, 246,664

PARAGUAY
Official Name: Republic of Paraguay
Population: 5,810,000
Area: 157,048 sq mi (406,752 sq km)
Pop. Density: 37/sq mi (14/sq km)
Capital: Asunción, 502,426

PERU
Official Name: Republic of Peru
Population: 27,720,000
Area: 496,225 sq mi (1,285,216 sq km)
Pop. Density: 56/sq mi (22/sq km)
Capital: Lima, 371,122

PHILIPPINES
Official Name: Republic of the Philippines
Population: 83,685,000
Area: 115,831 sq mi (300,000 sq km)
Pop. Density: 722/sq mi (279/sq km)
Capital: Manila, 1,654,761

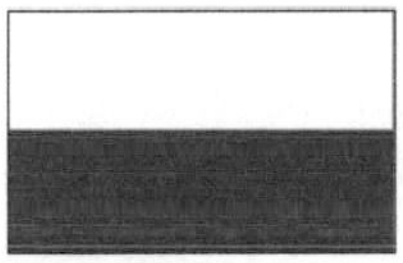

POLAND
Official Name: Republic of Poland
Population: 38,630,000
Area: 120,728 sq mi (312,685 sq km)
Pop. Density: 320/sq mi (124/sq km)
Capital: Warsaw (Warszawa), 1,615,369

PORTUGAL
Official Name: Portuguese Republic
Population: 10,075,000
Area: 35,516 sq mi (91,985 sq km)
Pop. Density: 284/sq mi (110/sq km)
Capital: Lisbon (Lisboa), 663,394

PUERTO RICO
Official Name: Commonwealth of Puerto Rico
Population: 3,950,000
Area: 3,515 sq mi (9,104 sq km)
Pop. Density: 1,124/sq mi (434/sq km)
Capital: San Juan, 421,958

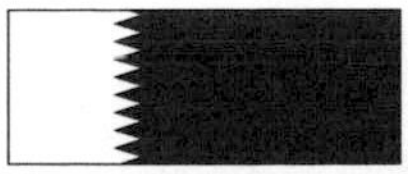

QATAR
Official Name: State of Qatar
Population: 780,000
Area: 4,412 sq mi (11,427 sq km)
Pop. Density: 177/sq mi (68/sq km)
Capital: Ad Dawḥah (Doha), 361,540

ROMANIA
Official Name: Romania
Population: 22,340,000
Area: 91,699 sq mi (237,500 sq km)
Pop. Density: 244/sq mi (94/sq km)
Capital: Bucharest (Bucureşti), 2,067,545

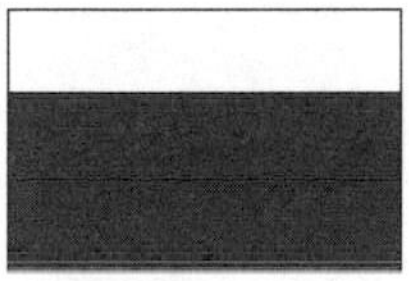

RUSSIA
Official Name: Russian Federation
Population: 145,215,000
Area: 6,592,849 sq mi (17,075,400 sq km)
Pop. Density: 22/sq mi (8.5/sq km)
Capital: Moscow (Moskva), 8,368,449

RWANDA
Official Name: Republic of Rwanda
Population: 7,355,000
Area: 10,169 sq mi (26,338 sq km)
Pop. Density: 723/sq mi (279/sq km)
Capital: Kigali, 232,733

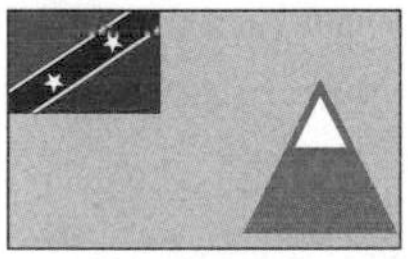

ST. KITTS AND NEVIS
Official Name: Federation of St. Kitts and Nevis
Population: 39,000
Area: 104 sq mi (269 sq km)
Pop. Density: 375/sq mi (145/sq km)
Capital: Basseterre, 11,295

ST. LUCIA
Official Name: St. Lucia
Population: 160,000
Area: 238 sq mi (616 sq km)
Pop. Density: 672/sq mi (260/sq km)
Capital: Castries, 11,147

Countries and Flags *continued*

ST. VINCENT AND THE GRENADINES
Official Name: St. Vincent and the Grenadines
Population: 115,000
Area: 150 sq mi (388 sq km)
Pop. Density: 767/sq mi (296/sq km)
Capital: Kingstown, 15,466

SAMOA
Official Name: Independent State of Samoa
Population: 180,000
Area: 1,093 sq mi (2,831 sq km)
Pop. Density: 165/sq mi (64/sq km)
Capital: Apia, 34,126

SAN MARINO
Official Name: Republic of San Marino
Population: 28,000
Area: 24 sq mi (61 sq km)
Pop. Density: 1,186/sq mi (459/sq km)
Capital: San Marino, 2,794

SAO TOME AND PRINCIPE
Official Name: Democratic Republic of Sao Tome and Principe
Population: 170,000
Area: 372 sq mi (964 sq km)
Pop. Density: 457/sq mi (176/sq km)
Capital: São Tomé, 5,245

SAUDI ARABIA
Official Name: Kingdom of Saudi Arabia
Population: 23,130,000
Area: 830,000 sq mi (2,149,690 sq km)
Pop. Density: 28/sq mi (11/sq km)
Capital: Riyadh (Ar Riyād), 1,250,000

SENEGAL
Official Name: Republic of Senegal
Population: 10,435,000
Area: 75,951 sq mi (196,712 sq km)
Pop. Density: 137/sq mi (53/sq km)
Capital: Dakar, 1,490,450

SERBIA AND MONTENEGRO
Official Name: Serbia and Montenegro
Population: 10,665,000
Area: 39,449 sq mi (102,173 sq km)
Pop. Density: 270/sq mi (104/sq km)
Capital: Belgrade (Beograd), 1,136,786

SEYCHELLES
Official Name: Republic of Seychelles
Population: 80,000
Area: 176 sq mi (455 sq km)
Pop. Density: 455/sq mi (176/sq km)
Capital: Victoria, 24,907

SIERRA LEONE
Official Name: Republic of Sierra Leone
Population: 5,525,000
Area: 27,925 sq mi (72,325 sq km)
Pop. Density: 198/sq mi (76/sq km)
Capital: Freetown, 469,776

SINGAPORE
Official Name: Republic of Singapore
Population: 4,375,000
Area: 246 sq mi (636 sq km)
Pop. Density: 17,814/sq mi (6,879/sq km)
Capital: Singapore, 4,017,700

SLOVAKIA
Official Name: Slovak Republic
Population: 5,420,000
Area: 18,933 sq mi (49,035 sq km)
Pop. Density: 286/sq mi (111/sq km)
Capital: Bratislava, 441,453

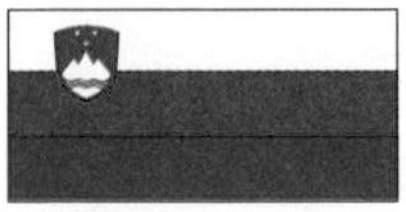

SLOVENIA
Official Name: Republic of Slovenia
Population: 1,930,000
Area: 7,821 sq mi (20,256 sq km)
Pop. Density: 247/sq mi (95/sq km)
Capital: Ljubljana, 292,589

SOLOMON ISLANDS
Official Name: Solomon Islands
Population: 490,000
Area: 10,954 sq mi (28,370 sq km)
Pop. Density: 45/sq mi (17/sq km)
Capital: Honiara, 30,413

SOMALIA
Official Name: Somalia
Population: 7,620,000
Area: 246,201 sq mi (637,657 sq km)
Pop. Density: 31/sq mi (12/sq km)
Capital: Mogadishu (Muqdisho), 600,000

SOUTH AFRICA
Official Name: Republic of South Africa
Population: 43,645,000
Area: 470,693 sq mi (1,219,090 sq km)
Pop. Density: 93/sq mi (36/sq km)
Capital: Pretoria (administrative), 525,583, Cape Town (legislative), 854,616, and Bloemfontein (judicial), 126,867

SPAIN
Official Name: Kingdom of Spain
Population: 40,060,000
Area: 194,885 sq mi (504,750 sq km)
Pop. Density: 206/sq mi (79/sq km)
Capital: Madrid, 2,882,860

SRI LANKA
Official Name: Democratic Socialist Republic of Sri Lanka
Population: 19,495,000
Area: 24,962 sq mi (64,652 sq km)
Pop. Density: 781/sq mi (302/sq km)
Capital: Colombo (designated), 612,000, and Sri Jayewardenepura Kotte (seat of government), 108,000

SUDAN
Official Name: Republic of the Sudan
Population: 36,585,000
Area: 967,500 sq mi (2,505,813 sq km)
Pop. Density: 38/sq mi (15/sq km)
Capital: Khartoum (Al Kharṭum), 473,597

SURINAME
Official Name: Republic of Suriname
Population: 435,000
Area: 63,251 sq mi (163,820 sq km)
Pop. Density: 6.9/sq mi (2.7/sq km)
Capital: Paramaribo, 241,000

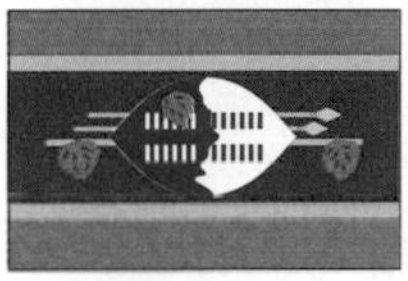

SWAZILAND
Official Name: Kingdom of Swaziland
Population: 1,115,000
Area: 6,704 sq mi (17,364 sq km)
Pop. Density: 166/sq mi (64/sq km)
Capital: Mbabane (administrative), 38,290, and Lobamba (legislative)

SWEDEN
Official Name: Kingdom of Sweden
Population: 8,875,000
Area: 173,732 sq mi (449,964 sq km)
Pop. Density: 51/sq mi (20/sq km)
Capital: Stockholm, 674,452

SWITZERLAND
Official Name: Swiss Confederation
Population: 7,295,000
Area: 15,943 sq mi (41,293 sq km)
Pop. Density: 458/sq mi (177/sq km)
Capital: Bern (Berne), 136,338

SYRIA
Official Name: Syrian Arab Republic
Population: 16,940,000
Area: 71,498 sq mi (185,180 sq km)
Pop. Density: 237/sq mi (91/sq km)
Capital: Damascus (Dimashq), 1,549,932

TAIWAN
Official Name: Republic of China
Population: 22,460,000
Area: 13,901 sq mi (36,002 sq km)
Pop. Density: 1,616/sq mi (624/sq km)
Capital: T'aipei, 2,706,453

TAJIKISTAN
Official Name: Republic of Tajikistan
Population: 6,650,000
Area: 55,251 sq mi (143,100 sq km)
Pop. Density: 120/sq mi (46/sq km)
Capital: Dushanbe, 582,400

TANZANIA
Official Name: United Republic of Tanzania
Population: 36,705,000
Area: 364,900 sq mi (945,087 sq km)
Pop. Density: 101/sq mi (39/sq km)
Capital: Dar es Salaam (de facto), 1,096,000, and Dodoma (legislative), 85,000

THAILAND
Official Name: Kingdom of Thailand
Population: 62,080,000
Area: 198,115 sq mi (513,115 sq km)
Pop. Density: 313/sq mi (121/sq km)
Capital: Bangkok (Krung Thep), 5,620,591

TOGO
Official Name: Republic of Togo
Population: 5,220,000
Area: 21,925 sq mi (56,785 sq km)
Pop. Density: 238/sq mi (92/sq km)
Capital: Lomé, 500,000

TONGA
Official Name: Kingdom of Tonga
Population: 105,000
Area: 288 sq mi (747 sq km)
Pop. Density: 364/sq mi (141/sq km)
Capital: Nuku'alofa, 22,400

TRINIDAD AND TOBAGO
Official Name: Republic of Trinidad and Tobago
Population: 1,165,000
Area: 1,980 sq mi (5,128 sq km)
Pop. Density: 588/sq mi (227/sq km)
Capital: Port of Spain, 50,878

TUNISIA
Official Name: Republic of Tunisia
Population: 9,760,000
Area: 63,170 sq mi (163,610 sq km)
Pop. Density: 155/sq mi (60/sq km)
Capital: Tunis, 674,142

TURKEY
Official Name: Republic of Turkey
Population: 66,905,000
Area: 302,541 sq mi (783,577 sq km)
Pop. Density: 221/sq mi (85/sq km)
Capital: Ankara, 2,559,471

TURKMENISTAN
Official Name: Turkmenistan
Population: 4,645,000
Area: 188,457 sq mi (488,100 sq km)
Pop. Density: 25/sq mi (10/sq km)
Capital: Ashgabat, 412,200

TUVALU
Official Name: Tuvalu
Population: 11,000
Area: 10 sq mi (26 sq km)
Pop. Density: 1,100/sq mi (423/sq km)
Capital: Funafuti, 2,191

UGANDA
Official Name: Republic of Uganda
Population: 24,335,000
Area: 93,104 sq mi (241,139 sq km)
Pop. Density: 261/sq mi (101/sq km)
Capital: Kampala, 773,463

Countries and Flags *continued*

UKRAINE
Official Name: Ukraine
Population: 48,570,000
Area: 233,090 sq mi (603,700 sq km)
Pop. Density: 208/sq mi (80/sq km)
Capital: Kiev (Kyyiv), 2,630,000

UNITED ARAB EMIRATES
Official Name: United Arab Emirates
Population: 2,425,000
Area: 32,278 sq mi (83,600 sq km)
Pop. Density: 75/sq mi (29/sq km)
Capital: Abū Ẓaby (Abu Dhabi), 242,975

UNITED KINGDOM
Official Name: United Kingdom of Great Britain and Northern Ireland
Population: 59,715,000
Area: 94,249 sq mi (244,101 sq km)
Pop. Density: 634/sq mi (245/sq km)
Capital: London, 7,650,944

UNITED STATES
Official Name: United States of America
Population: 279,310,000
Area: 3,717,796 sq mi (9,629,091 sq km)
Pop. Density: 75/sq mi (29/sq km)
Capital: Washington, D.C., 572,059

URUGUAY
Official Name: Oriental Republic of Uruguay
Population: 3,375,000
Area: 68,500 sq mi (177,414 sq km)
Pop. Density: 49/sq mi (19/sq km)
Capital: Montevideo, 1,303,182

UZBEKISTAN
Official Name: Republic of Uzbekistan
Population: 25,355,000
Area: 172,742 sq mi (447,400 sq km)
Pop. Density: 147/sq mi (57/sq km)
Capital: Tashkent, 2,113,300

VANUATU
Official Name: Republic of Vanuatu
Population: 195,000
Area: 4,707 sq mi (12,190 sq km)
Pop. Density: 41/sq mi (16/sq km)
Capital: Port Vila, 19,311

VATICAN CITY
Official Name: State of the Vatican City
Population: 1,000
Area: 0.2 sq mi (0.4 sq km)
Pop. Density: 5,000/sq mi (2,500/sq km)
Capital: Vatican City, 1,000

VENEZUELA
Official Name: Republic of Venezuela
Population: 24,105,000
Area: 352,145 sq mi (912,050 sq km)
Pop. Density: 68/sq mi (26/sq km)
Capital: Caracas, 1,822,465

VIETNAM
Official Name: Socialist Republic of Vietnam
Population: 80,520,000
Area: 127,428 sq mi (330,036 sq km)
Pop. Density: 632/sq mi (244/sq km)
Capital: Hanoi, 905,939

YEMEN
Official Name: Republic of Yemen
Population: 18,385,000
Area: 203,850 sq mi (527,968 sq km)
Pop. Density: 90/sq mi (35/sq km)
Capital: San'ā', 427,150

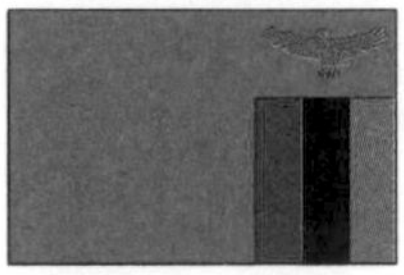

ZAMBIA
Official Name: Republic of the Zambia
Population: 9,865,000
Area: 290,586 sq mi (752,614 sq km)
Pop. Density: 34/sq mi (13/sq km)
Capital: Lusaka, 982,362

ZIMBABWE
Official Name: Republic of Zimbabwe
Population: 11,375,000
Area: 150,873 sq mi (390,759 sq km)
Pop. Density: 75/sq mi (29/sq km)
Capital: Harare (Salisbury), 1,189,103

Introduction to the Maps and Legend

Continental and regional coverage of the world's land areas is provided by the following section of thematic maps and physical-political reference maps. The reference map section falls into a continental arrangement: North America, South America, Europe, Africa, Asia, and Oceania. Introducing each regional reference map section are several basic thematic maps.

To aid the reader in understanding the relative sizes of continents and of some of the countries and regions, uniform scales for comparable areas were used as far as possible. Most of the world is covered by a series of regional maps at scales of 1:16,000,000 and 1:12,000,000. Maps at 1:10,000,000 provide even greater detail for parts of Europe. The United States and parts of South America are mapped at 1:4,000,000.

Many of the symbols used are self-explanatory. A complete legend below provides a key to the symbols on the reference maps in the atlas.

The color tints on the maps depict the varying elevations and depths of land areas and bodies of water. The Relief legend that accompanies each map shows the specific elevation or depth that each color tint represents.

The surface configuration is represented by hill-shading, which gives the three-dimensional impression of landforms. This terrain representation is superimposed on the layer tints to convey a realistic and readily visualized impression of the surface. The combination of altitudinal tints and hill-shading best shows elevation, relief, steepness of slope, and ruggedness of terrain.

If the world used one alphabet and language, no particular difficulty would arise in understanding place-names. However, some of the people of the world, the Chinese and the Japanese, for example, use non-alphabetic languages. Their symbols are transliterated into the Roman alphabet. In this atlas, a "local-name" policy generally was used for naming cities, towns, and all local topographic and water features. However, for a few major cities the Anglicized name was preferred and the local name given in parentheses: for instance, Moscow (Moskva), Vienna (Wien), Bangkok (Krung Thep). In countries where more than one official language is used, a name appears in the dominant local language. The generic parts of local names for topographic and water features are self-explanatory in many cases because of the associated map symbols or type styles. A complete list of foreign generic names is given in the Glossary.

Physical-Political Reference Map Legend

Cultural Features

Political Boundaries

(over water)	International (Demarcated, Undemarcated, and Administrative)
	Disputed de facto
	Claim Boundary
	Indefinite or Undefined
(over water)	Secondary, State, Provincial, etc.
	Parks, Indian Reservations
	City Limits Urbanized Areas
□	Neighborhoods, Sections of City

Populated Places

◉	1,000,000 and over
◎	250,000 to 1,000,000
⊙	100,000 to 250,000
•	25,000 to 100,000
○	0 to 25,000
TŌKYŌ	National Capitals
Boise	Secondary Capitals

Note: On maps at 1:20,000,000 and smaller the town symbols do not follow the specific population classification shown above. On all maps, type size indicates the relative importance of the city.

Transportation

	Railroads
	Railroads On 1:1,000,000 scale maps
	Railroad Ferries
	Roads
Major	On 1:1,000,000 scale maps
Other	
Major	On 1:4,000,000 scale maps
Other	
	On other scale maps
⋯⋯	Caravan Routes
✈	Airports

Other Cultural Features

	Dams
	Pipelines
▲	Points of Interest
∴	Ruins

Land Features

△	Peaks, Spot Heights
=	Passes
	Sand
	Contours

Water Features

Lakes and Reservoirs

	Fresh Water
	Fresh Water: Intermittent
	Salt Water
	Salt Water: Intermittent

Other Water Features

	Salt Basins, Flats
	Swamps
	Ice Caps and Glaciers
	Rivers
	Intermittent Rivers
	Aqueducts and Canals
	Ship Channels
	Falls
	Rapids
♪	Springs
△	Water Depths
	Fishing Banks
	Sand Bars
	Reefs

Note: Country populations used throughout the atlas are 2002 estimates based on 2001 U.S. Census Bureau figures and other available information. City populations in the continent "At a Glance" sections reflect the latest available official data.

ARCTIC OCEAN
Beaufort Sea
VICTORIA ISLAND
BAFFIN ISLAND
Baffin Bay
GREENLAND
(Den.)
Godthåb
Reykjavik
ICELAND
FAROE ISLANDS
(Den.)
RUSSIA
UNITED STATES
Arctic Circle
Mount McKinley
6194
Anchorage
Yellowknife
Hudson Bay
Bering Sea
Gulf of Alaska
Juneau
ROCKY MOUNTAINS
CANADA
ALEUTIAN ISLANDS
Winnipeg
NEWFOUNDLAND
IRELAND
Vancouver
Seattle
Saint Lawrence
Montréal
Toronto
NORTH AMERICA
DETROIT
CHICAGO
NEW YORK
ATLANTIC OCEAN
Denver
St. Louis
APPALACHIAN MOUNTAINS
Washington
PORTUGAL
SAN FRANCISCO
UNITED STATES
PACIFIC
AÇORES AZORES
(Port.)
LOS ANGELES
Phoenix
Mississippi
Atlanta
ARQUIPÉLAGO DA MADEIRA
(Port.)
Casablanca
MOROCCO
BERMUDA
(U.K.)
MIDWAY ISLANDS
(U.S.)
OCEAN
Houston
New Orleans
Gulf of Mexico
Miami
ISLAS CANARIAS
CANARY ISLANDS
(Sp.)
BAHAMAS
WESTERN SAHARA
Tropic of Cancer
Monterrey
La Habana
HAWAI'IAN ISLANDS
(U.S.)
Honolulu
MEXICO
CUBA
Guadalajara
CIUDAD DE MÉXICO
BELIZE
Caribbean Sea
HAITI
DOMINICAN REPUBLIC
PUERTO RICO (U.S.)
MAURITANIA
JAMAICA
GUADELOUPE (Fr.)
CAPE VERDE
GUATEMALA
HONDURAS
MARTINIQUE (Fr.)
SENEGAL
EL SALVADOR
NICARAGUA
TRINIDAD AND TOBAGO
THE GAMBIA
GUINEA-BISSAU
GUINEA
CLIPPERTON
(Fr.)
Caracas
COSTA RICA
Panamá
PANAMA
VENEZUELA
GUYANA
SIERRA LEONE
LIBERIA
Bogotá
SURINAME
FRENCH GUIANA
POLYNESIA
COLOMBIA
Equator
ARCHIPIÉLAGO DE COLÓN
GALAPAGOS ISLANDS
(Ec.)
Quito
ECUADOR
Amazon
Belém
Equator
Manaus
Fortaleza
ANDES
PERU
BRAZIL
Recife
TOKELAU ISLANDS
(N.Z.)
ÎLES MARQUISES
WALLIS AND FUTUNA
(Fr.)
SAMOA
AM. SAMOA
Lima
SOUTH AMERICA
Salvador
ATLANTIC OCEAN
FIJI
La Paz
BOLIVIA
Brasília
NIUE
(N.Z.)
COOK ISLANDS
(N.Z.)
FRENCH POLYNESIA
TONGA
PARAGUAY
PITCAIRN
(U.K.)
Tropic of Capricorn
SÃO PAULO
RIO DE JANEIRO
ISLA DE PASCUA
EASTER ISLAND
(Chile)
Antofagasta
Asunción
International Date Line
CHILE
Pôrto Alegre
Córdoba
URUGUAY
Santiago
BUENOS AIRES
Montevideo
PACIFIC
Co. Aconcagua
6959
ARGENTINA
OCEAN
CHATHAM ISLAND
(N.Z.)
FALKLAND ISLANDS
(U.K.)
Punta Arenas
SOUTH GEORGIA
(Falk. Is.)
CABO DE HORNOS
CAPE HORN
SOUTH ORKNEY ISLANDS
(B.A.T.)
Antarctic Circle
Bellingshausen Sea
Weddell Sea
Ross Sea
Vinson Massif
4897
ANTAR

14 30° 15 45° 16 60° 17 75° 18 90° 19 105° 20 120° 21 135° 22 150° 23 165° 24 180°
90°
ARCTIC OCEAN
ZEML'A FRANCA-IOSIFA
SVALBARD (Nor.)
Barents Sea
NOVAJA ZEML'A
Karskoje More
More Laptevych
NOVOSIBIRSKIJE OSTROVA
A
75°
Noril'sk
Jenisej
Arctic Circle
B
SWEDEN
FINLAND
Helsinki
Oslo
Stockholm
Archangel'sk
SANKT PETERBURG
URAL'SKIJE GORY
Ob'
Lena
Jakutsk
Anadyr'
60°
MOSKVA
Nižnij Novgorod
Jekaterinburg
R U S S I A
Sea of Okhotsk
Bering Sea
EST.
LAT.
LITH.
BELA.
Novosibirsk
Ozero Bajkal
ALEUTIAN IS. (U.S.)
Petropavlovsk-Kamčatskij
C
GERMANY
POLAND
Kyiv
UKRAINE
MOLD.
E U R O P E
ALTAI
OSTROV SACHALIN
HUNG.
AUS.
ROM.
Volga
Gora El'brus 5633
Caspian Sea
K A Z A K H S T A N
MONGOLIA
A S I A
Harbin
45°
BUL.
Black Sea
GEOR.
Aral Sea
UZBEK.
GOBI
Sea of Japan
International Date Line
Roma
ITALY
ALB.
Istanbul
ARM.
AZER.
Taškent
KYRG.
TAJIK.
BEIJING PEKING
KOREA
JAPAN
Mediterranean Sea
GREECE
TURKEY
TURKMENISTAN
SOUL
Yellow Sea
D
MALTA
TUNISIA
SYRIA
Tehrān
C H I N A
ŌSAKA
TŌKYŌ
LEB.
IRAQ
IRAN
AFGHANISTAN
Xi'an
ISRAEL
JORDAN
HIMALAYAS
Wuhan
SHANGHAI
AL-QĀHIRAH CAIRO
KUWAIT
NEPAL
BHU.
Chongqing
30°
LIBYA
EGYPT
PAKISTAN
DELHI
Mount Everest 8848
S A H A R A
QATAR
UNITED ARAB EMIRATES
Karāchi
Tropic of Cancer
BANGL.
Guangzhou
P A C I F I C
SAUDI ARABIA
Red Sea
KOLKATA
TAIWAN
E
A F R I C A
OMAN
INDIA
MYANMAR (BURMA)
Xianggang (Hong Kong)
Philippine Sea
NIGER
CHAD
Nile
Al-Kharṭūm
MUMBAI
Bay of Bengal
LAOS
South China Sea
O C E A N
WAKE ISLAND (U.S.)
ERITREA
THAILAND
VIETNAM
SUDAN
YEMEN
Aden
Arabian Sea
Chennai
Krung Thep Bangkok
CAMB.
MANILA
15°
NIGERIA
DJIBOUTI
GUAM (U.S.)
PHILIPPINES
ETHIOPIA
SRI LANKA
Lagos
CAMEROON
CEN. AFR. REP.
SOMALIA
Colombo
M I C R O N E S I A
BRUNEI
F
MALDIVES
MALAYSIA
EQUATORIAL GUINEA
DEM. REP. OF THE CONGO ZAIRE
UGANDA
Muqdisho
Equator
Singapore
GABON
CONGO
KENYA
Lake Victoria
BORNEO
SULAWESI
Equator
KIRIBATI
0°
RWANDA
Nairobi
SUMATERA
PAPUA NEW GUINEA
IRIAN JAYA
SOLOMON ISLANDS
TUVALU
Kinshasa
BURUNDI
Kilimanjaro 5895
SEYCHELLES
CHAGOS ARCHIPELAGO (B.I.O.T.)
INDONESIA
NEW GUINEA
Luanda
TANZANIA
JAKARTA
JAWA
EAST TIMOR
G
Port Moresby
SOLOMON ISLANDS
M E L A N E S I A
TIMOR
CHRISTMAS ISLAND (Austl.)
ANGOLA
ZAMBIA
MALAWI
I N D I A N
VANUATU
Cairns
Coral Sea
15°
ZIMBABWE
MOZAMBIQUE
Mozambique Channel
MADAGASCAR
O C E A N
FIJI
NAMIBIA
MAURITIUS
BOTSWANA
REUNION (Fr.)
Tropic of Capricorn
NEW CALEDONIA (Fr.)
H
Johannesburg
SWAZILAND
AUSTRALIA
Brisbane
LESOTHO
Durban
30°
SOUTH AFRICA
Perth
Cape Town
Sydney
CAPE OF GOOD HOPE
Mount Kosciuszko 2230
Melbourne
Tasman Sea
NEW ZEALAND
I
TASMANIA
Wellington
45°
ÎLES KERGUELEN (F.S.A.T.)
J
60°
Antarctic Circle
ENDERBY LAND
K
WILKES LAND
75°
Copyright © by Rand McNally & Co.
Map prepared by Rand McNally & Co.
C-510000-264 23-1-47EL
L
A N T A R C T I C A
14 30° 15 45° 16 60° 17 75° 18 90° 19 105° 20 120° 21 135° 22 150° 23 165° 24 180°
90°
Kilometers 0 1000 2000 3000 Km.
Miles 0 1000 2000 3000 Mi.
Robinson Projection

World Physical

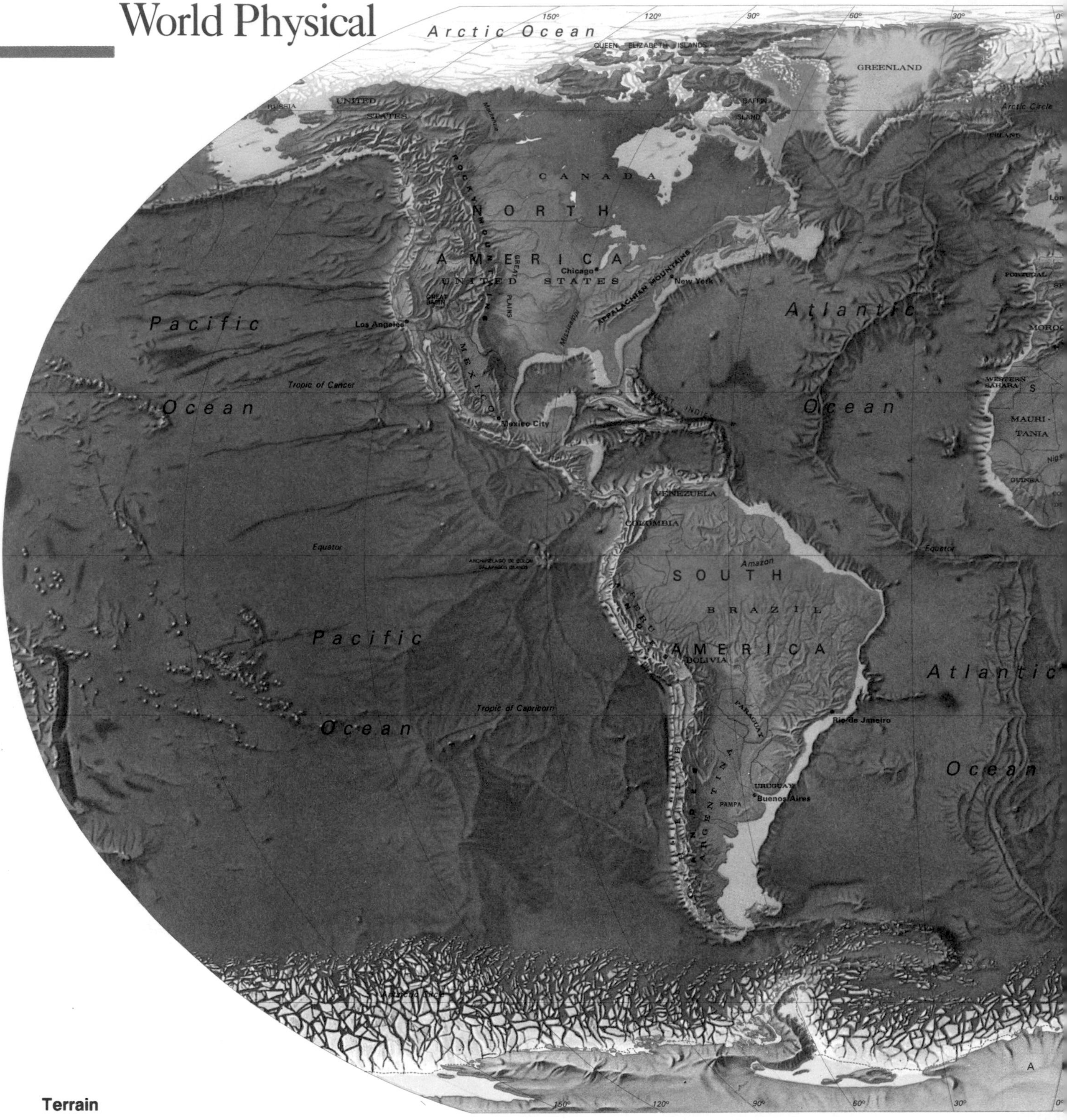

Terrain

Land Elevations in Profile

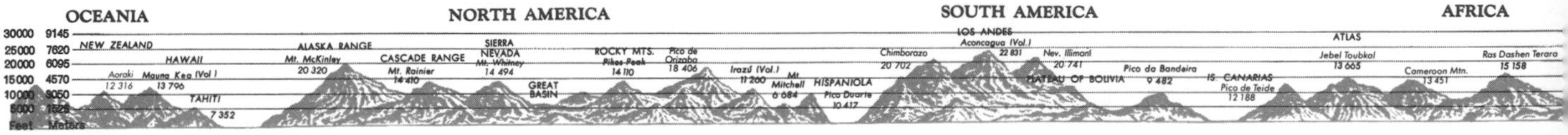

Ocean Depths in Profile

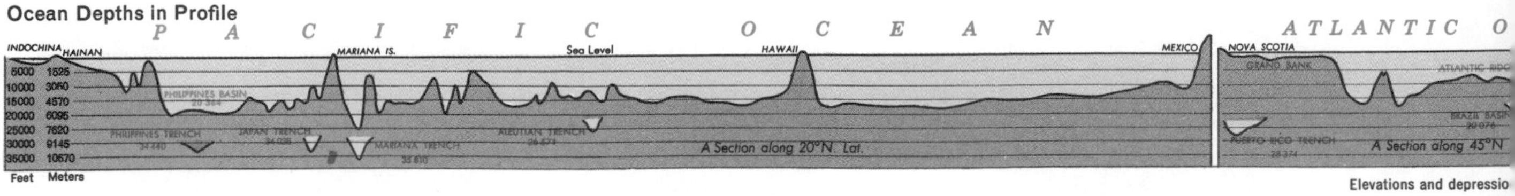

Elevations and depressio

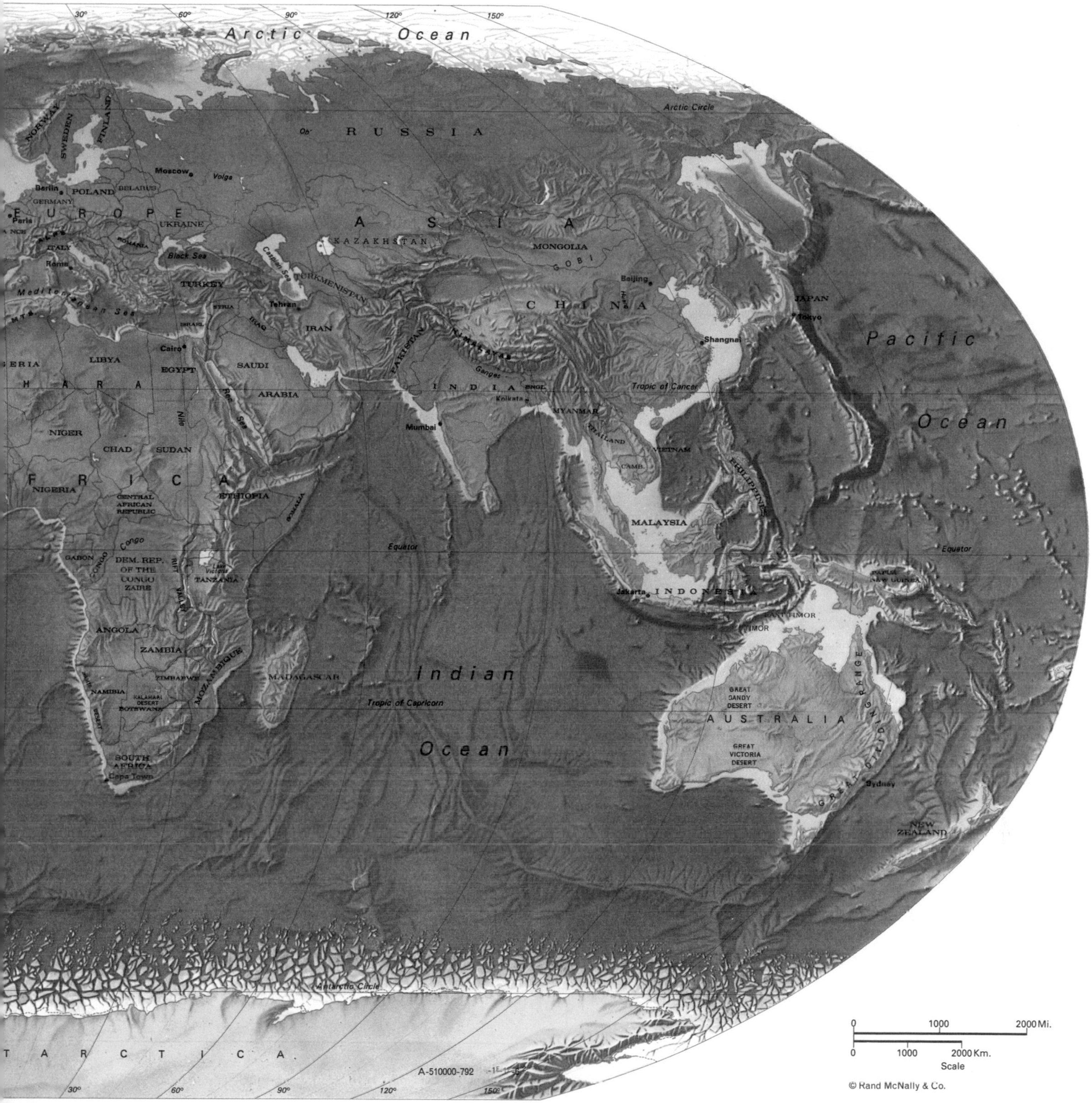

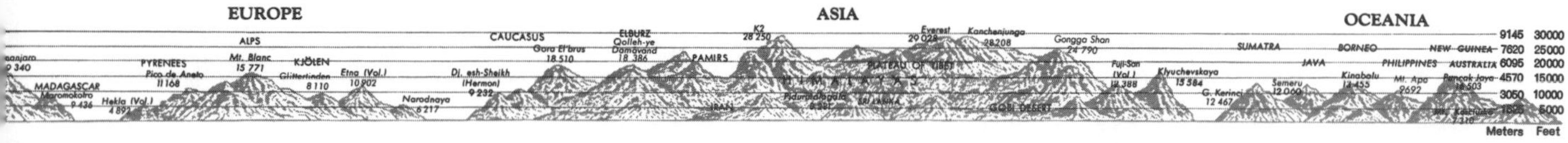

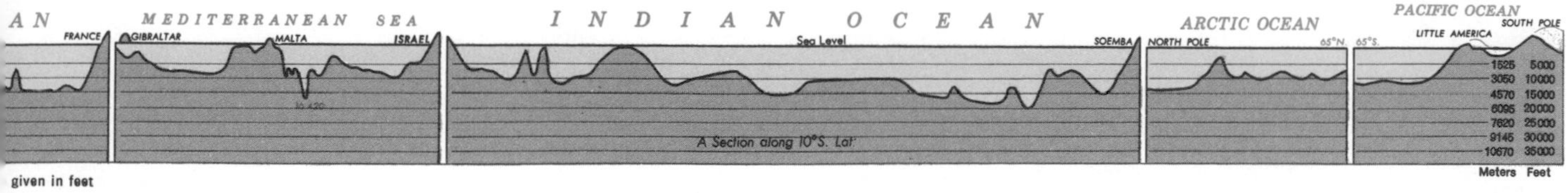

given in feet

World Climate

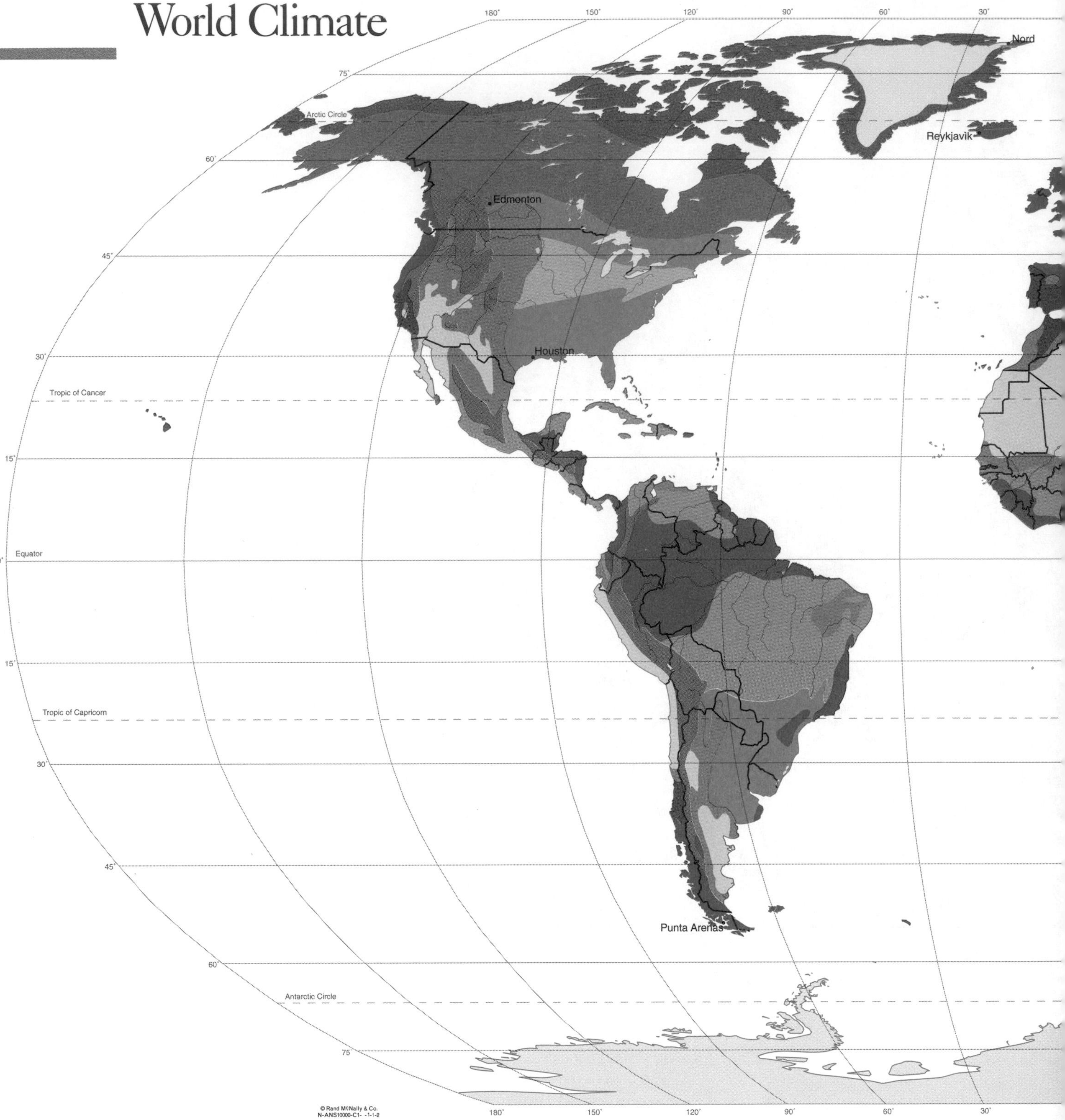

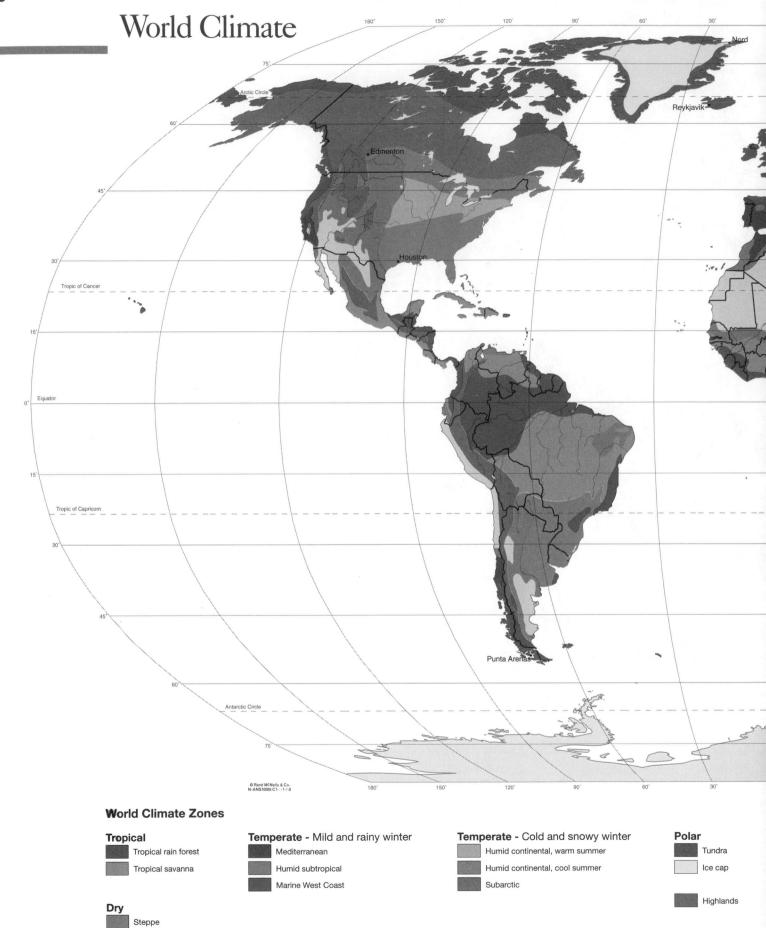

World Climate Zones

Tropical
- Tropical rain forest
- Tropical savanna

Temperate - Mild and rainy winter
- Mediterranean
- Humid subtropical
- Marine West Coast

Temperate - Cold and snowy winter
- Humid continental, warm summer
- Humid continental, cool summer
- Subarctic

Polar
- Tundra
- Ice cap

- Highlands

Dry
- Steppe
- Desert

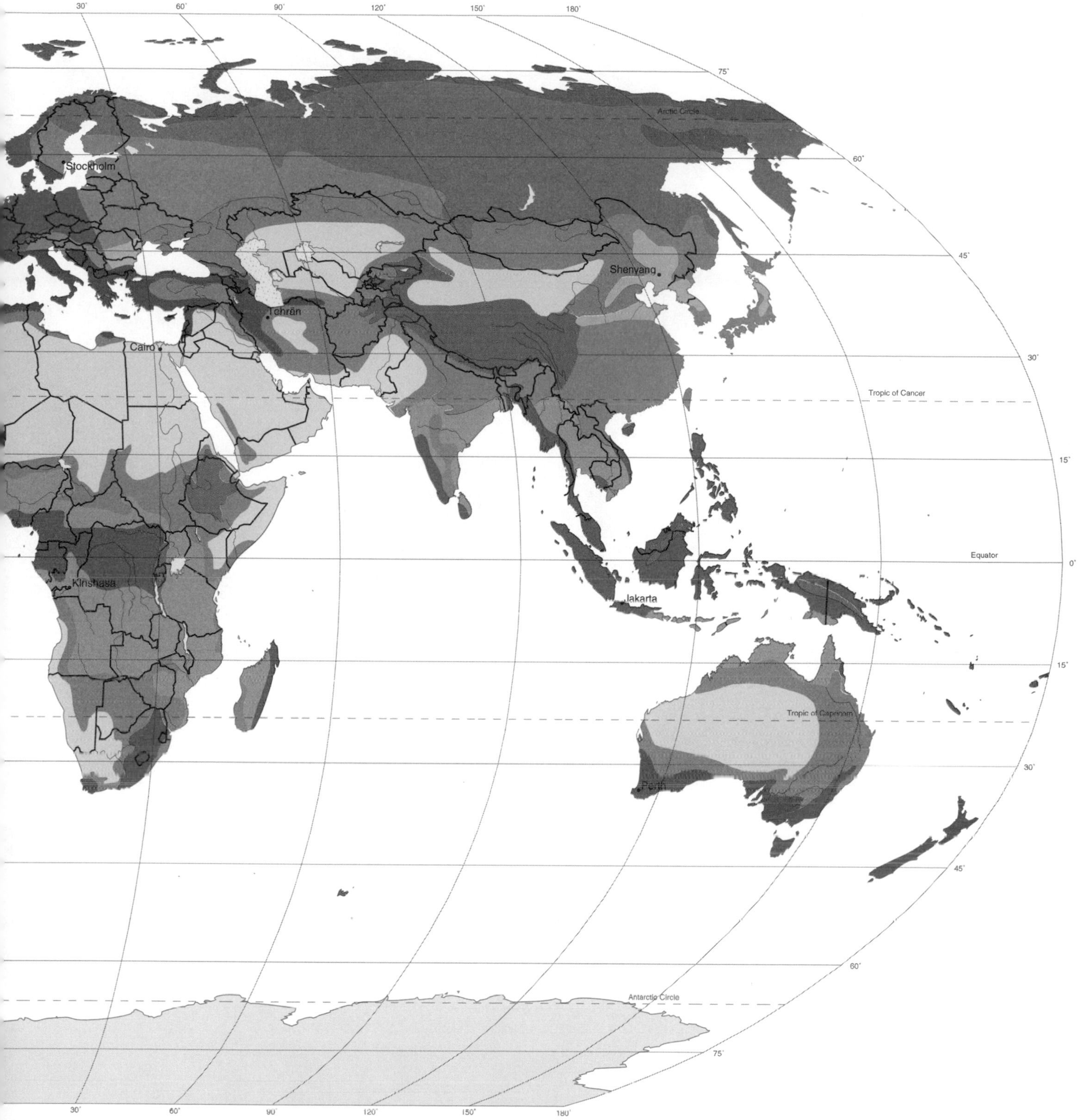

Tinted areas show temperature in degrees Fahrenheit. Vertical bars show precipitation in inches.

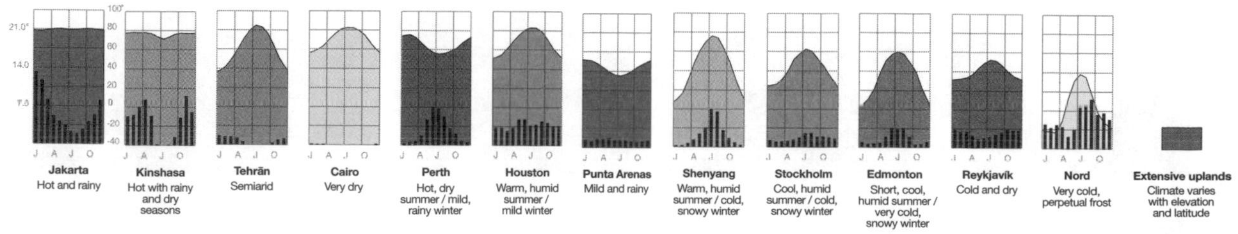

World Vegetation

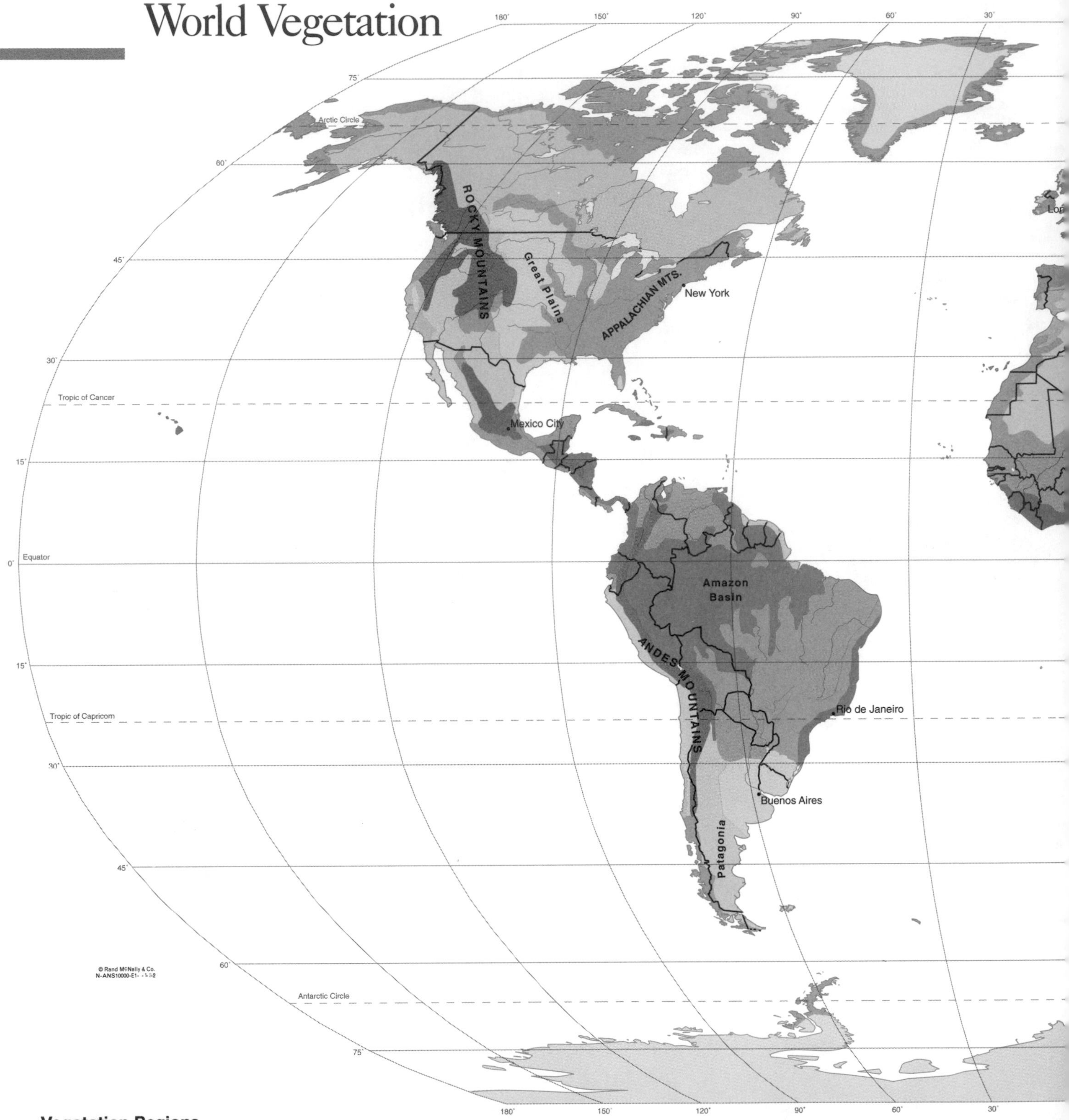

Vegetation Regions

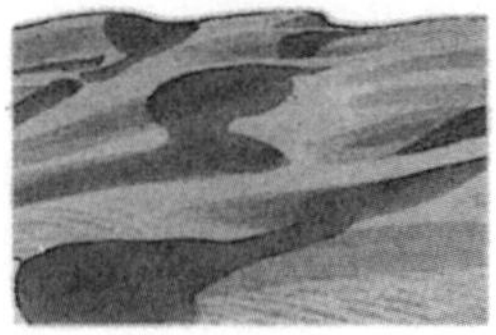

Tropical and subtropical forests

Savanna

Desert

Mediterranean

Temperate grassland

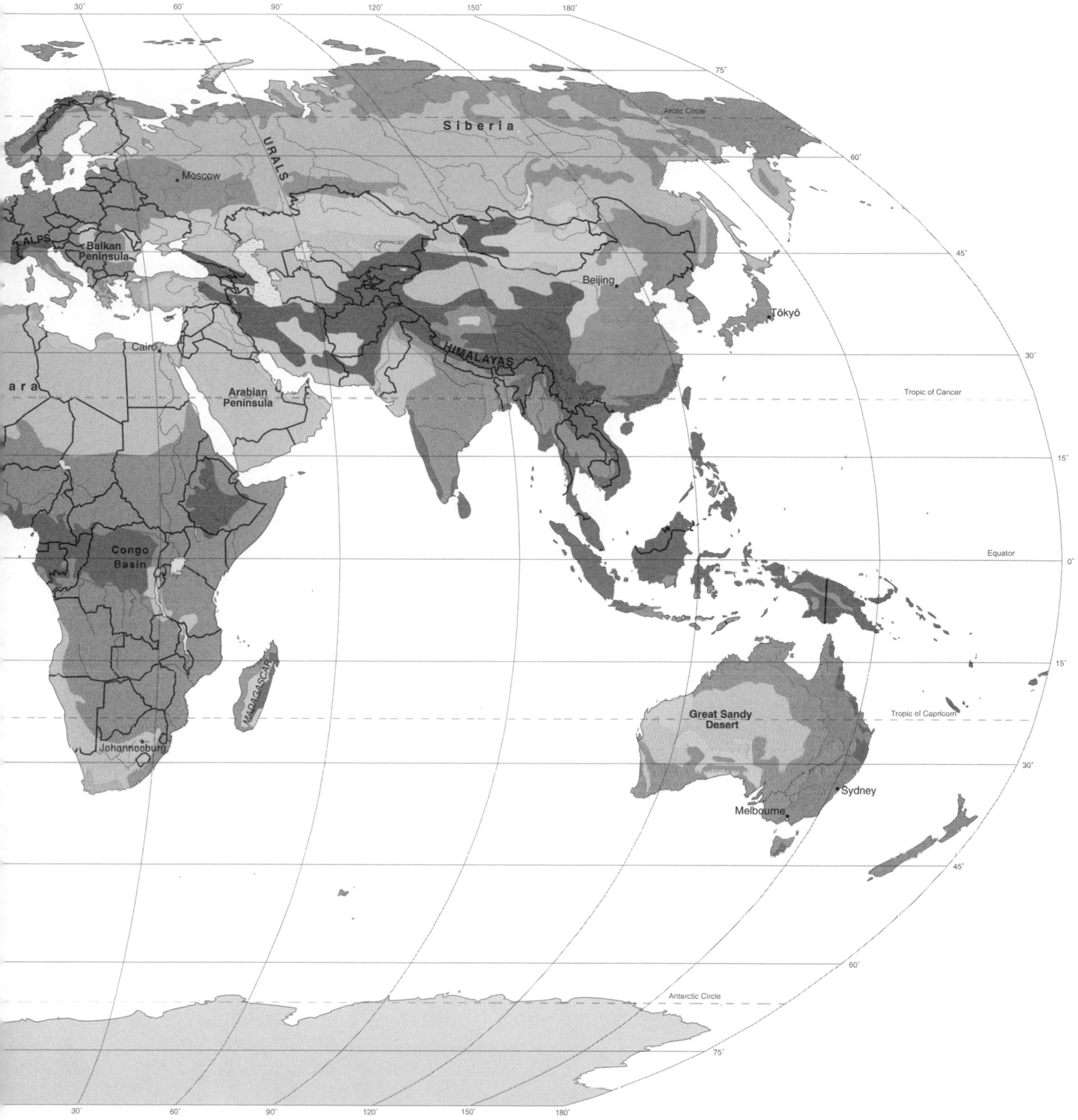

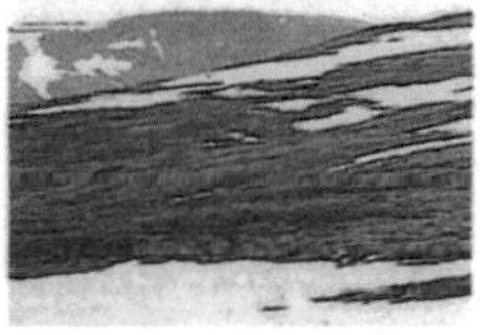

- Temperate forest
- Taiga (northern forests)
- Tundra (lichen and moss)
- Mountain
- Polar and high mountain

World Population

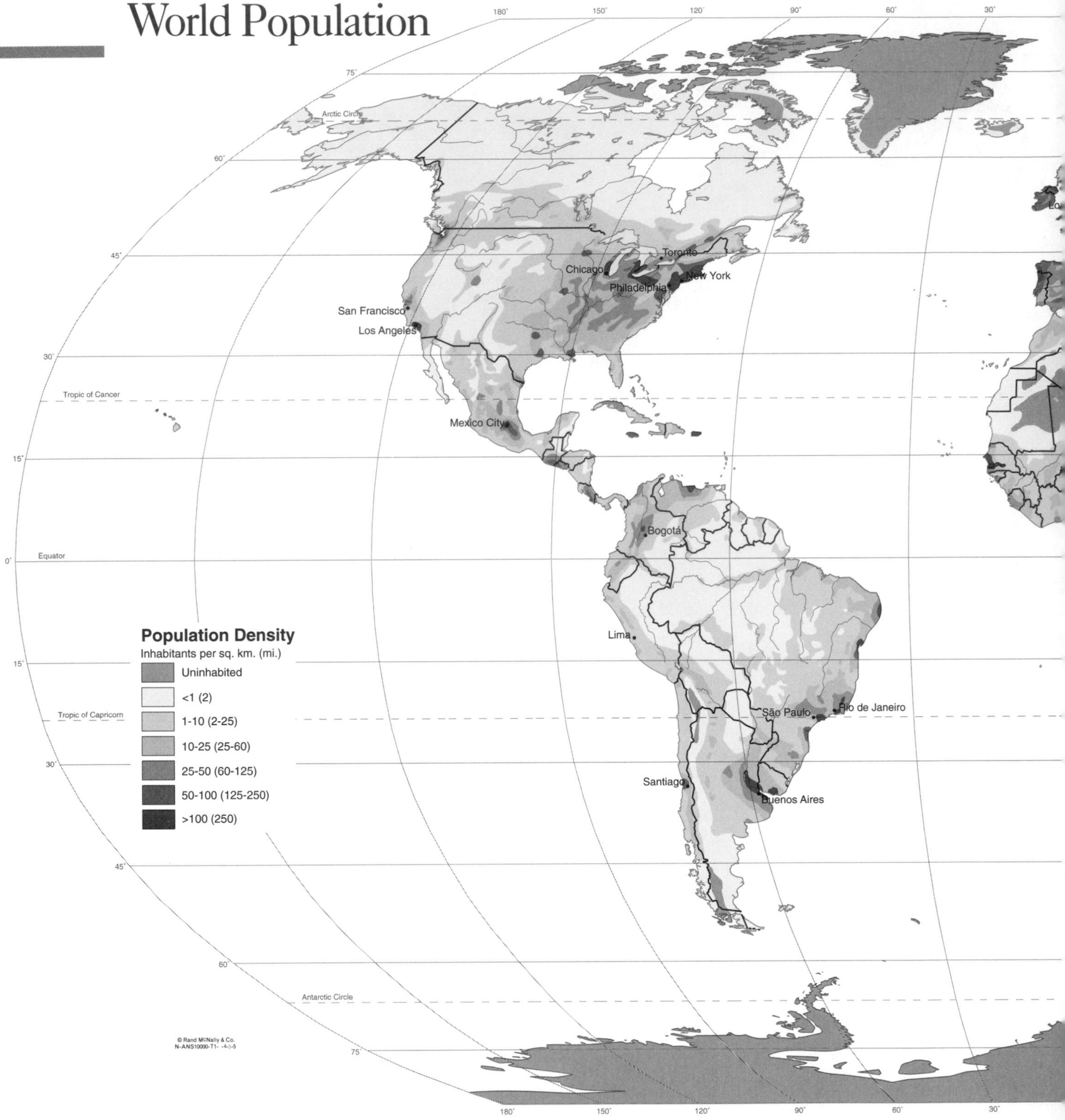

Comparative Land Areas (Land and inland water. Numbers indicate thousands of square miles.)

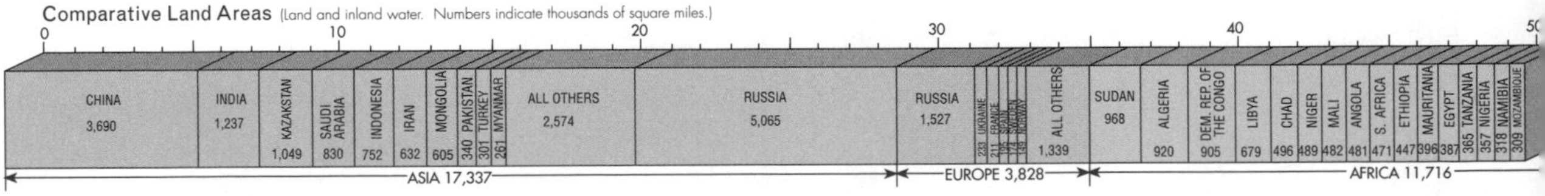

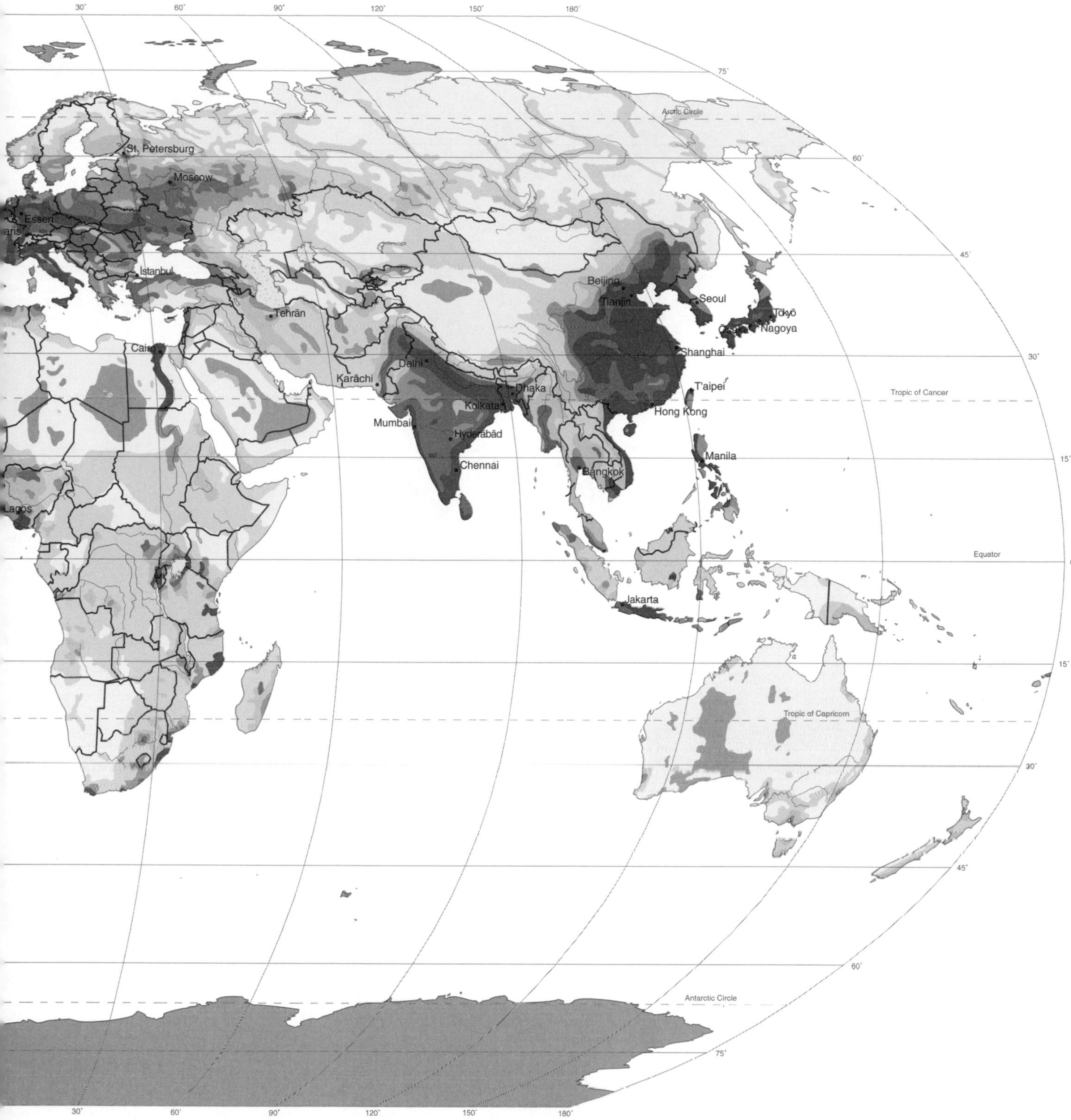
30°
60°
90°
120°
150°
180°
75°
Arctic Circle
60°
45°
30°
Tropic of Cancer
15°
Equator
0°
15°
Tropic of Capricorn
30°
45°
60°
Antarctic Circle
75°
St. Petersburg
Moscow
Essen
Istanbul
Tehrān
Karāchi
Delhi
Beijing
Tianjin
Seoul
Tōkyō
Nagoya
Shanghai
T'aipei
Dhaka
Kolkata
Hong Kong
Mumbai
Hyderābād
Chennai
Manila
Bangkok
Lagos
Jakarta

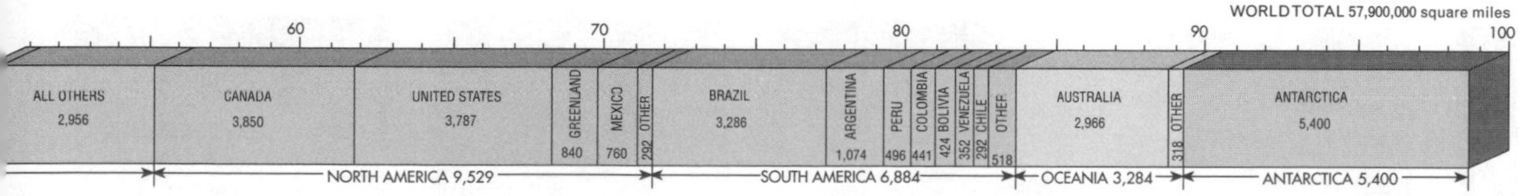
WORLD TOTAL 57,900,000 square miles
60
70
80
90
100
ALL OTHERS 2,956
CANADA 3,850
UNITED STATES 3,787
GREENLAND 840
MEXICO 760
OTHER 292
BRAZIL 3,286
ARGENTINA 1,074
PERU 496
COLOMBIA 441
BOLIVIA 424
VENEZUELA 352
CHILE 292
OTHER 518
AUSTRALIA 2,966
OTHER 318
ANTARCTICA 5,400
NORTH AMERICA 9,529
SOUTH AMERICA 6,884
OCEANIA 3,284
ANTARCTICA 5,400

World Environments

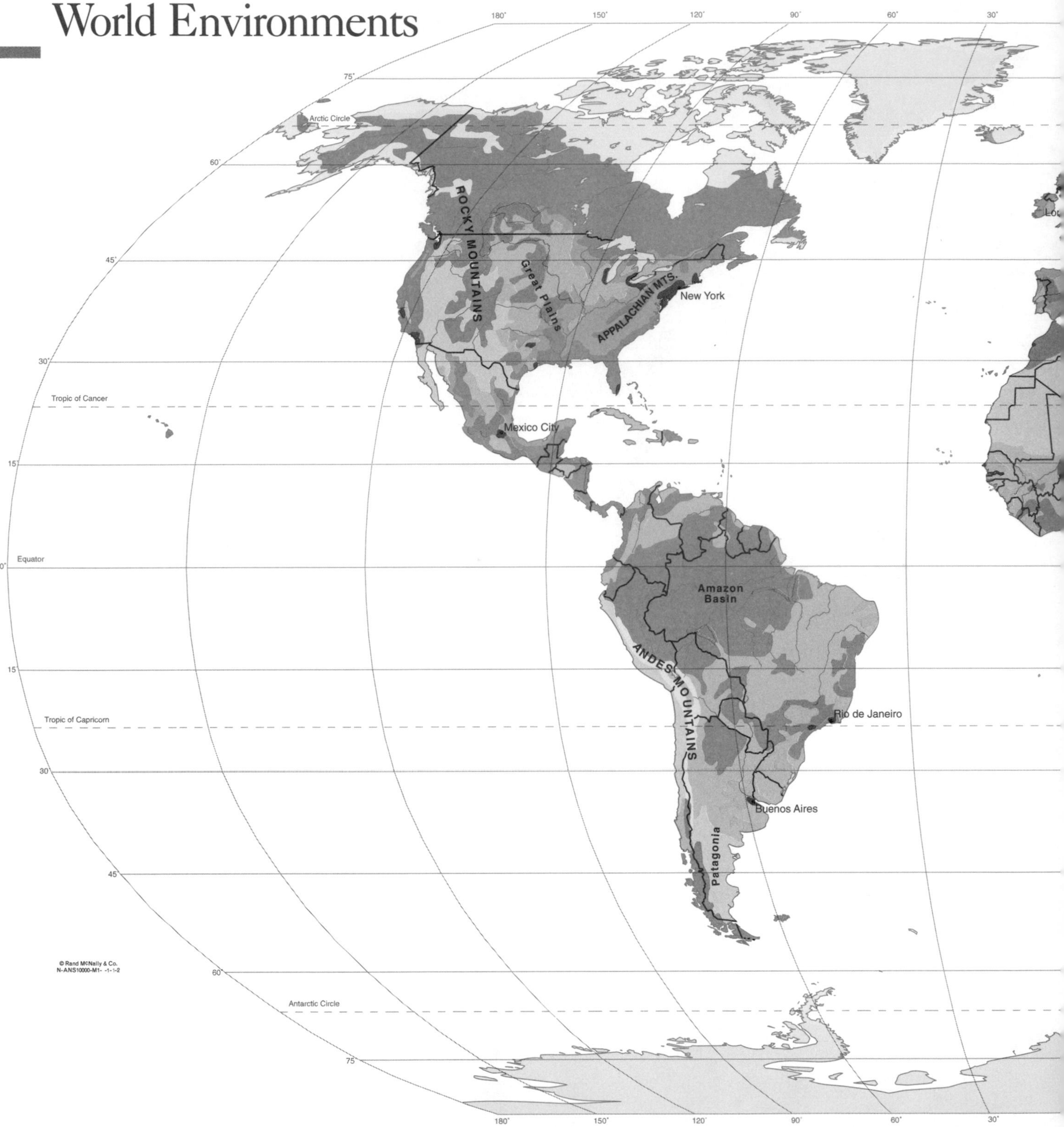

Environments

Urban

Cropland

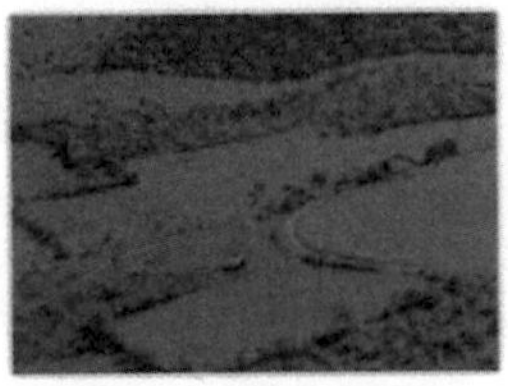

Cropland, woodland

Cropland, grazing land

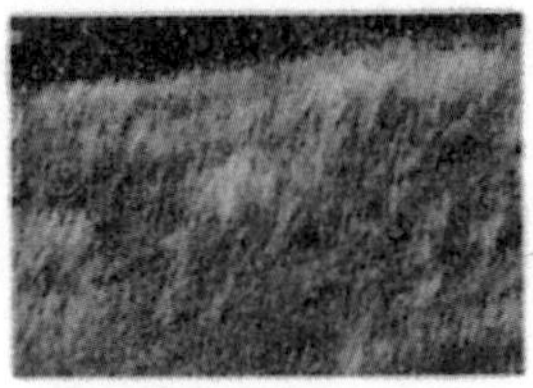

Grassland, grazing land

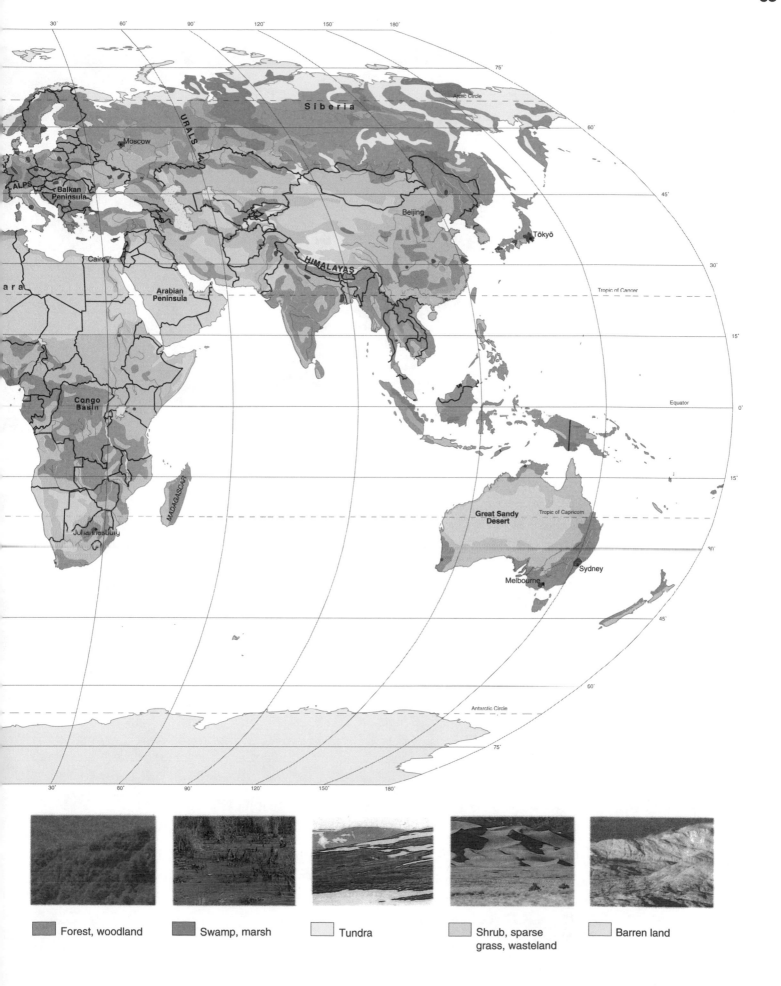

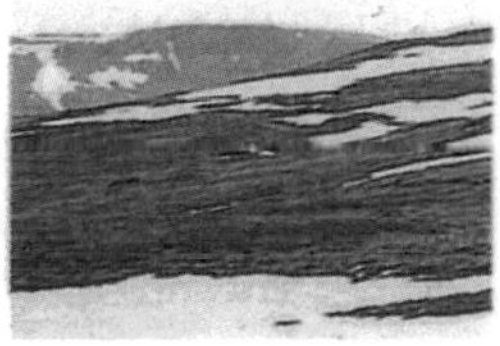

Forest, woodland

Swamp, marsh

Tundra

Shrub, sparse grass, wasteland

Barren land

Time Zones

- Standard time zone of even-numbered hours from Greenwich time
- Standard time zone of odd-numbered hours from Greenwich time
- Time varies from the standard time zone by half an hour
- Time varies from the standard time zone by other than half an hour

h m — hours, minutes

The standard time zone system, fixed by international agreement and by law in each country, is based on a theoretical division of the globe into 24 zones of 15° longitude each. The mid-meridian of each zone fixes the hour for the entire zone. The zero time zone extends 7½° east and 7½° west of the Greenwich meridian, 0° longitude. Since the earth rotates toward the east, time zones to the west of Greenwich are earlier, to the east, later.
Plus and minus hours at the top of the map are added to or subtracted from local time to find Greenwich time. Local standard time can be determined for any area in the world by adding one hour for each time zone counted in an easterly direction from one's own, or by subtracting one hour for each zone counted in a westerly direction. To separate one day from the next, the 180th meridian has been designated as the international date line.
On both sides of the line the time of day is the same, but west of the line it is one day later than it is to the east.
Countries that adhere to the international zone system adopt the zone applicable to their location. Some countries, however, establish time zones based on political boundaries, or adopt the time zone of a neighboring unit. For all or part of the year some countries also advance their time by one hour, thereby utilizing more daylight hours each day.

North America

North America is the world's third-largest continent, covering an area of 9.5 million square miles (24.7 million sq km). It lies primarily between the Arctic Circle and the Tropic of Cancer, and comes within 500 miles (800 km) of both the North Pole and the Equator. The continent's western flank is dominated by the spectacular Rocky Mountains. Covering vast stretches of the central United States and Canada are the fertile Great Plains, a large part of which is drained by the Mississippi River and its tributaries.

In the north, Hudson Bay is frozen for much of the year. Mexico, located in the continent's southern third, is mostly mountainous and dry, but farther south, the climate is wet. Many of the small Central American countries have volcanoes along the Pacific Coast.

North America at a glance

Land area: 9,500,000 square miles (24,700,000 sq km)

Estimated population: 488,780,000

Population density: 51/square mile (20/sq km)

Mean elevation: 2,000 feet (610 m)

Highest point: Mt. McKinley, Alaska, U.S. 20,230 feet (6,194 m)

Lowest point: Death Valley, California, U.S., 282 feet (86 m) below sea level

Longest river: Mississippi-Missouri, 3,740 mi (6,019 km)

Number of countries (incl. dependencies): 38

Largest independent country: Canada, 3,855,103 square miles (9,984,670 sq km)

Smallest independent country: St. Kitts and Nevis, 104 square miles (269 sq km)

Most populous independent country: United States, 279,310,000

Least populous independent country: St. Kitts and Nevis, 39,000

Largest city: Mexico City, pop. 8,489,007

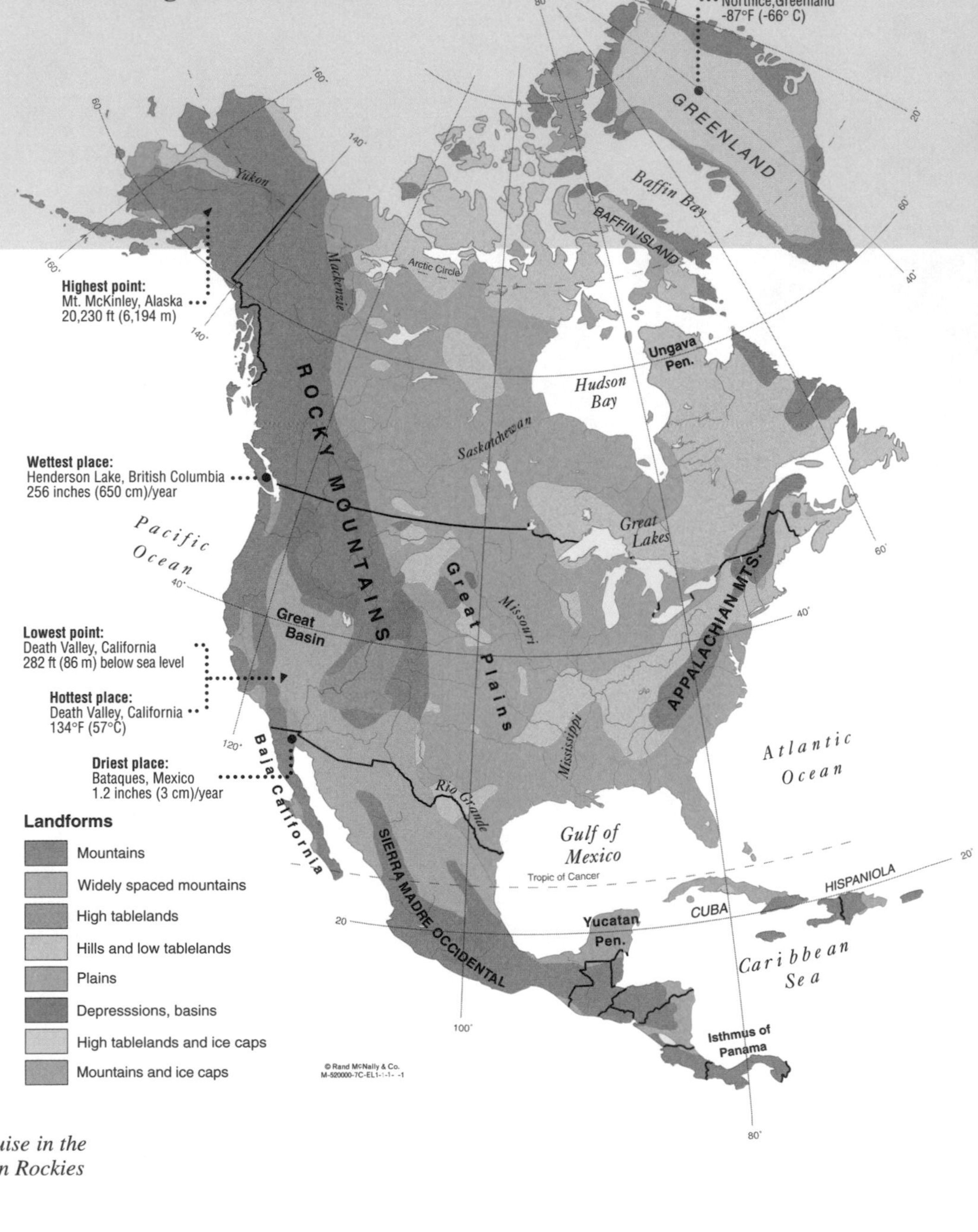

Lake Louise in the Canadian Rockies

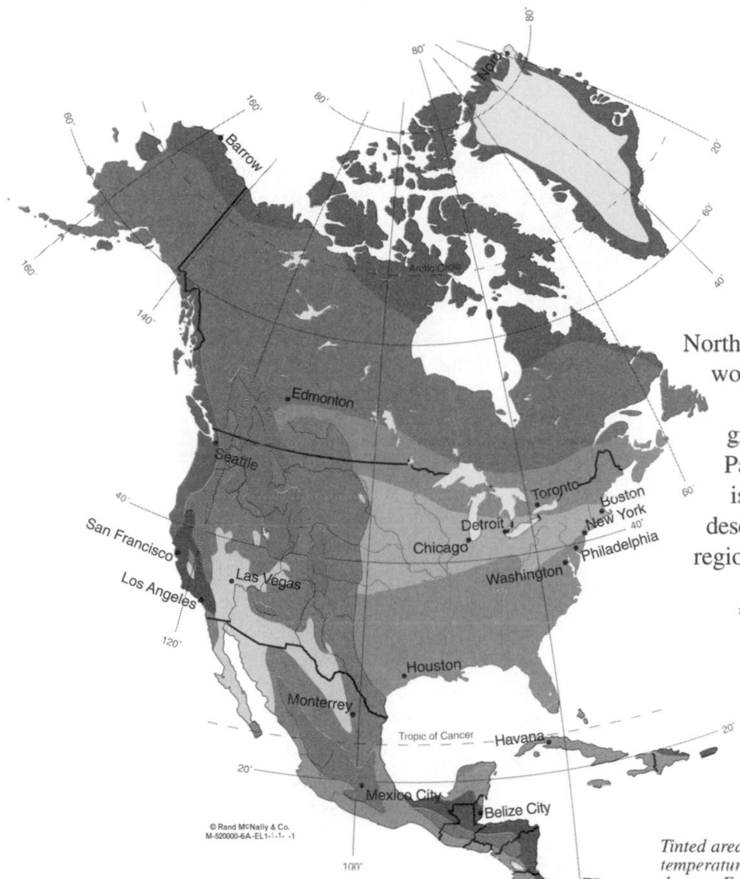

Climate

North America contains almost every type of climate that can be found in the world. Ice and tundra cover northern Canada and Greenland. Much of the central and eastern parts of the U.S. and Canada are temperate, with great seasonal changes marked by warm summers and cold winters. The Pacific Ocean moderates weather changes along the west coast, where it is cool and wet in the north and warm and dry in the south. Desert and semi-desert cover much of the southwestern U.S. and Mexico. The tropical southern region of the continent and the islands of the Caribbean Sea are hot and rainy.

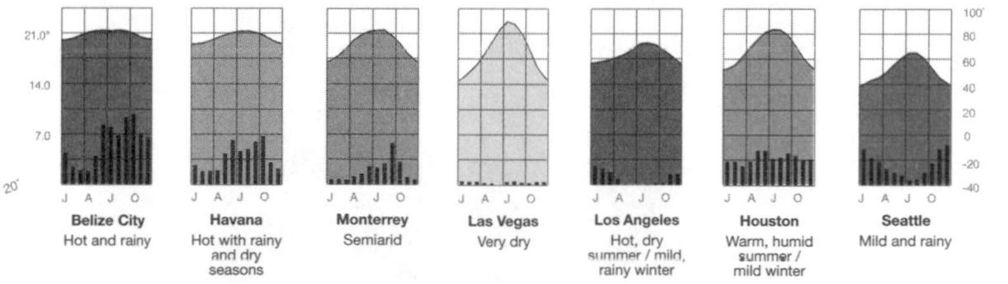

Tinted areas show temperature in degrees Fahrenheit. Vertical bars show precipitation in inches.

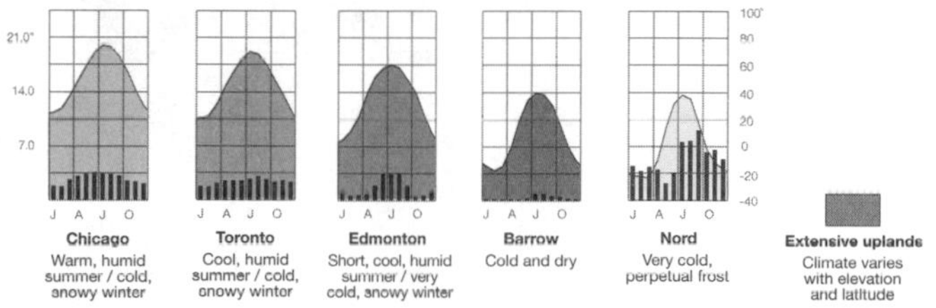

Population

About 60% of all North Americans live in the United States, the world's third most-populous country. Canada is the continent's largest country, but one of the world's least densely populated; most Canadians live within 100 miles (160 km) of the country's southern border. Mexico, with approximately 20% of North America's inhabitants, has one of the world's largest and fastest growing metropolitan areas, Mexico City, which is home to more than 20 million people.

Canada is populated mostly by descendants of French and British settlers, as well as native Americans, such as the Inuit (Eskimos) of the far north. The United States' populace reflects the country's diverse history of immigration, with European ancestry being the most common. The people of Mexico and Central America trace their origins to Spaniards and native Americans. The population of the Caribbean islands includes many descendants of African slaves and European settlers.

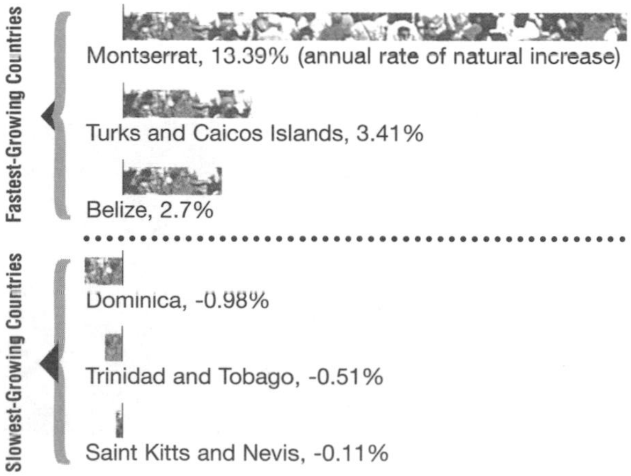

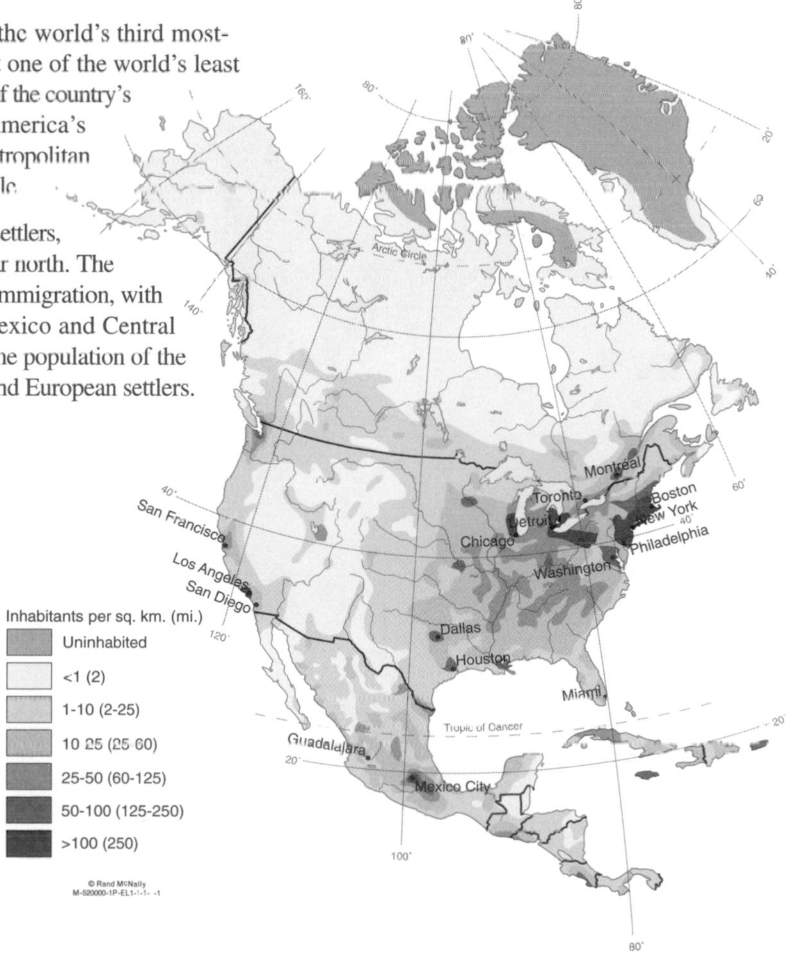

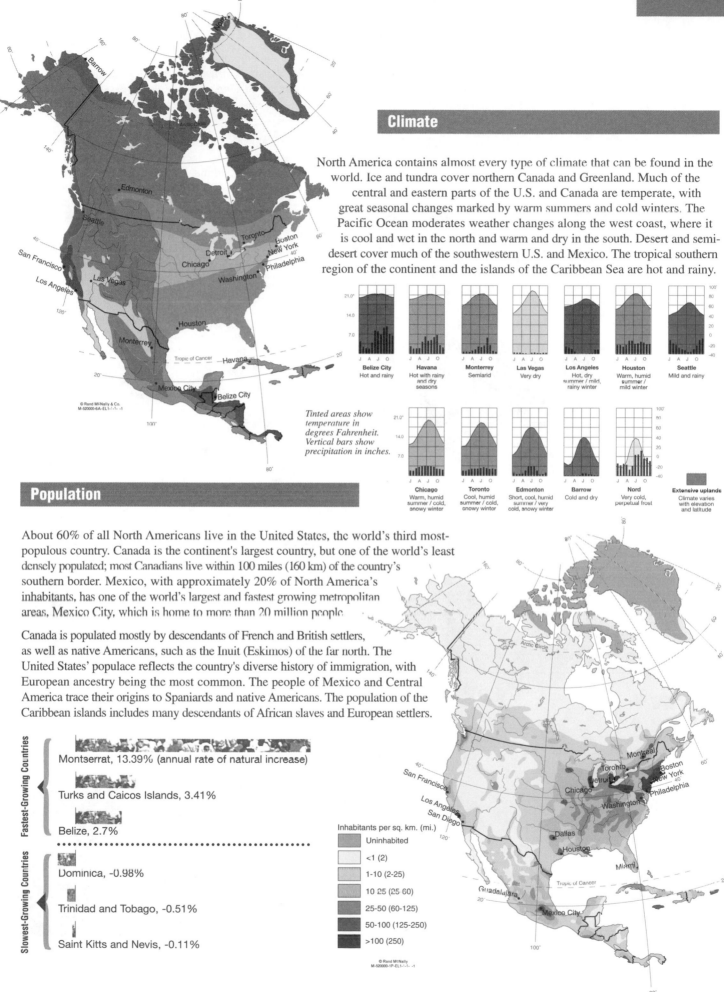

Environments and Land Use

Although only 12% of the continent is suitable for agriculture, North America is the world's leading food producer. Unlike other parts of the world, famine is virtually unknown. Large quantities of food, such as grains from the central U.S. and Canada, are exported worldwide. Sixteen percent of the continent is used for grazing, and the livestock raised on these lands are also an important source of food at home and abroad.

Forests cover one-third of the land, and the timber and paper industries are important to the U.S. and Canada. The continent has an extremely long coastline, and many countries send great fishing fleets to sea. This is especially true of Canada, whose eastern-most provinces are fittingly known as the "Maritime Provinces." However, sharp declines in catches due to over-fishing have put the industry in economic turmoil.

Blue waters, sunny skies, and idyllic beaches draw millions of tourists to the Caribbean each year. While tourism provides income for island countries that have few other assets, the economic gap between the visitors and the people who serve them remains dramatic.

One of the greatest challenges facing North America in the coming decades is a familiar one: coping with a growing population and dwindling resources. Pollution and the environment are divisive issues. Although the United States has begun to clean up its air and water, economic pressures will continue to be an argument for a relaxation of policies. Meanwhile, in Mexico, environmental issues have been pushed aside by concerns about the economy and the exploding population.

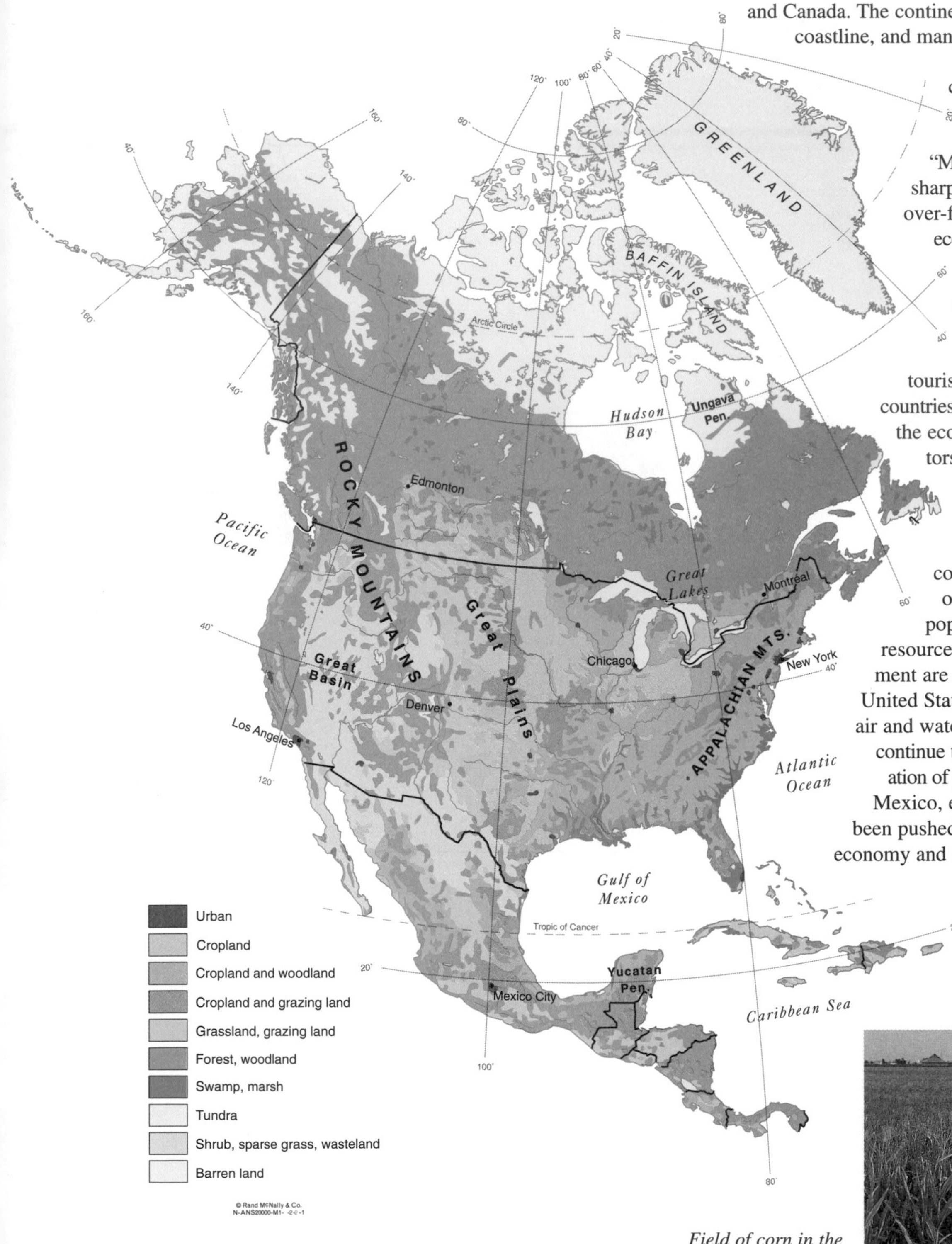

Field of corn in the midwestern United States

Urbanization in North America

Seen from the air, large portions of North America still bear the checkerboard imprint left by the people who settled the continent: a vast array of small farms that could be worked by one man and a horse. As industrialization swept through the United States in the second half of the 19th century, many farmers left their farms. Great numbers moved to fast-growing cities such as Chicago and St. Louis. Many small towns saw their populations dwindle.

In the cities, change was continuous. The former farm families were joined by waves of European immigrants. Over the next 100 years, urban populations continued to grow, and cities that had once been separate became part of vast urban megalopolises. An example can be seen in the eastern United States, where a band of urban centers stretches almost continuously from Boston south through New York City to Washington D.C. (see map at right).

After World War II, as the U. S. middle class expanded, large numbers of families moved out of the city centers into suburban communities of mass-produced, affordable homes. Many of those who remained were economically disadvantaged. A shrinking tax base meant that cities could not support their infrastructures, and conditions in the inner cities worsened. In the suburbs the opposite was true: vast sums were spent building new roads, houses, and shopping centers.

The same process that transformed the U.S. is now occurring in Mexico. In 1945, 25% of the population was considered urban, but today the figure surpasses 70% (see graph above). Not content to lead lives as subsistence farmers, scores of Mexicans arrive in the cities each day in search of jobs that will enable them to provide a better life for their families.

Sadly, these dreams are often elusive. Most of the people end up in low-paying jobs, with their meager wages going to pay for the food that they once grew themselves. City officials are hard-pressed to provide clean water to their ever-growing populations, let alone electricity, transportation and education.

As elsewhere in the world, coping with the pressures of growing populations is one of the greatest challenges facing North Americans today.

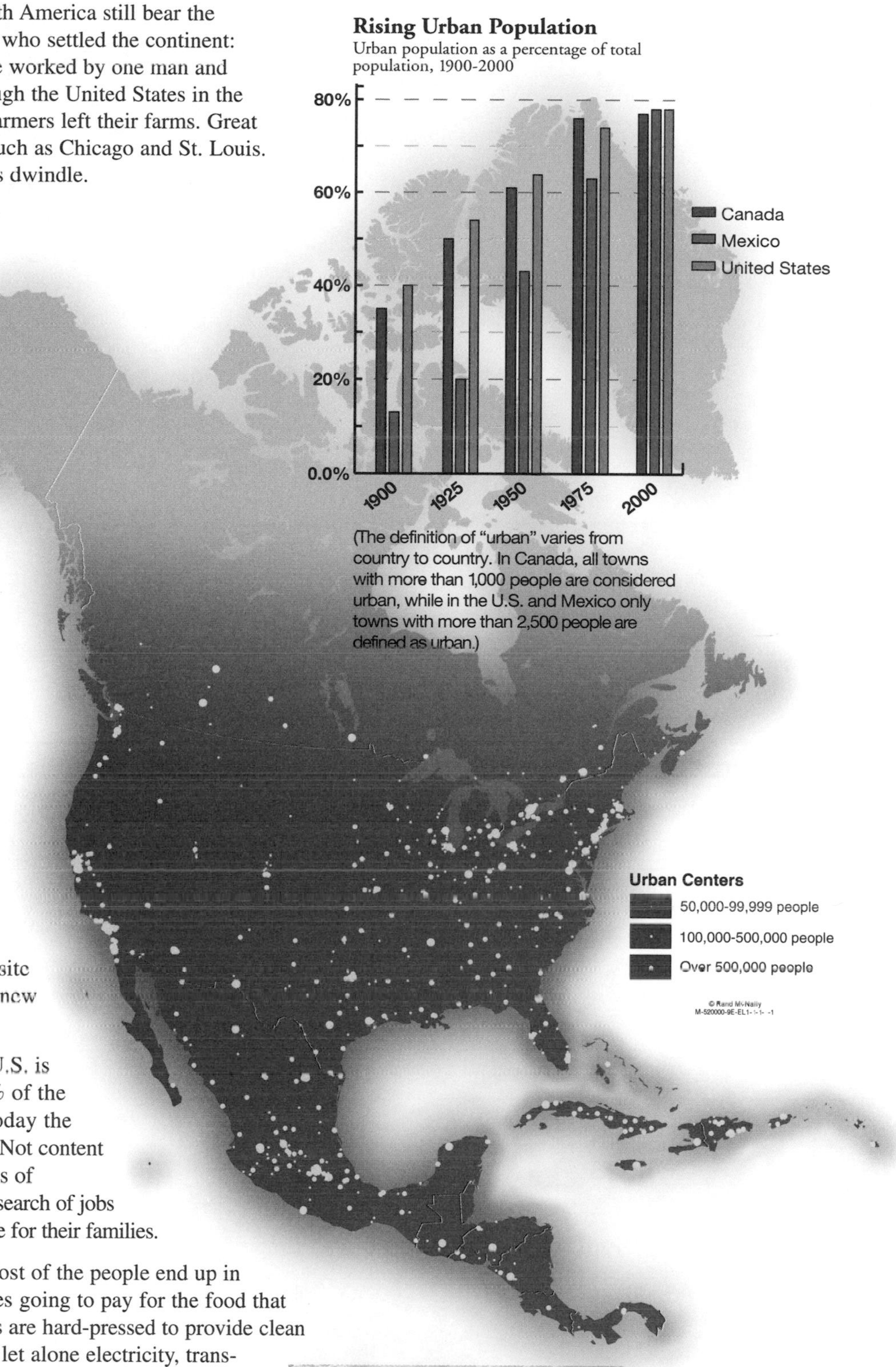

Mexico City, whose metropolitan area population exceeds 20 million, sprawls toward the distant mountains.

Scale 1:40 000 000; one inch to 630 miles. Lambert's Azimuthal Equal Area Projection
Elevations and depressions are given in feet

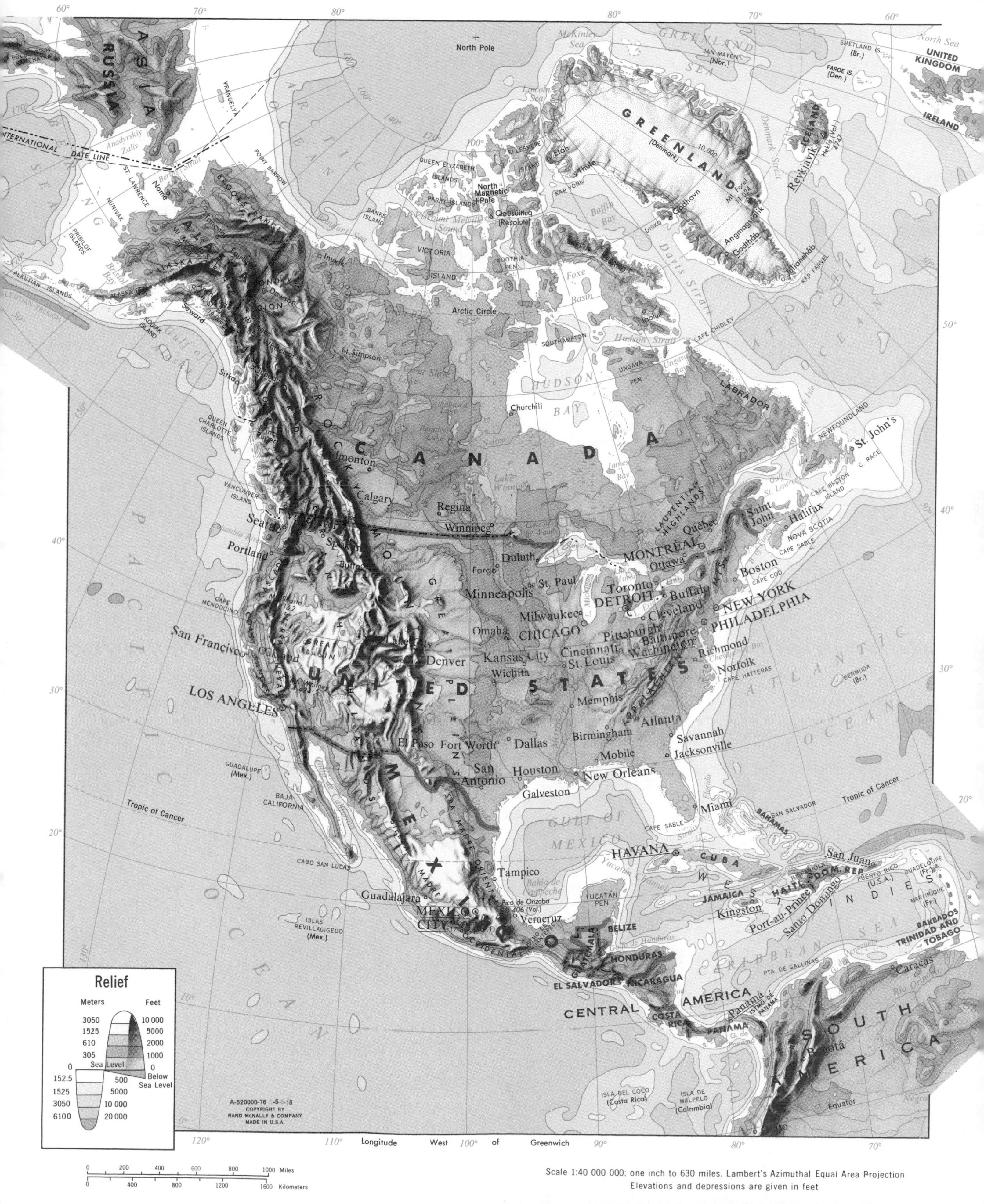

Scale 1:40 000 000; one inch to 630 miles. Lambert's Azimuthal Equal Area Projection
Elevations and depressions are given in feet

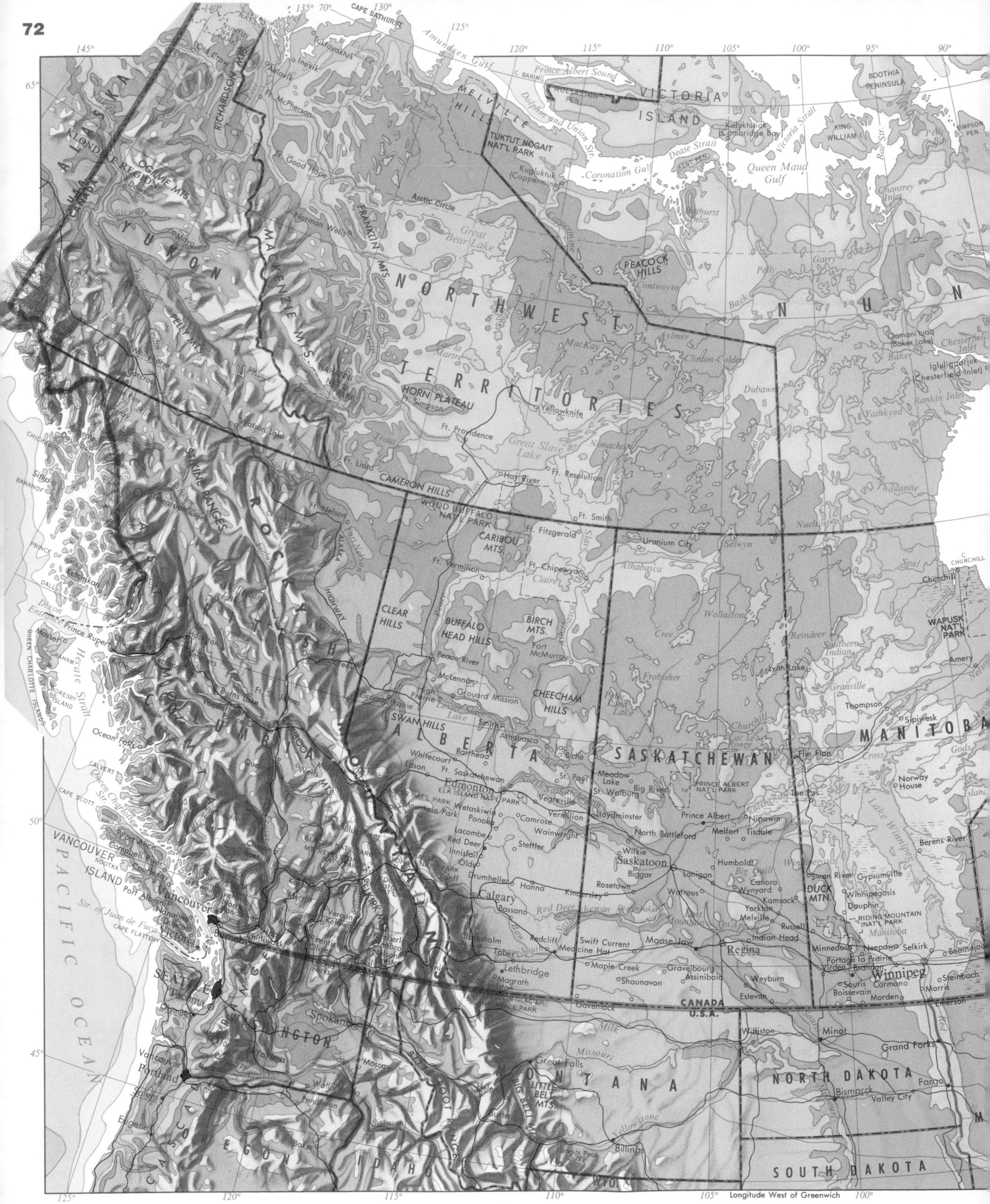

Longitude West of Greenwich

Scale 1: 12 000 000; one inch to 190 miles. Conic Projection

Elevations and depressions are given in feet

NEWFOUNDLAND AND LABRADOR
Same scale as main map
QUEBEC
Gulf of St. Lawrence
LONG RANGE MTS.
GROS MORNE NAT'L PARK
Deer Lake
Corner Brook
Stephenville
Botwood
Windsor
Gander
Grand Falls
Twillingate
Bonavista
TERRA NOVA NAT'L PARK
NEWFOUNDLAND
St. George's
Channel-Port-aux-Basques
Cabot Strait
Grand Bank
Burin
St. John's
CAPE BAULD
C. ST. JOHN
CAPE RAY
CAPE NORTH
CAPE BRETON ISLAND
ST. PIERRE AND MIQUELON (Fr.)
ATLANTIC OCEAN
©RMcN
60° Longitude West of Greenwich 55°
BAFFIN ISLAND
MELVILLE PENINSULA
Foxe Basin
Arctic Circle
Iqaluit
Frobisher Bay
EVERETT MTS.
Cumberland Sound
Pangnirtung
Igloolik
SOUTHAMPTON ISLAND
Roes Welcome Sound
Foxe Channel
Hudson Strait
NUNAVUT
C. LOW
COATS
MANSEL
NOTTINGHAM ISLAND
AKPATOK
Ungava Bay
Ivujivik
PENINSULE D'UNGAVA
Povungnituk
Kuujjuaq
TORNGAT MTS.
Hebron
Nain
Hopedale
Makkovik
Cartwright
Battle Harbour
NEWFOUNDLAND AND LABRADOR
LABRADOR
MEALY MTS.
Happy Valley-Goose Bay
Churchill Falls
Schefferville
Lac Bienville
Caniapiscau
MTS. OTISH
Natashquan
Minga
ILE D'ANTICOSTI
Sept-Îles
HUDSON BAY
All islands within bays and straits lie within Nunavut.
OTTAWA ISLANDS
BELCHER ISLANDS
C. HENRIETTA MARIA
Ft. Severn
James Bay
Chisasibi
AKIMISKI
Ft. Albany
Moosonee
Chibougamau
QUEBEC
ONTARIO
Gaspé
CHIC-CHOCS MTS.
NEW BRUNSWICK
NOVA SCOTIA
P.E.I.
Charlottetown
Halifax
Sydney
Saint John
Fredericton
Moncton
Yarmouth
Shelburne
Chicoutimi
Québec
Trois-Rivières
Sherbrooke
MONTREAL
Ottawa
Hull
Kingston
Sudbury
North Bay
Timmins
Kapuskasing
Hearst
Cochrane
Kirkland Lake
Rouyn
Val-d'Or
Amos
Chapleau
Geraldton
Longlac
Nipigon
Marathon
Thunder Bay
Sault Ste. Marie
Red Lake
Sioux Lookout
Dryden
Lake Superior
Lake Huron
Georgian Bay
Lake Michigan
Lake Ontario
Lake Erie
TORONTO
Hamilton
Peterborough
Oshawa
Kitchener
London
St. Catharines
Windsor
Sarnia
Niagara
BUFFALO
Rochester
DETROIT
Toledo
MILWAUKEE
CHICAGO
MINNEAPOLIS
St. Paul
Duluth
Madison
Green Bay
Grand Rapids
Lansing
Flint
Saginaw
Marquette
WISCONSIN
MICHIGAN
PENNSYLVANIA
NEW YORK
MAINE
VERMONT
NEW HAMPSHIRE
MASS.
CONN.
R.I.
N.J.
OHIO
BOSTON
Portland
Augusta
Concord
Albany
Hartford
Providence
Scranton
CAPE COD
CAPE SABLE
ATLANTIC OCEAN
Relief
Meters
Feet
3050
1525
610
305
152.5
0
Sea Level
10 000
5000
2000
1000
500
0
152.5
1525
3050
500
5000
10 000
A-520200-76
COPYRIGHT BY RAND McNALLY & COMPANY MADE IN U.S.A.
0 25 50 75 100 200 300 400 500 Miles
0 100 200 400 600 800 Kilometers

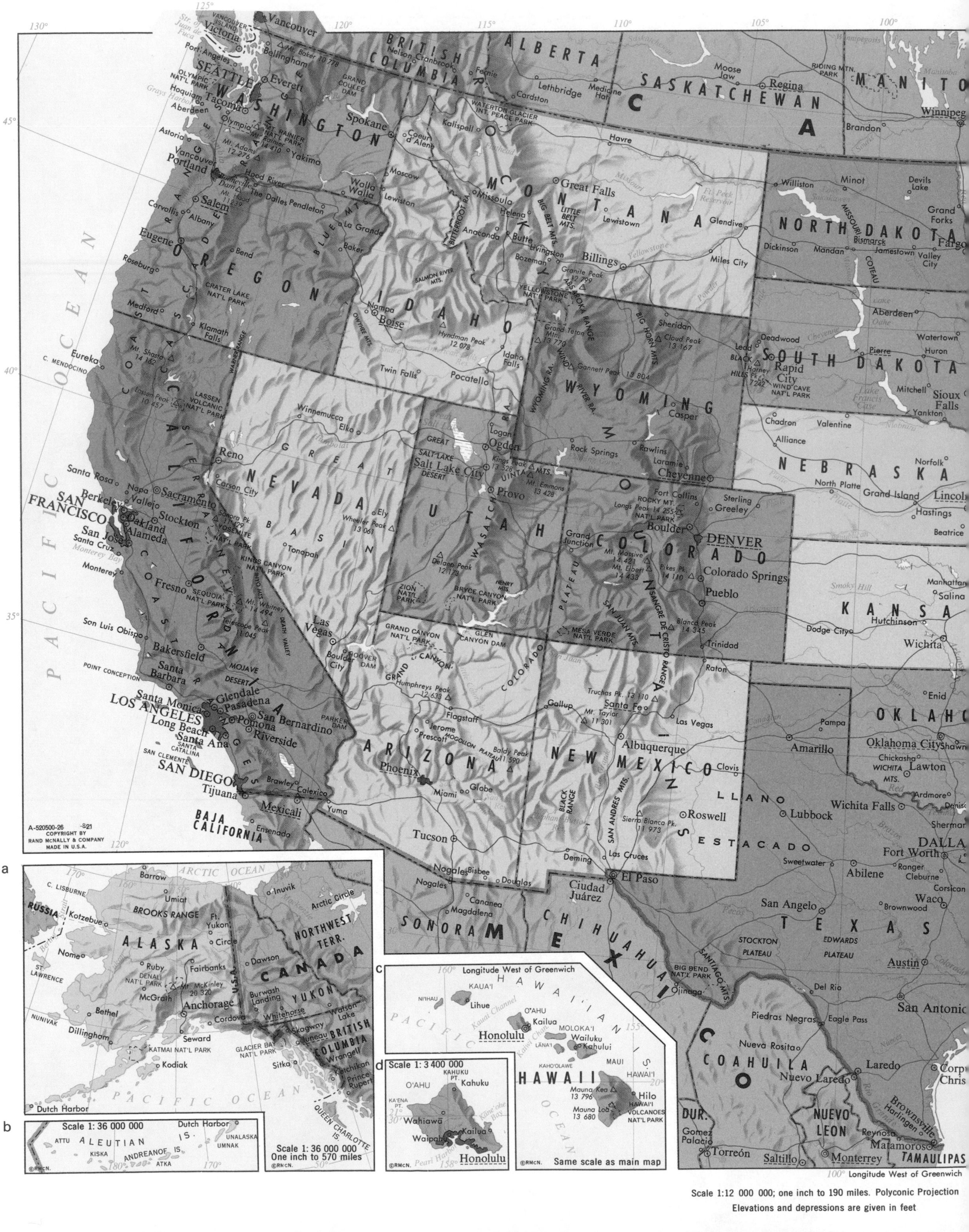

Scale 1:12 000 000; one inch to 190 miles. Polyconic Projection

Elevations and depressions are given in feet

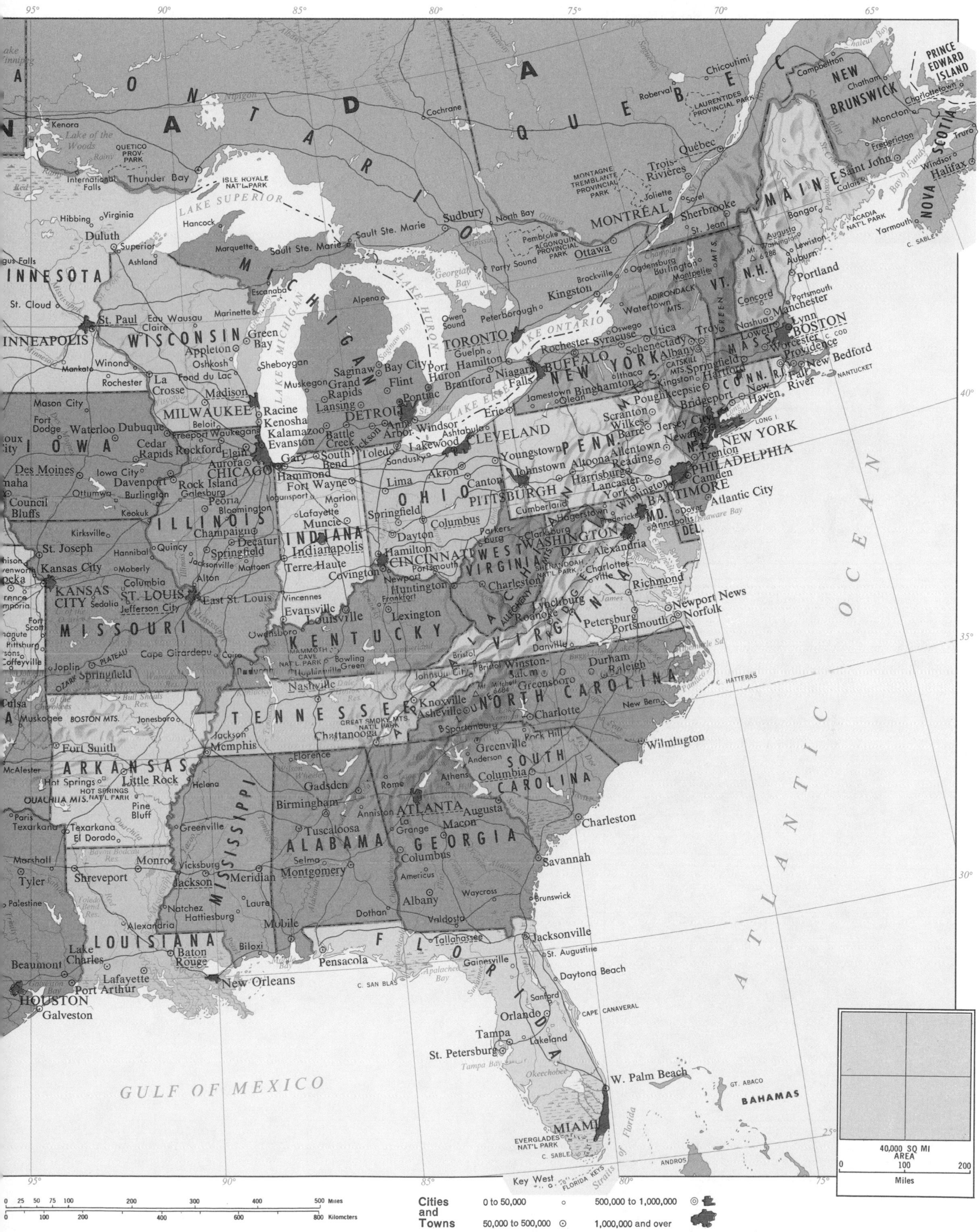
95°
90°
85°
80°
75°
70°
65°
40°
35°
30°
25°
C A N A D A
Q U E B E C
O N T A R I O
PRINCE EDWARD ISLAND
NEW BRUNSWICK
NOVA SCOTIA
M A I N E
N.H.
VT.
MASS.
CONN.
R.I.
NEW YORK
N.J.
PENN.
MD.
DEL.
D.C.
WEST VIRGINIA
VIRGINIA
NORTH CAROLINA
SOUTH CAROLINA
GEORGIA
FLORIDA
ALABAMA
MISSISSIPPI
LOUISIANA
ARKANSAS
TENNESSEE
KENTUCKY
OHIO
INDIANA
ILLINOIS
MICHIGAN
WISCONSIN
MINNESOTA
IOWA
MISSOURI
KANSAS CITY
LAKE SUPERIOR
LAKE MICHIGAN
LAKE HURON
LAKE ERIE
LAKE ONTARIO
Lake of the Woods
Georgian Bay
Saginaw Bay
Green Bay
Bay of Fundy
ATLANTIC OCEAN
GULF OF MEXICO
BAHAMAS
GT. ABACO
ANDROS
Straits of Florida
FLORIDA KEYS
Key West
C. SABLE
EVERGLADES NAT'L PARK
MIAMI
W. Palm Beach
Okeechobee
St. Petersburg
Tampa
Tampa Bay
Lakeland
Orlando
Sanford
CAPE CANAVERAL
Daytona Beach
St. Augustine
Jacksonville
Gainesville
Tallahassee
Apalachee Bay
C. SAN BLAS
Pensacola
Mobile
Biloxi
New Orleans
Baton Rouge
Lafayette
Lake Charles
Port Arthur
Beaumont
HOUSTON
Galveston
Alexandria
Shreveport
Monroe
Natchez
Hattiesburg
Laurel
Meridian
Jackson
Vicksburg
Greenville
Tyler
Marshall
Palestine
Texarkana
El Dorado
Pine Bluff
Little Rock
Hot Springs
HOT SPRINGS NAT'L PARK
OUACHITA MTS.
McAlester
Fort Smith
BOSTON MTS.
Muskogee
Tulsa
Jonesboro
Memphis
Jackson
Helena
Florence
Huntsville
Gadsden
Birmingham
Tuscaloosa
Anniston
Montgomery
Selma
Dothan
Columbus
Americus
Albany
Valdosta
Waycross
Brunswick
Savannah
Macon
La Grange
ATLANTA
Rome
Athens
Augusta
Columbia
Charleston
Anderson
Greenville
Spartanburg
Rock Hill
Charlotte
Wilmington
New Bern
C. HATTERAS
Durham
Raleigh
Greensboro
Winston-Salem
Mt. Mitchell 6684
Asheville
Knoxville
Chattanooga
GREAT SMOKY MTS. NAT'L PARK
Nashville
Johnson City
Bristol
Danville
Lynchburg
Roanoke
Petersburg
Portsmouth
Norfolk
Newport News
Richmond
Charlottesville
SHENANDOAH NAT'L PARK
Alexandria
WASHINGTON
Annapolis
Dover
BALTIMORE
Wilmington
Atlantic City
Delaware Bay
Camden
PHILADELPHIA
Trenton
Newark
Jersey City
NEW YORK
LONG I.
New Haven
Bridgeport
Hartford
Springfield
Worcester
Providence
Fall River
New Bedford
NANTUCKET
C. COD
BOSTON
Lynn
Lowell
Nashua
Manchester
Concord
Portsmouth
Portland
Auburn
Lewiston
Augusta
Mt. Washington 6288
Bangor
ACADIA NAT'L PARK
GREEN MTS.
Burlington
Montpelier
Troy
Albany
Schenectady
Utica
Syracuse
Rochester
Oswego
Watertown
ADIRONDACK MTS.
CATSKILL MTS.
Kingston
Poughkeepsie
Binghamton
Ithaca
Elmira
Olean
Jamestown
BUFFALO
Niagara Falls
Erie
Scranton
Wilkes-Barre
Allentown
Reading
Lancaster
York
Harrisburg
Altoona
Johnstown
PITTSBURGH
Cumberland
Hagerstown
Frederick
Youngstown
CLEVELAND
Ashtabula
Lakewood
Akron
Canton
Sandusky
Toledo
Lima
Springfield
Dayton
Columbus
Hamilton
CINCINNATI
Covington
Newport
Portsmouth
Huntington
Charleston
Parkersburg
Clarksburg
Ashland
Frankfort
Lexington
Louisville
Owensboro
Evansville
MAMMOTH CAVE NAT'L PARK
Bowling Green
Hopkinsville
Paducah
Cairo
Cape Girardeau
Vincennes
Terre Haute
Indianapolis
Muncie
Lafayette
Marion
Logansport
Fort Wayne
South Bend
Gary
Hammond
CHICAGO
Elgin
Aurora
Evanston
Waukegan
Kenosha
Racine
MILWAUKEE
Madison
Beloit
Freeport
Rockford
Rock Island
Galesburg
Peoria
Bloomington
Champaign
Decatur
Springfield
Quincy
Jacksonville
Mattoon
Alton
East St. Louis
ST. LOUIS
Jefferson City
Sedalia
Columbia
Moberly
Hannibal
Kirksville
St. Joseph
Kansas City
Joplin
Springfield
OZARK PLATEAU
Keokuk
Burlington
Ottumwa
Des Moines
Iowa City
Davenport
Cedar Rapids
Waterloo
Dubuque
Fort Dodge
Mason City
Council Bluffs
Rochester
Winona
Mankato
La Crosse
Eau Claire
Wausau
Oshkosh
Fond du Lac
Appleton
Green Bay
Sheboygan
Marinette
Escanaba
Marquette
Hancock
Ashland
Superior
Duluth
Hibbing
Virginia
International Falls
Thunder Bay
ISLE ROYALE NAT'L PARK
QUETICO PROV. PARK
Kenora
Nipigon
St. Cloud
St. Paul
MINNEAPOLIS
Sault Ste. Marie
Sault Ste. Marie
Alpena
Saginaw
Bay City
Flint
Pontiac
Grand Rapids
Muskegon
Lansing
Kalamazoo
Battle Creek
Jackson
Ann Arbor
DETROIT
Windsor
Port Huron
London
Brantford
Hamilton
Guelph
TORONTO
Owen Sound
Peterborough
Kingston
Brockville
Ottawa
Ogdensburg
Pembroke
ALGONQUIN PROVINCIAL PARK
Parry Sound
North Bay
Sudbury
Cochrane
MONTRÉAL
Sherbrooke
St. Jean
Sorel
Joliette
Trois-Rivières
MONTAGNE TREMBLANTE PROVINCIAL PARK
Québec
Roberval
Chicoutimi
LAURENTIDES PROVINCIAL PARK
Campbellton
Chatham
Moncton
Fredericton
Saint John
Calais
Charlottetown
Truro
Windsor
Halifax
Yarmouth
C. SABLE
Chaleur Bay
40,000 SQ MI AREA
0 100 200
Miles
0 25 50 75 100 200 300 400 500 Miles
0 100 200 400 600 800 Kilometers
Cities and Towns
0 to 50,000
50,000 to 500,000
500,000 to 1,000,000
1,000,000 and over

Scale 1:12 000 000; one inch to 190 miles. Polyconic Projection
Elevations and depressions are given in feet

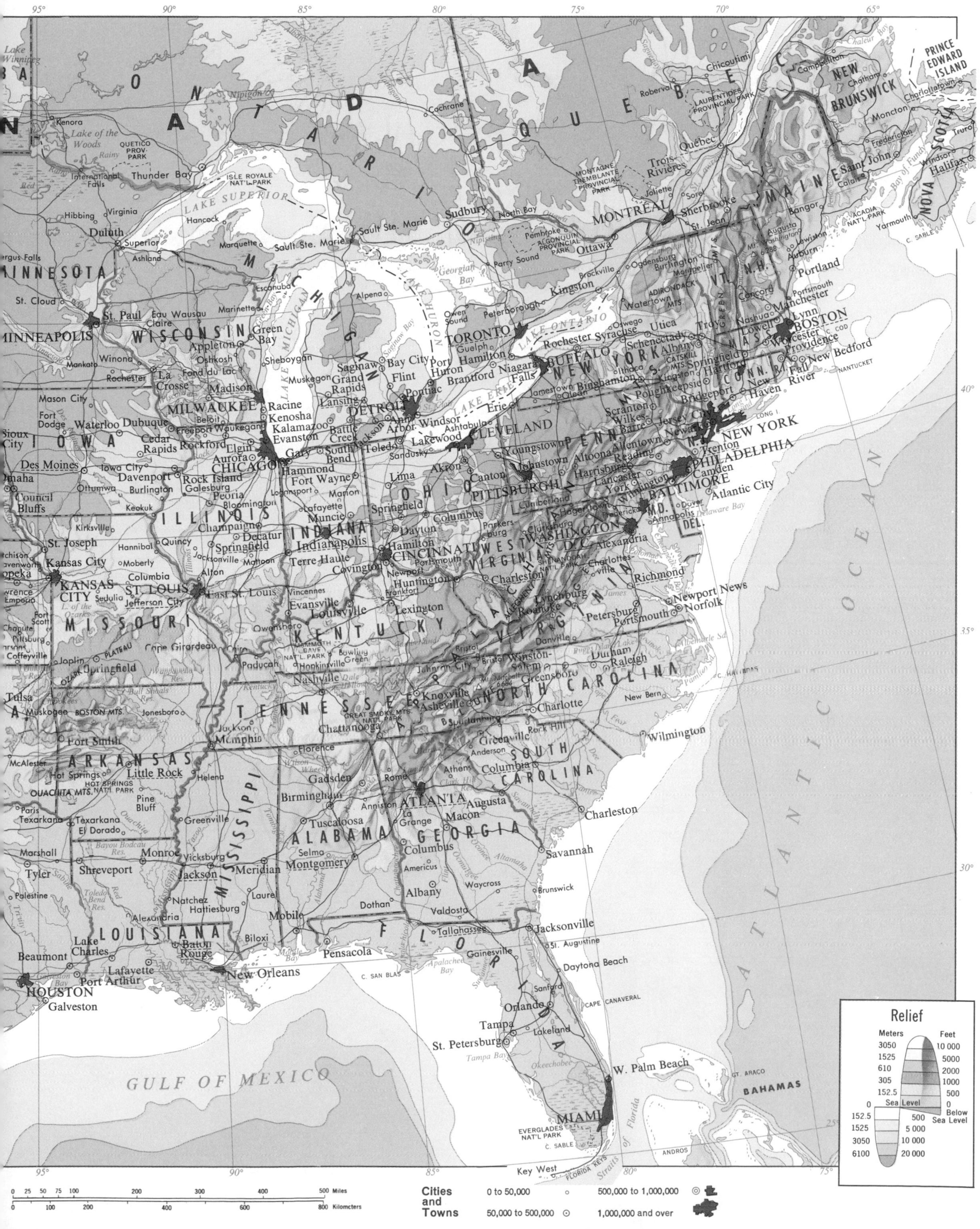
95°
90°
85°
80°
75°
70°
65°
40°
35°
30°
ONTARIO
QUEBEC
NEW BRUNSWICK
PRINCE EDWARD ISLAND
NOVA SCOTIA
MINNESOTA
WISCONSIN
MICHIGAN
IOWA
ILLINOIS
INDIANA
OHIO
PENN.
NEW YORK
VT.
N.H.
MAINE
MASS.
CONN.
R.I.
N.J.
MD.
DEL.
WEST VIRGINIA
VIRGINIA
KENTUCKY
TENNESSEE
NORTH CAROLINA
SOUTH CAROLINA
GEORGIA
FLORIDA
ALABAMA
MISSISSIPPI
LOUISIANA
ARKANSAS
MISSOURI
APPALACHIAN
LAKE SUPERIOR
LAKE MICHIGAN
LAKE HURON
LAKE ERIE
LAKE ONTARIO
Lake of the Woods
Georgian Bay
Saginaw Bay
ISLE ROYALE NAT'L PARK
QUETICO PROV. PARK
ALGONQUIN PROVINCIAL PARK
LAURENTIDES PROVINCIAL PARK
MONTAGNE TREMBLANTE PROVINCIAL PARK
ACADIA NAT'L PARK
ADIRONDACK MTS.
GREEN MTS.
CATSKILL MTS.
Mt. Washington 6288
Mt. Mitchell 6684
GREAT SMOKY MTS. NAT'L PARK
SHENANDOAH NAT'L PARK
MAMMOTH CAVE NAT'L PARK
OZARK PLATEAU
BOSTON MTS.
OUACHITA MTS.
HOT SPRINGS NAT'L PARK
EVERGLADES NAT'L PARK
ATLANTIC OCEAN
GULF OF MEXICO
BAHAMAS
Straits of Florida
Bay of Fundy
Delaware Bay
Chesapeake Bay
Albemarle Sd.
Pamlico Sd.
Tampa Bay
Okeechobee
Apalachee Bay
Mobile Bay
C. COD
NANTUCKET
LONG I.
C. HATTERAS
CAPE CANAVERAL
C. SABLE
C. SAN BLAS
FLORIDA KEYS
GT. ABACO
ANDROS
Kenora
Thunder Bay
International Falls
Duluth
Superior
Hibbing
Virginia
Sault Ste. Marie
Sudbury
North Bay
Cochrane
Ottawa
MONTREAL
Quebec
Trois-Rivières
Sherbrooke
Chicoutimi
Roberval
Campbellton
Chatham
Moncton
Charlottetown
Fredericton
Saint John
Halifax
Truro
Yarmouth
Bangor
Augusta
Lewiston
Auburn
Portland
Kingston
TORONTO
Hamilton
Niagara Falls
BUFFALO
Rochester
Syracuse
Utica
Schenectady
Albany
Troy
Ithaca
Binghamton
Elmira
Jamestown
Springfield
Hartford
New Haven
Bridgeport
Worcester
BOSTON
Lynn
Lowell
Manchester
Concord
Nashua
Providence
Fall River
New Bedford
NEW YORK
Jersey City
Newark
Trenton
PHILADELPHIA
Camden
Atlantic City
Allentown
Scranton
Wilkes-Barre
Reading
Harrisburg
Lancaster
York
Wilmington
BALTIMORE
Annapolis
Dover
WASHINGTON D.C.
Alexandria
Hagerstown
Frederick
Altoona
Johnstown
PITTSBURGH
Erie
CLEVELAND
Akron
Canton
Youngstown
Toledo
DETROIT
Pontiac
Flint
Saginaw
Bay City
Lansing
Grand Rapids
Muskegon
Kalamazoo
Battle Creek
Jackson
Ann Arbor
Windsor
Port Huron
MILWAUKEE
Racine
Kenosha
Madison
Green Bay
Appleton
Oshkosh
Sheboygan
Fond du Lac
La Crosse
Eau Claire
Wausau
St. Paul
MINNEAPOLIS
St. Cloud
Rochester
Winona
CHICAGO
Evanston
Gary
Hammond
Elgin
Aurora
Rockford
Peoria
Bloomington
Champaign
Decatur
Springfield
Quincy
Davenport
Rock Island
Cedar Rapids
Waterloo
Dubuque
Des Moines
Sioux City
Council Bluffs
Omaha
South Bend
Fort Wayne
Indianapolis
Muncie
Lafayette
Terre Haute
Evansville
Lima
Dayton
Springfield
Columbus
Hamilton
CINCINNATI
Covington
Newport
Portsmouth
Huntington
Charleston
Parkersburg
Clarksburg
Louisville
Lexington
Frankfort
Owensboro
Paducah
Bowling Green
Hopkinsville
Nashville
Knoxville
Chattanooga
Memphis
Jackson
Bristol
Johnson City
Asheville
Winston-Salem
Greensboro
Durham
Raleigh
Charlotte
Wilmington
New Bern
Danville
Lynchburg
Roanoke
Charlottesville
Richmond
Petersburg
Newport News
Norfolk
Portsmouth
Greenville
Spartanburg
Rock Hill
Anderson
Columbia
Charleston
Augusta
Athens
ATLANTA
Rome
Macon
Columbus
Savannah
Brunswick
Albany
Americus
Valdosta
Waycross
Jacksonville
St. Augustine
Daytona Beach
Gainesville
Tallahassee
Pensacola
Orlando
Sanford
Tampa
St. Petersburg
Lakeland
W. Palm Beach
MIAMI
Key West
Birmingham
Gadsden
Anniston
Florence
Tuscaloosa
Montgomery
Selma
Dothan
Mobile
Biloxi
Meridian
Hattiesburg
Natchez
Vicksburg
Greenville
New Orleans
Baton Rouge
Lafayette
Lake Charles
Alexandria
Monroe
Shreveport
Texarkana
El Dorado
Pine Bluff
Little Rock
Hot Springs
Helena
Fort Smith
Jonesboro
ST. LOUIS
East St. Louis
Jefferson City
Columbia
Moberly
Hannibal
Kirksville
St. Joseph
KANSAS CITY
Sedalia
Springfield
Joplin
Cape Girardeau
Tulsa
Muskogee
McAlester
HOUSTON
Galveston
Beaumont
Port Arthur
Tyler
Marshall
Palestine
Relief
Meters
Feet
3050
1525
610
305
152.5
0
10 000
5000
2000
1000
500
0
Sea Level
Below Sea Level
152.5
1525
3050
6100
500
5 000
10 000
20 000
0 25 50 75 100 200 300 400 500 Miles
0 100 200 400 600 800 Kilometers
Cities and Towns
0 to 50,000
50,000 to 500,000
500,000 to 1,000,000
1,000,000 and over

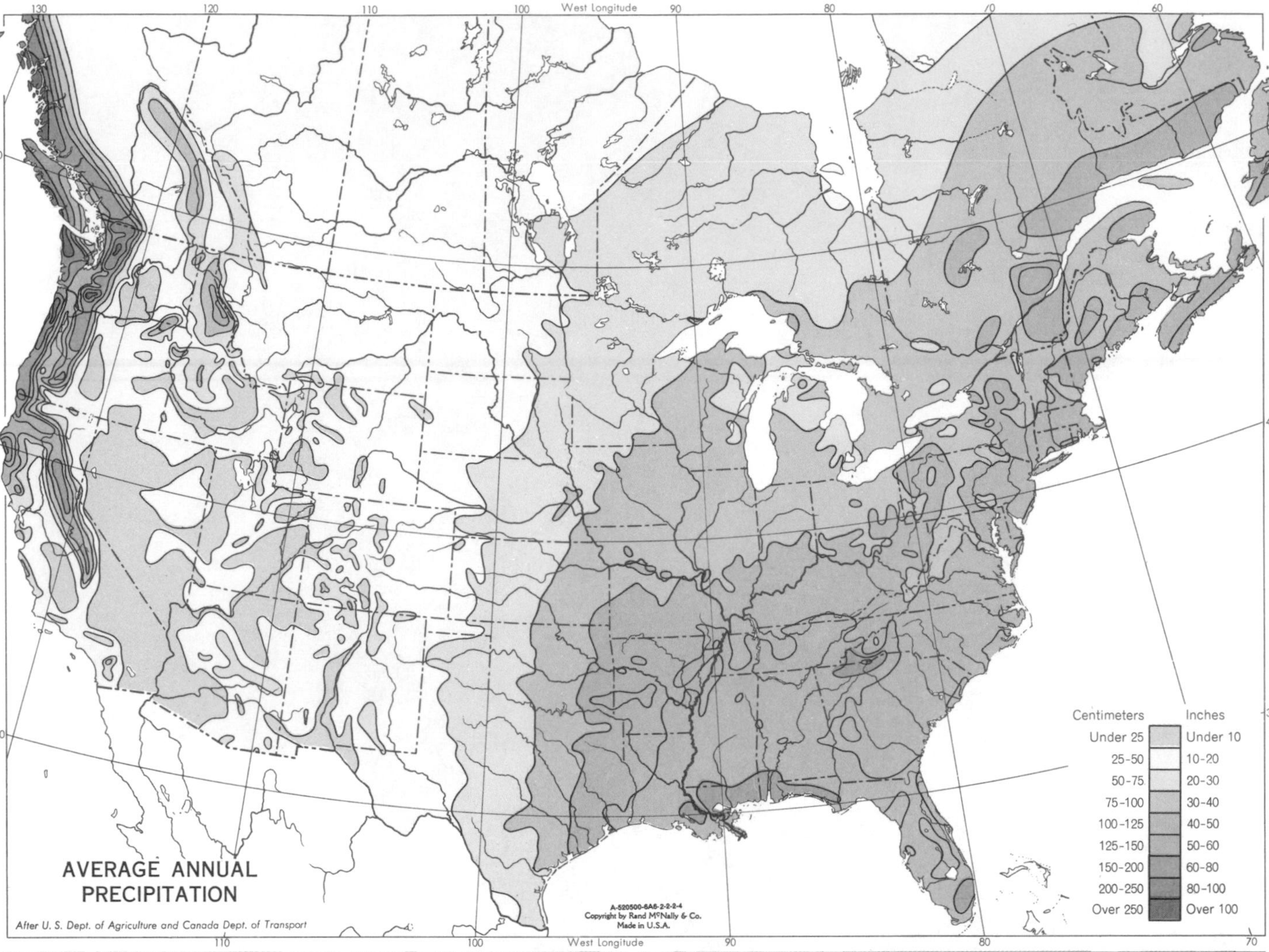
West Longitude
130
120
110
100
90
80
70
60
50
40
30
AVERAGE ANNUAL PRECIPITATION
After U. S. Dept. of Agriculture and Canada Dept. of Transport
A-520500-6A6-2-2-2-4
Copyright by Rand McNally & Co.
Made in U.S.A.
Centimeters
Inches
Under 25
Under 10
25-50
10-20
50-75
20-30
75-100
30-40
100-125
40-50
125-150
50-60
150-200
60-80
200-250
80-100
Over 250
Over 100

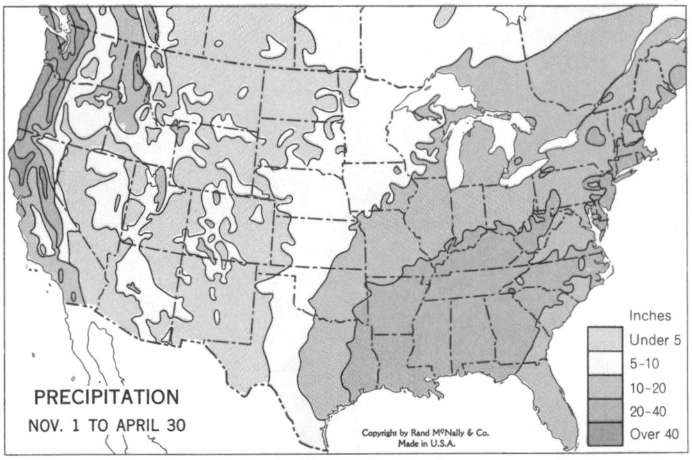
PRECIPITATION
NOV. 1 TO APRIL 30
Inches
Under 5
5-10
10-20
20-40
Over 40
Copyright by Rand McNally & Co.
Made in U.S.A.

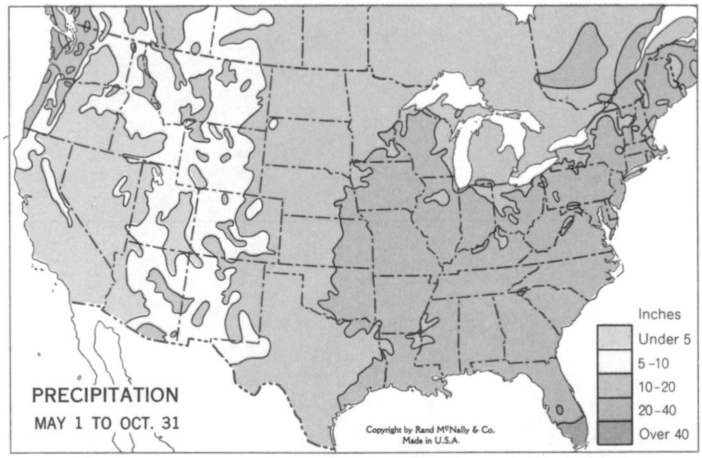
PRECIPITATION
MAY 1 TO OCT. 31
Inches
Under 5
5-10
10-20
20-40
Over 40
Copyright by Rand McNally & Co.
Made in U.S.A.

GLACIAL LAKE AGASSIZ
After Warren Upham, U. S. G. S., and others
0 50 100 150 200 Miles
0 100 200 300 Km.
Present lakes and rivers are shown in black.
SASKATCHEWAN
MANITOBA
ONTARIO
Lake Winnipeg
Lake Winnipegosis
NORTH DAKOTA
MINNESOTA
Lake Dakota
Lake Minnesota
100 West Longitude 95

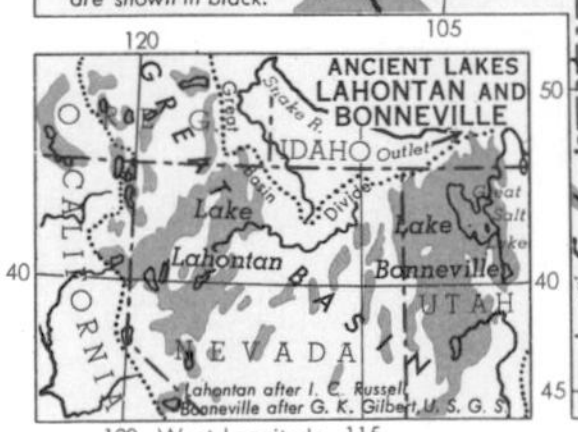
ANCIENT LAKES LAHONTAN AND BONNEVILLE
IDAHO
UTAH
NEVADA
Lake Lahontan
Lake Bonneville
Lahontan after I. C. Russell
Bonneville after G. K. Gilbert, U. S. G. S.
120 West Longitude 115

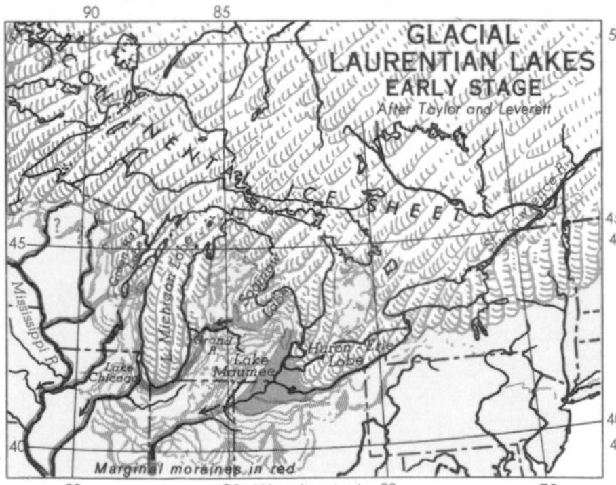
GLACIAL LAURENTIAN LAKES
EARLY STAGE
After Taylor and Leverett
Lake Maumee
Lake Chicago
Marginal moraines in red
85 West Longitude 80

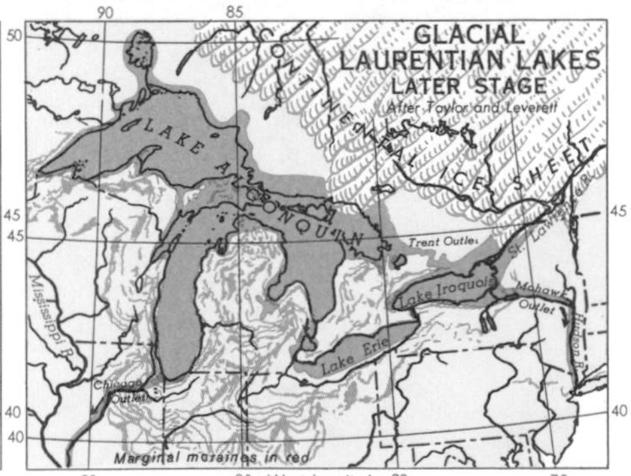
GLACIAL LAURENTIAN LAKES
LATER STAGE
After Taylor and Leverett
LAKE ALGONQUIN
Lake Iroquois
Lake Erie
Trent Outlet
Marginal moraines in red
85 West Longitude 80

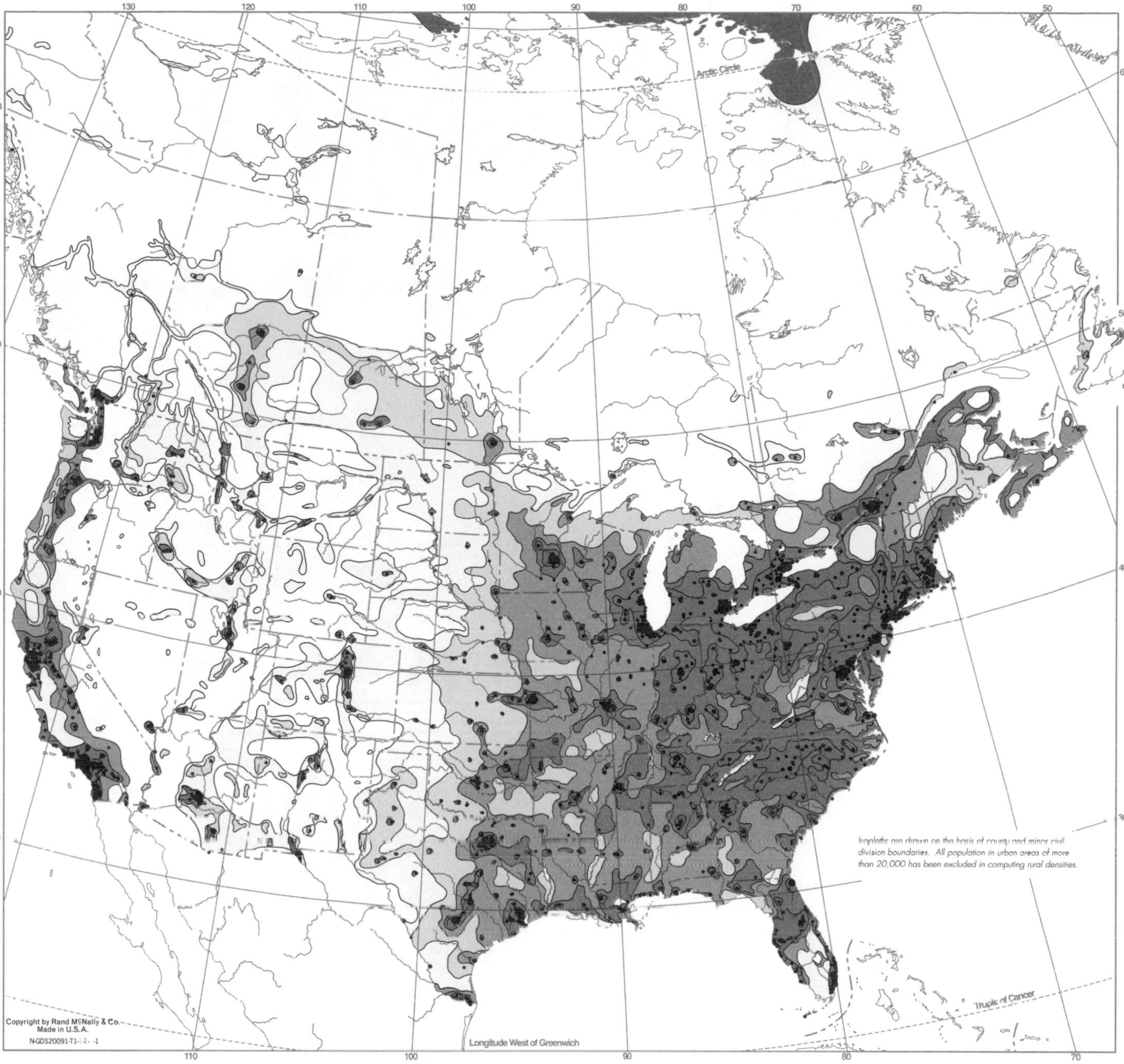

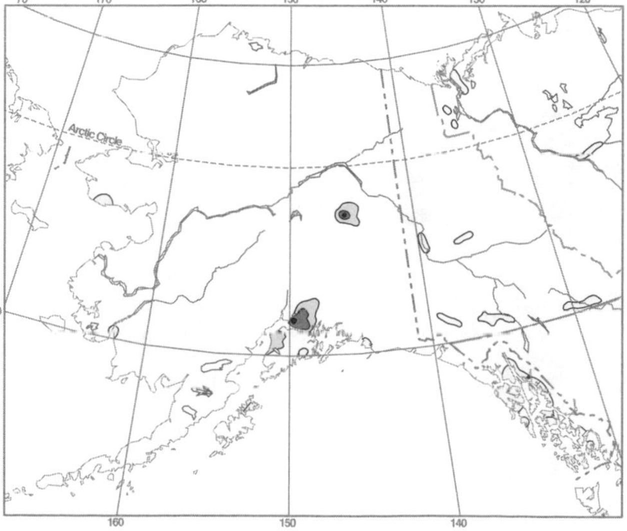

U.S.A.

Total Population
279,310,000

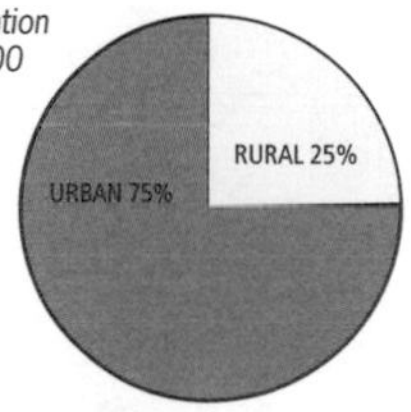

CANADA

Total Population
31,750,000

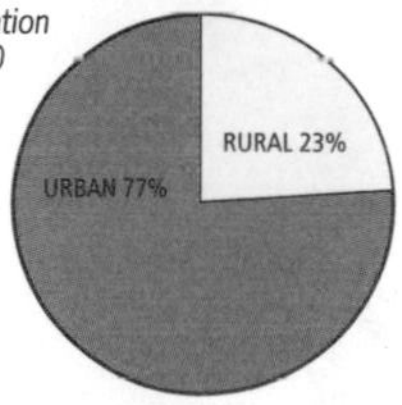

DENSITY OF POPULATION

INHABITANTS PER UNIT AREA

Per Sq. Km.	Per Sq. Mile
Uninhabited	Uninhabited
Under 1	Under 2
1 - 2	2 - 6
2 - 7	6 - 18
7 - 17	18 - 45
17 - 35	45 - 90
Over 35	Over 90

POPULATION OF URBAN CENTERS

- Over 1,000,000
- 500,000-1,000,000
- 200,000-500,000
- 100,000-200,000
- 50,000-100,000
- 20,000-50,000

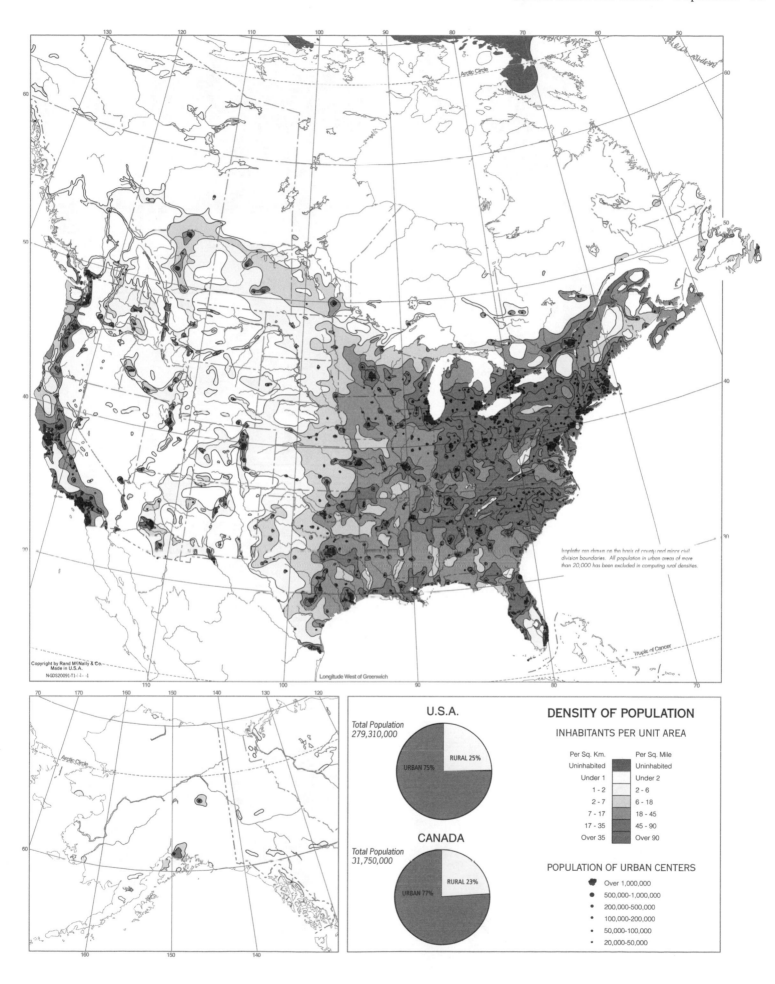

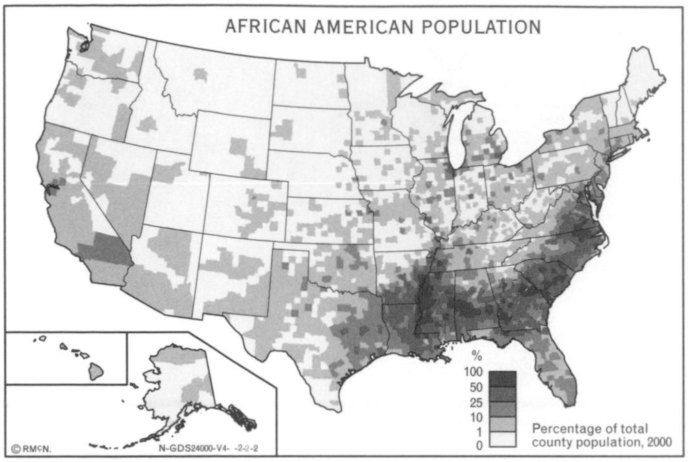
AFRICAN AMERICAN POPULATION
%
100
50
25
10
1
0
Percentage of total county population, 2000
©RMcN.

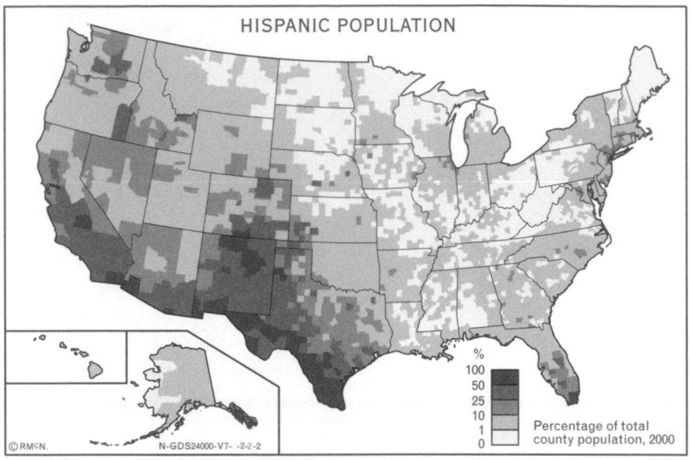
HISPANIC POPULATION
%
100
50
25
10
1
0
Percentage of total county population, 2000
©RMcN.

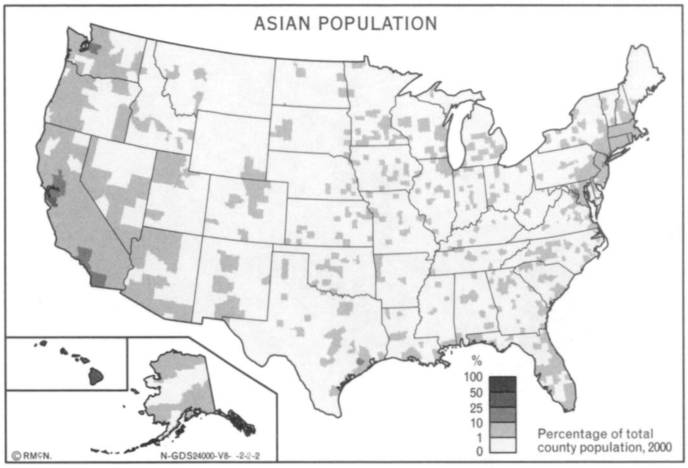
ASIAN POPULATION
%
100
50
25
10
1
0
Percentage of total county population, 2000
©RMcN.

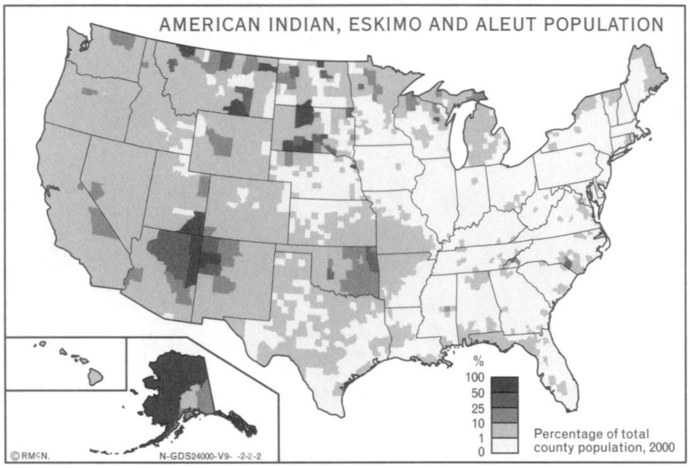
AMERICAN INDIAN, ESKIMO AND ALEUT POPULATION
%
100
50
25
10
1
0
Percentage of total county population, 2000
©RMcN.

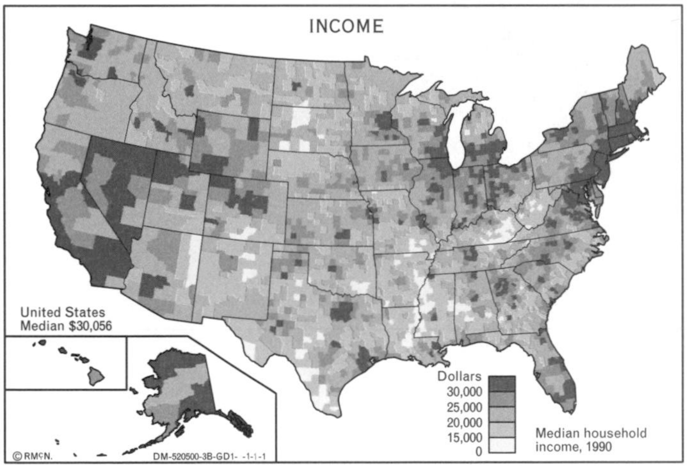
INCOME
United States Median $30,056
Dollars
30,000
25,000
20,000
15,000
0
Median household income, 1990
©RMcN.

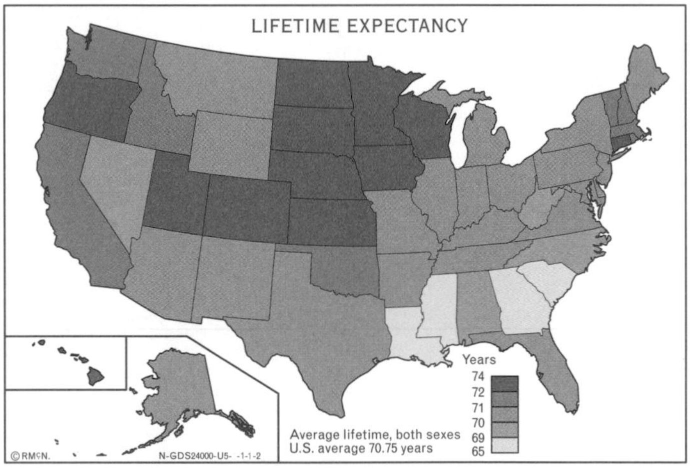
LIFETIME EXPECTANCY
Years
74
72
71
70
69
65
Average lifetime, both sexes
U.S. average 70.75 years
©RMcN.

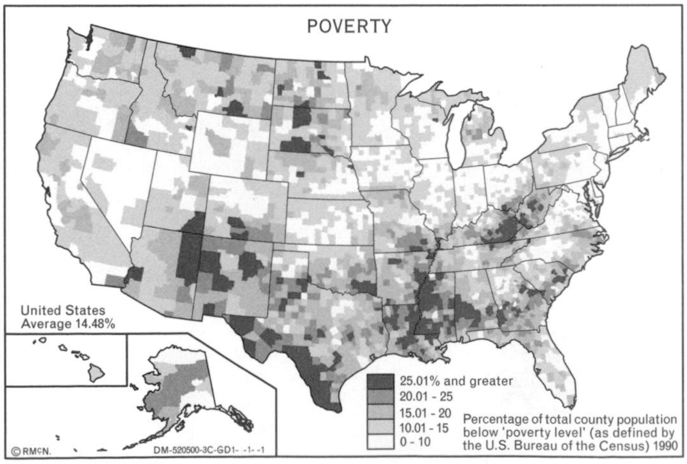
POVERTY
United States Average 14.48%
25.01% and greater
20.01 - 25
15.01 - 20
10.01 - 15
0 - 10
Percentage of total county population below 'poverty level' (as defined by the U.S. Bureau of the Census) 1990
©RMcN.

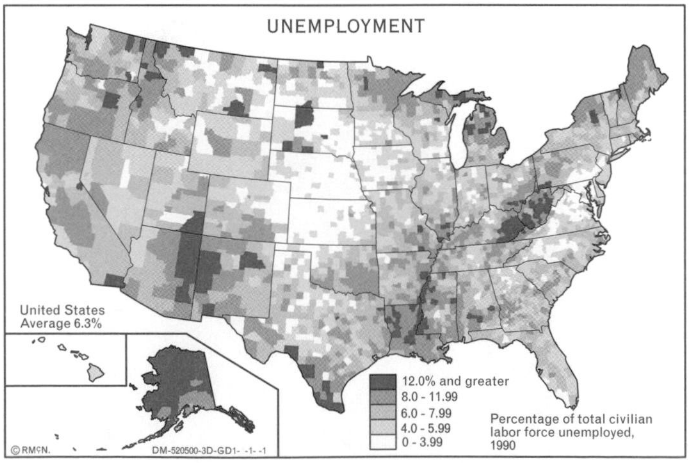
UNEMPLOYMENT
United States Average 6.3%
12.0% and greater
8.0 - 11.99
6.0 - 7.99
4.0 - 5.99
0 - 3.99
Percentage of total civilian labor force unemployed, 1990
©RMcN.

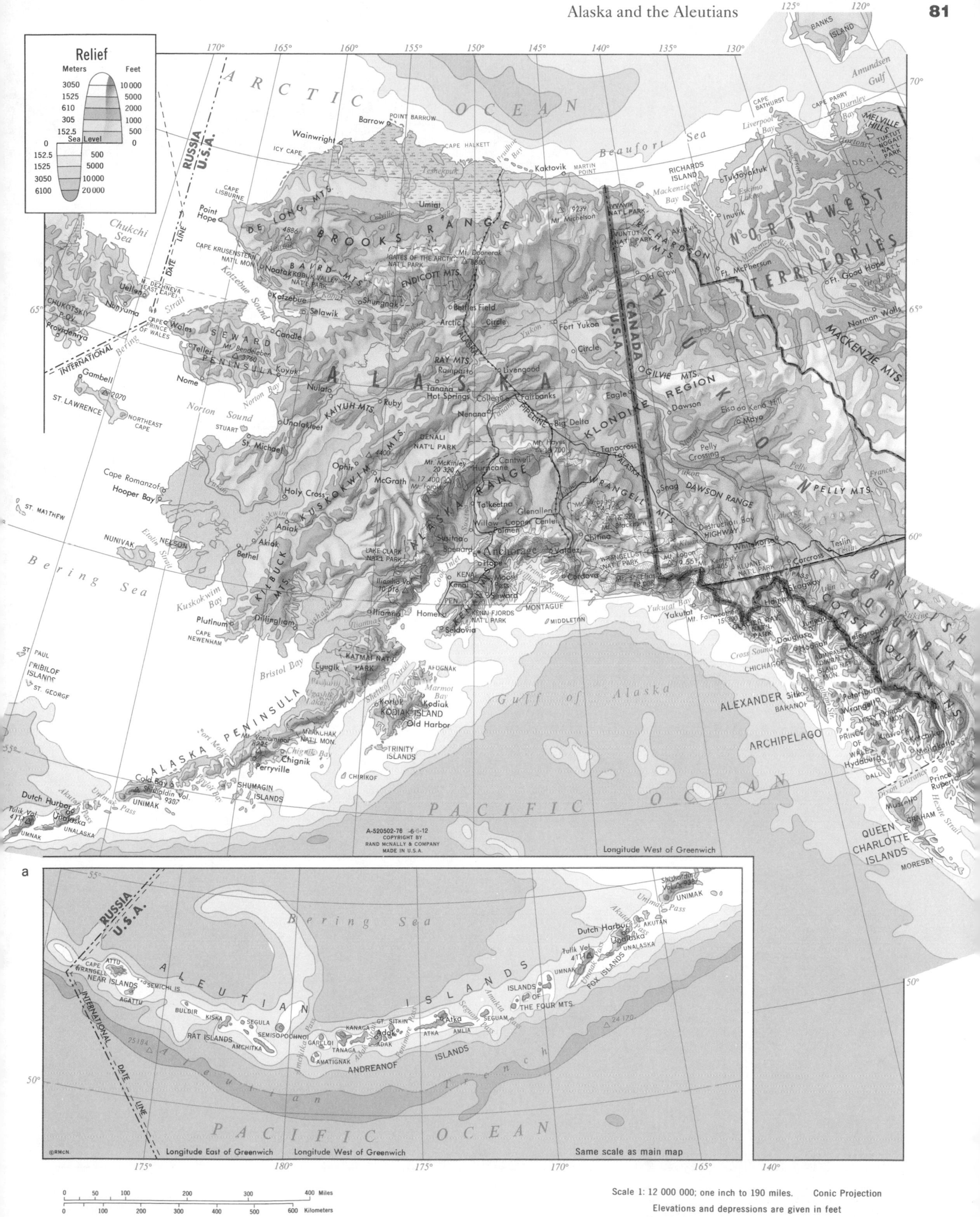

Scale 1: 12 000 000; one inch to 190 miles. Conic Projection

Elevations and depressions are given in feet

Scale 1: 4,000 000; one inch to 64 miles. Conic Projection
Elevations and depressions are given in feet

ALBERTA
SASKATCHEWAN
CANADA
U.S.A.
WATERTON-GLACIER INTERNATIONAL PEACE PARK
BLACKFEET IND. RES.
Cut Bank
Sunburst
Shelby
Browning
Whitefish
Kalispell
Valier
Conrad
Lake Elwell
Marias
Havre
Chinook
Harlem
Hogeland
Malta
FT. BELKNAP IND. RES.
ROCKY BOYS IND. RES.
Fresno Res.
Milk
Morgan
Opheim
Scobey
Plentywood
Grenora
FORT PECK IND. RES.
Medicine Lake
Williston
Glasgow
Wolf Point
Poplar
Missouri
Ft. Peck
Fort Peck Lake
Sidney
N. DAK.
Fort Benton
Winifred
Choteau
Polson
Ronan
SWAN RANGE
NATIONAL BISON RANGE
Great Falls
Belt
LITTLE BELT MTS.
Neihart
Lewistown
Winnett
Brockway
Glendive
Beach
Terry
MONTANA
ROCKY MTS.
BIG BELT MTS.
Missoula
Lolo
Helena
East Helena
Stevensville
Hamilton
Deer Lodge
Townsend
Philipsburg
Anaconda
Butte
Walkerville
Three Forks
White Sulphur Spgs.
Harlowton
Roundup
Musselshell
Big Porcupine Cr.
Miles City
Baker
Marmarth
Forsyth
Yellowstone
CRAZY MTS.
Big Timber
Colstrip
Huntley
Billings
Hardin
Laurel
Columbus
Bozeman
Livingston
Crow Agency
CROW IND. RES.
LITTLE BIGHORN BATTLEFIELD NAT'L MON.
Lame Deer
NORTHERN CHEYENNE IND. RES.
BIG HOLE NAT'L BATTLEFIELD
Twin Bridges
PIONEER MTS.
Homer Youngs Peak 10 621
Dillon
Salmon
Hap Hawkins Lake
Lima Res.
Electric Peak 10 992
Gardiner
Mt. Washburn 10 243
Red Lodge
Granite Peak
Bear Creek
Sheridan
BIGHORN MOUNTAINS
Lovell
Powell
Bighorn Lake
DEVILS TOWER NAT'L MON.
Sundance
Moorcroft
Gillette
Buffalo
Cody
Greybull
Basin
Cloud Peak 13 167
Ten Sleep
Worland
YELLOWSTONE NATIONAL PARK
7733 ft. above Sea level
ABSAROKA RANGE
IDAHO
LEMHI RANGE
LOST RIVER RA
BEAVERHEAD MTS.
Borah Pk. 12 662
Mackay
Hyndman Peak 12 009
Arco
St. Anthony
Ashton
Rexburg
Rigby
Idaho Falls
GRAND TETON NAT'L PARK
Grand Teton 13 770
Jackson
Gebo
Thermopolis
Kaycee
Antelope
Midwest
WIND RIVER
Shoshoni
Riverton
Powder River
WIND RIVER IND. RES.
Gannett Peak 13 804
Fremont Peak 13 745
WIND RIVER RANGE
WYOMING RANGE
Lander
Casper
Glenrock
Douglas
Platte
Orin
CRATERS OF THE MOON NAT'L MON.
SNAKE RIVER PLAIN
Shelley
Blackfoot
FORT HALL IND. RES.
Pocatello
American Falls Res.
American Falls
Shoshone
Soda Springs
Meade Peak 9957
Lava Hot Sprs.
Afton
WYOMING
Alcova Res.
Pathfinder Res.
Seminoe Res.
Rupert
Burley
Twin Falls
Oakley
Montpelier
Malad City
Preston
GREAT DIVIDE BASIN
Sweetwater
Fontenelle Res.
Big Sandy
Wheatland
Wheatland Res. No. 2
Medicine Bow
Hanna
Rawlins
Superior
Kemmerer
Granger
Green River
Rock Springs
Flaming Gorge Res.
Lewiston
Richmond
Smithfield
Logan
Garland
Wellsville
Providence
Brigham
Bear Lake
BEAR RIVER RANGE
Huntsville
Ogden
Morgan
Farmington
Evanston
Lucin
GREAT SALT LAKE DESERT
Great Salt Lake
UTAH
Bountiful
Salt Lake City
Wendover
Murray
Midvale
Tooele
Park City
Heber City
UINTA MTS.
Kings Peak 13 528
Mt. Emmons 13 440
UINTAH AND OURAY IND. RES.
DINOSAUR NAT'L MON.
Vernal
COLO.
Craig
Steamboat Spr.
Oak Creek
PARK RANGE
114°
112°
110°
108°
106°
104°
48°
44°
42°
Relief
Meters
Feet
3050
1525
610
305
152.5
0
1525
10000
5000
2000
1000
500
0
Sea Level
500
0 20 40 60 80 100 120 Miles
0 20 40 60 80 100 120 140 160 180 200 Kilometers

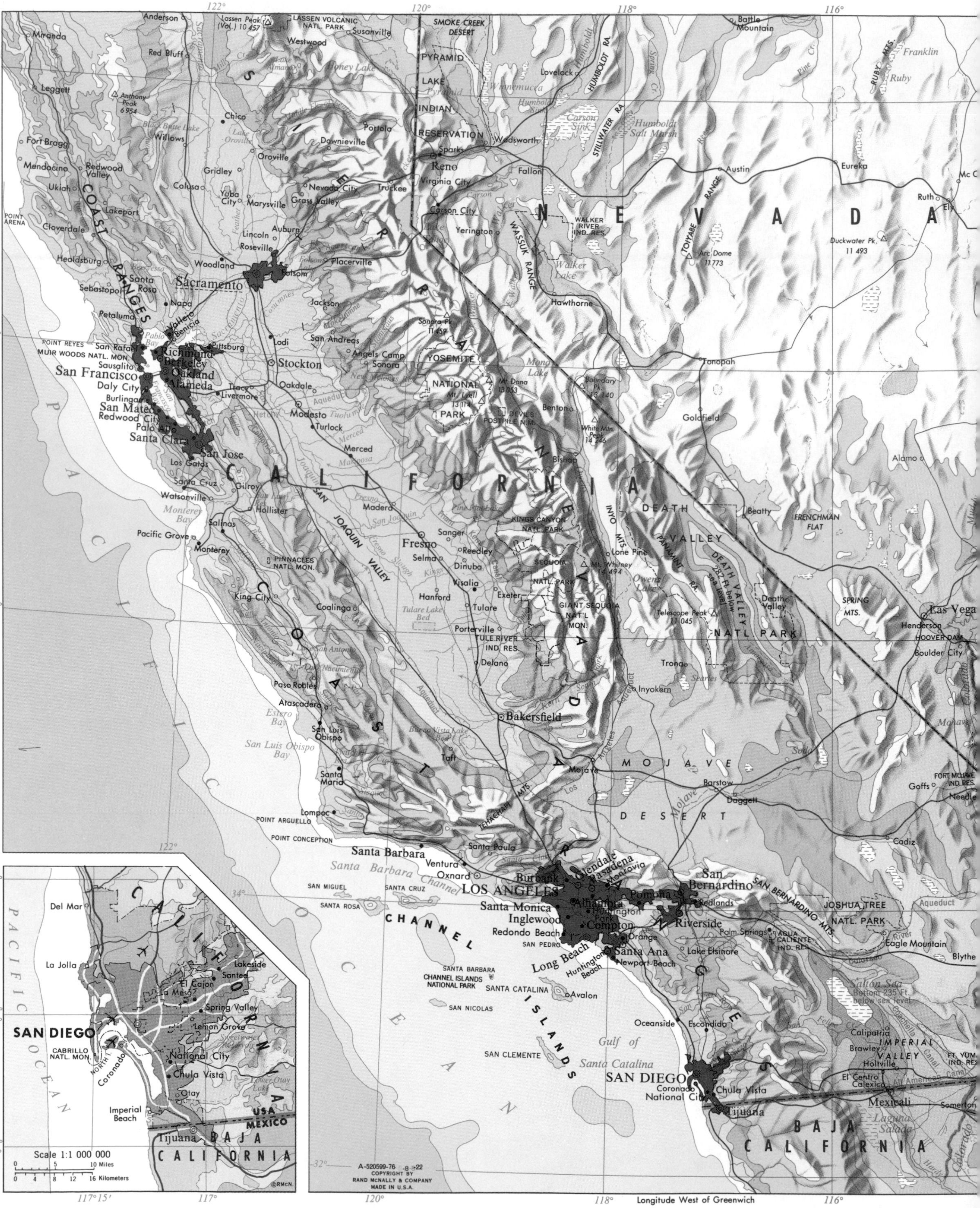

Scale 1:4 000 000; one inch to 64 miles. Conic Projection

Elevations and depressions are given in feet

0 20 40 60 80 100 120 Miles

0 20 40 60 80 100 120 140 160 180 200 Kilometers

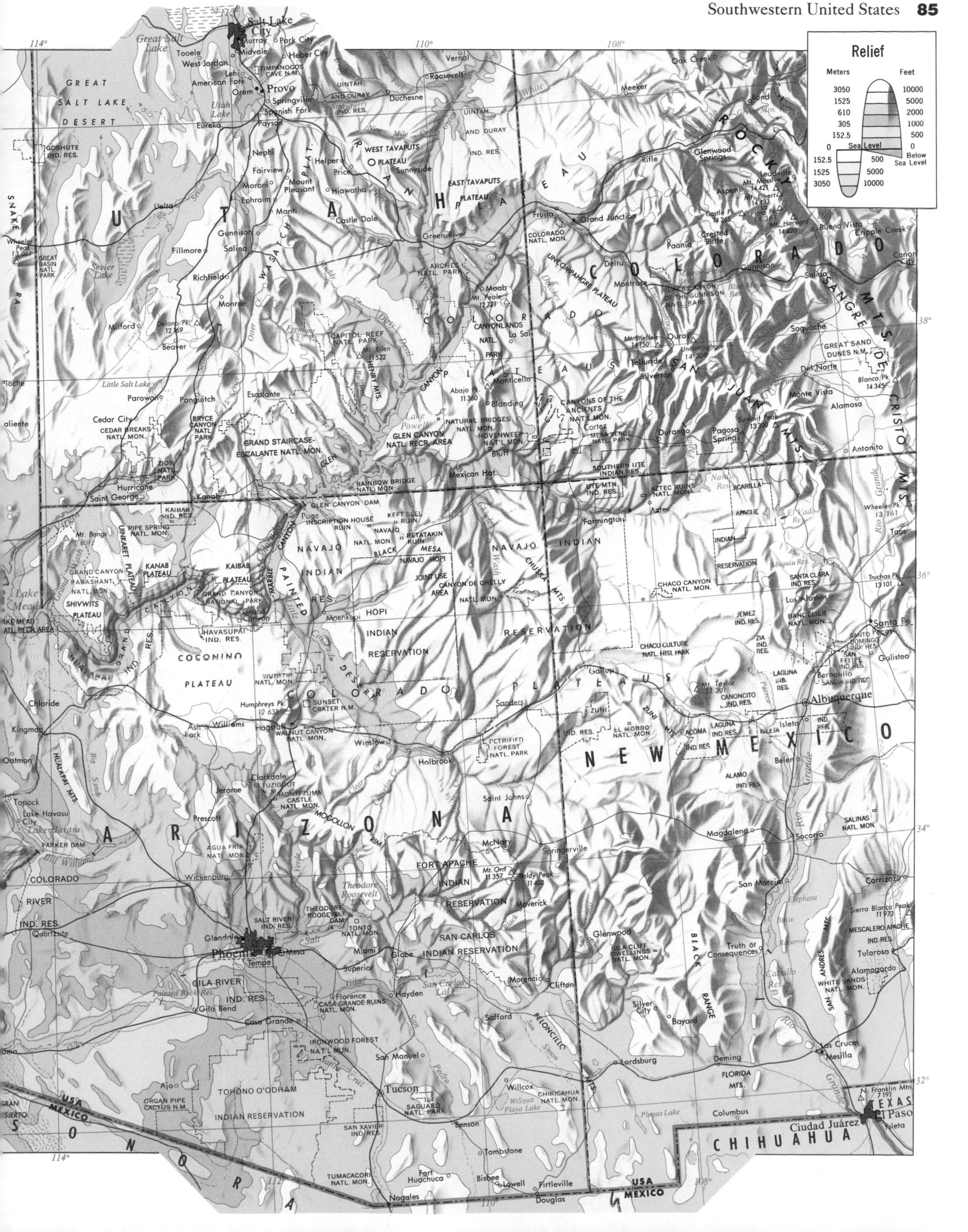
Relief
Meters
Feet
3050
1525
610
305
152.5
0
152.5
1525
3050
10000
5000
2000
1000
500
0
Sea Level
Below Sea Level
500
5000
10000
114°
110°
108°
38°
36°
34°
32°
112°
U T A H
C O L O R A D O
A R I Z O N A
N E W M E X I C O
S O N O R A
CHIHUAHUA
TEXAS
USA
MEXICO
GREAT SALT LAKE DESERT
Great Salt Lake
Salt Lake City
Murray
Midvale
Park City
Heber City
Tooele
West Jordan
Lehi
American Fork
Orem
Provo
Springville
Spanish Fork
Payson
Eureka
Utah Lake
TIMPANOGOS CAVE N.M.
UINTAH AND OURAY IND. RES.
Vernal
Roosevelt
Duchesne
GOSHUTE IND. RES.
Nephi
Fairview
Moroni
Mount Pleasant
Ephraim
Manti
Delta
Helper
Price
Sunnyside
Hiawatha
WEST TAVAPUTS PLATEAU
EAST TAVAPUTS PLATEAU
Castle Dale
Gunnison
Salina
Fillmore
Green River
Richfield
Monroe
WASATCH PLAT.
Sevier Lake
GREAT BASIN NATL. PARK
Wheeler Peak 13 063
SNAKE RA.
Milford
Delano Pk. 12 169
Beaver
CAPITOL REEF NATL. PARK
Mt. Ellen 11 522
HENRY MTS.
ARCHES NATL. PARK
Moab
Mt. Peale 12 721
CANYONLANDS NATL. PARK
La Sal
Little Salt Lake
Parowan
Panguitch
Escalante
Cedar City
CEDAR BREAKS NATL. MON.
BRYCE CANYON NATL. PARK
GRAND STAIRCASE-ESCALANTE NATL. MON.
Lake Powell
GLEN CANYON NATL. RECR. AREA
NATURAL BRIDGES NATL. MON.
HOVENWEEP NAT'L MON.
Abajo Pk. 11 360
Monticello
Blanding
Bluff
Mexican Hat
ZION NATL. PARK
Hurricane
Saint George
Kanab
RAINBOW BRIDGE NATL. MON.
Pioche
Caliente
Rifle
Meeker
Oak Creek
Bond
Glenwood Springs
Leadville
Mt. Massive 14 421
Mt. Elbert 14 433
Aspen
Castle Pk. 14 265
Pikes Pk. 14 361
Mt. Harvard 14 420
Buena Vista
Cripple Creek
Canon City
ROCKY
Fruita
Grand Junction
COLORADO NATL. MON.
Paonia
Crested Butte
Delta
Montrose
Gunnison
Salida
UNCOMPAHGRE PLATEAU
BLACK CANYON OF THE GUNNISON NATL. PARK
SANGRE DE CRISTO MTS.
Saguache
GREAT SAND DUNES N.M.
Mt. Sneffels 14 150
Ouray
Uncompahgre Pk. 14 309
Telluride
Silverton
SAN JUAN MTS.
Del Norte
Blanca Pk. 14 345
Monte Vista
Alamosa
CANYONS OF THE ANCIENTS NAT'L MON.
Cortez
MESA VERDE NATL. PARK
Durango
Pagosa Springs
Summit Peak 13 300
Antonito
SOUTHERN UTE INDIAN RES.
UTE MTN. IND. RES.
AZTEC RUINS NATL. MON.
Aztec
JICARILLA APACHE INDIAN RESERVATION
Farmington
Wheeler Pk. 13 161
Taos
Truchas Pk. 13 101
CHACO CANYON NATL. MON.
SANTA CLARA IND. RES.
Los Alamos
JEMEZ IND. RES.
BANDELIER NATL. MON.
Santa Fe
SANTO DOMINGO IND. RES.
ZIA IND. RES.
CHACO CULTURE NATL. HIST. PARK
Galisteo
Bernalillo
Gallup
Mt. Taylor
CANONCITO IND. RES.
Albuquerque
ZUNI
EL MORRO NATL. MON.
ACOMA
LAGUNA IND. RES.
ISLETA
Isleta
Belen
ALAMO IND. RES.
SALINAS NATL. MON.
Magdalena
Socorro
Carrizozo
San Marcial
Sierra Blanca Peak 11 973
MESCALERO APACHE IND. RES.
Tularosa
Alamogordo
WHITE SANDS NATL. MON.
SAN ANDRES MTS.
Elephant Butte Reservoir
Truth or Consequences
Caballo Res.
Las Cruces
Mesilla
Franklin Mtn. 7 192
El Paso
Ciudad Juárez
Ysleta
Deming
FLORIDA MTS.
Columbus
Lordsburg
Glenwood
GILA CLIFF DWELLINGS NATL. MON.
BLACK RANGE
Silver City
Bayard
Playas Lake
GLEN CANYON DAM
Page
INSCRIPTION HOUSE RUIN
KEET SEEL RUIN
BETATAKIN RUIN
NAVAJO NATL. MON.
KAIBAB IND. RES.
PIPE SPRING NATL. MON.
Mt. Bangs 8012
NAVAJO INDIAN RES.
BLACK MESA
NAVAJO HOPI JOINT USE AREA
CANYON DE CHELLY NATL. MON.
CHUSKA MTS.
NAVAJO INDIAN RESERVATION
GRAND CANYON-PARASHANT NATL. MON.
KANAB PLATEAU
KAIBAB PLATEAU
SHIVWITS PLATEAU
GRAND CANYON NATIONAL PARK
Grand Canyon
Lake Mead
LAKE MEAD NATL. RECR. AREA
Moenkopi
HOPI INDIAN RESERVATION
HAVASUPAI IND. RES.
HUALAPAI IND. RES.
COCONINO PLATEAU
PAINTED DESERT
WUPATKI NATL. MON.
SUNSET CRATER N.M.
Humphreys Pk. 12 633
Chloride
Kingman
Ash Fork
Williams
Flagstaff
WALNUT CANYON NATL. MON.
Winslow
Holbrook
PETRIFIED FOREST NATL. PARK
Sanders
Oatman
HUALAPAI MTS.
Topock
Lake Havasu City
Lake Havasu
PARKER DAM
Clarkdale
TUZIGOOT N.M.
Jerome
MONTEZUMA CASTLE NATL. MON.
Prescott
MOGOLLON RIM
Saint Johns
McNary
Springerville
AGUA FRIA NATL. MON.
FORT APACHE INDIAN RESERVATION
Mt. Ord 11 357
Baldy Peak 11 403
Maverick
COLORADO RIVER IND. RES.
Wickenburg
Quartzsite
Theodore Roosevelt Lake
THEODORE ROOSEVELT DAM
TONTO NATL. MON.
SALT RIVER IND. RES.
Glendale
Phoenix
Mesa
Tempe
Miami
Globe
SAN CARLOS INDIAN RESERVATION
Superior
San Carlos Lake
Morenci
Clifton
GILA RIVER IND. RES.
Painted Rock Res.
Gila Bend
Florence
CASA GRANDE RUINS NATL. MON.
Hayden
Casa Grande
Safford
PELONCILLO MTS.
IRONWOOD FOREST NAT'L MON.
San Manuel
Ajo
ORGAN PIPE CACTUS N.M.
TOHONO O'ODHAM INDIAN RESERVATION
Tucson
SAGUARO NATL. PARK
Willcox
Willcox Playa Lake
CHIRICAHUA NATL. MON.
SAN XAVIER IND. RES.
Benson
Tombstone
TUMACACORI NATL. MON.
Fort Huachuca
Bisbee
Lowell
Pirtleville
Nogales
Douglas

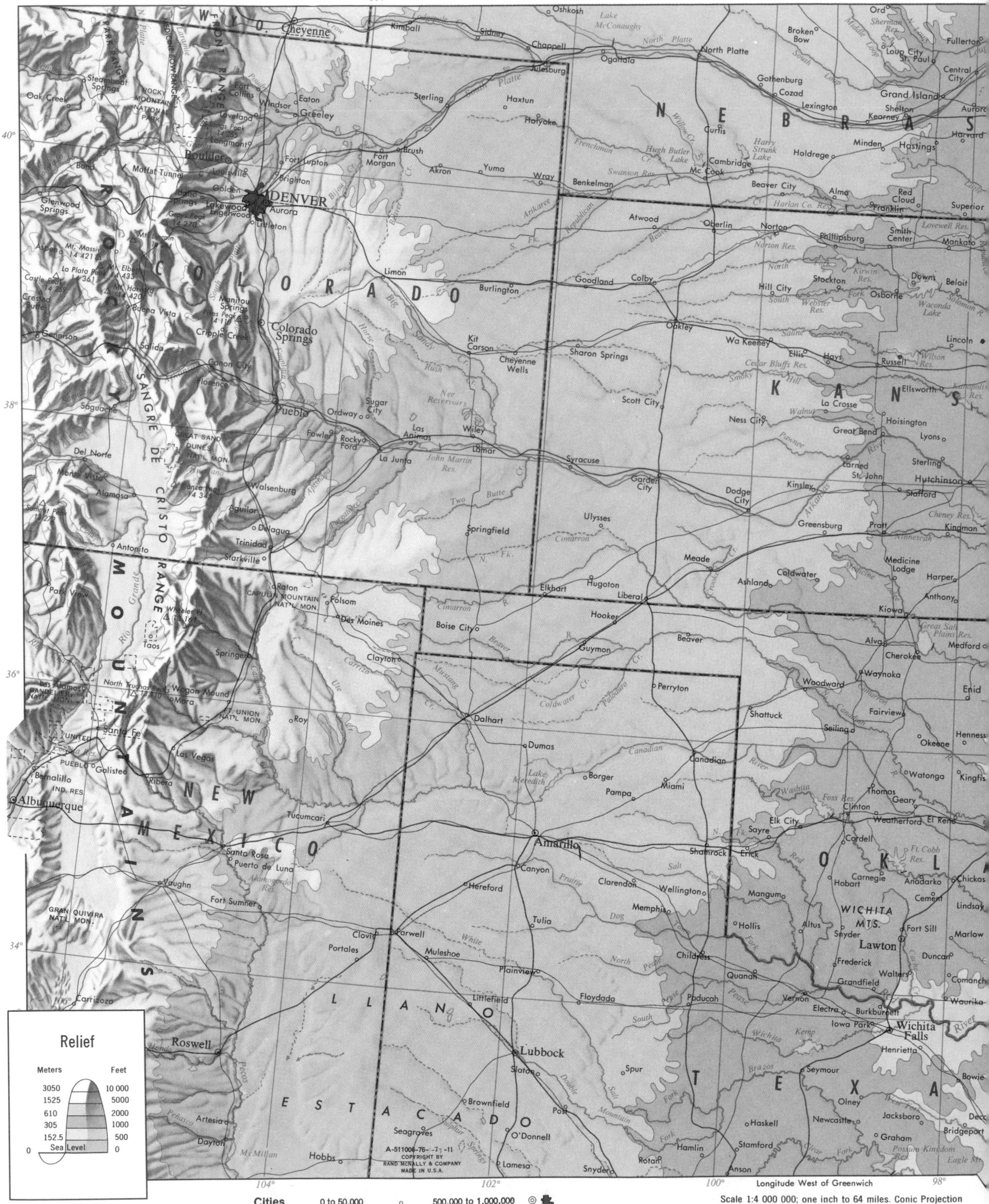

Cities and Towns	0 to 50,000 ○	500,000 to 1,000,000 ◎	
	50,000 to 500,000 ⊙	1,000,000 and over	

Scale 1:4 000 000; one inch to 64 miles. Conic Projection
Elevations and depressions are given in feet.

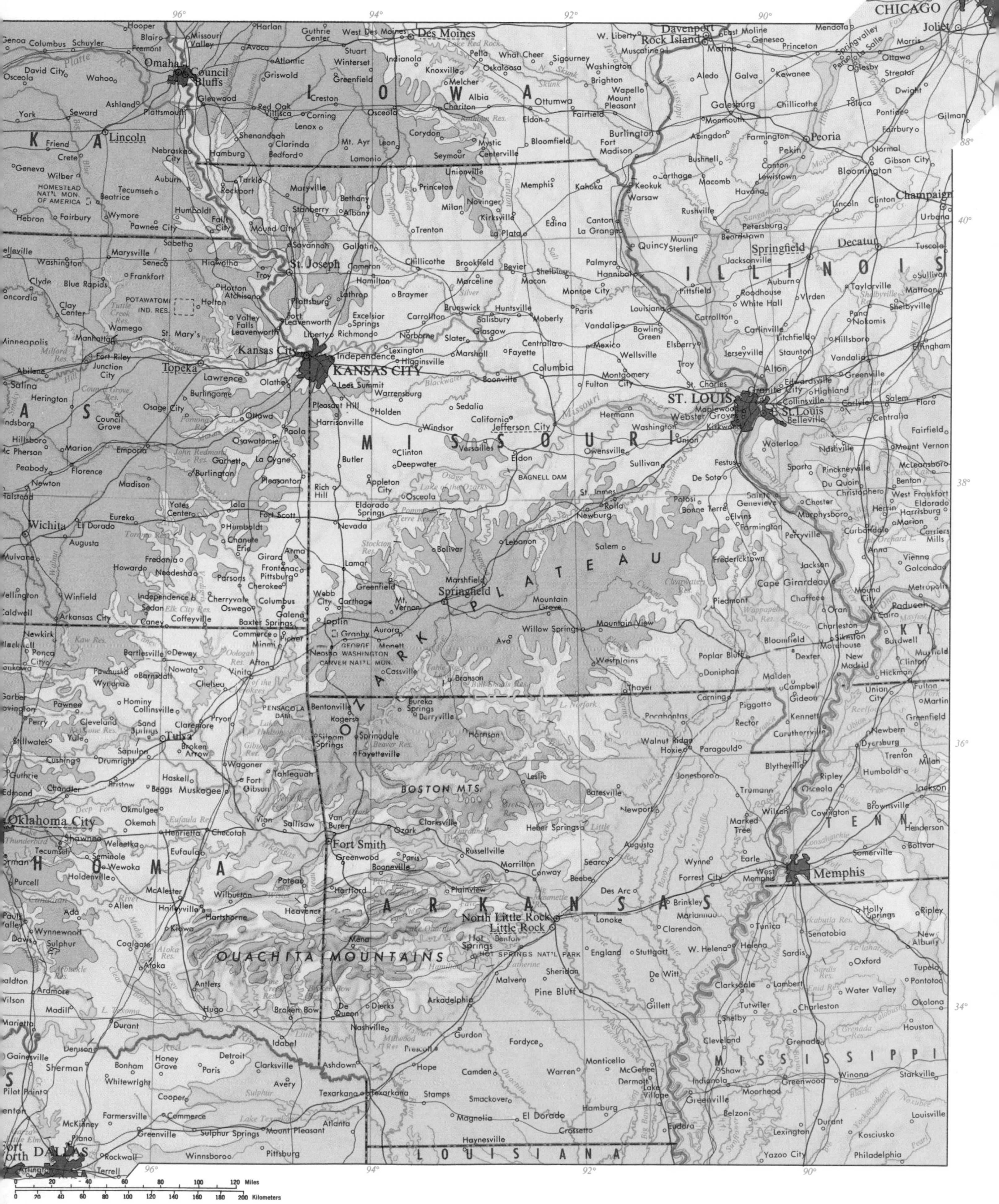
IOWA
MISSOURI
ILLINOIS
KANSAS
OKLAHOMA
ARKANSAS
TENN.
KY.
MISSISSIPPI
LOUISIANA
OZARK PLATEAU
BOSTON MTS.
OUACHITA MOUNTAINS
CHICAGO
Aurora
Joliet
Des Moines
Davenport
Rock Island
Moline
Omaha
Council Bluffs
Lincoln
Peoria
Springfield
Decatur
Champaign
Bloomington
KANSAS CITY
Kansas City
St. Joseph
Topeka
Wichita
ST. LOUIS
East St. Louis
Jefferson City
Columbia
Springfield
Joplin
Tulsa
Oklahoma City
Fort Smith
North Little Rock
Little Rock
Hot Springs
HOT SPRINGS NAT'L PARK
Pine Bluff
Memphis
West Memphis
Texarkana
DALLAS
Fort Worth
Arlington
Cape Girardeau
Paducah
Quincy
Hannibal
Burlington
Ottumwa
Galesburg
Jonesboro
El Dorado
Greenville
Sherman
Denison
Muskogee
Bartlesville
Lake of the Ozarks
BAGNELL DAM
PENSACOLA DAM
HOMESTEAD NAT'L MON. OF AMERICA
POTAWATOMI IND. RES.
GEORGE WASHINGTON CARVER NAT'L MON.
Mississippi River
Missouri River
96°
94°
92°
90°
88°
40°
38°
36°
34°
0 20 40 60 80 100 120 Miles
0 20 40 60 80 100 120 140 160 180 200 Kilometers

Scale 1:4 000 000; one inch to 64 miles. Conic Projection
Elevations and depressions are given in feet

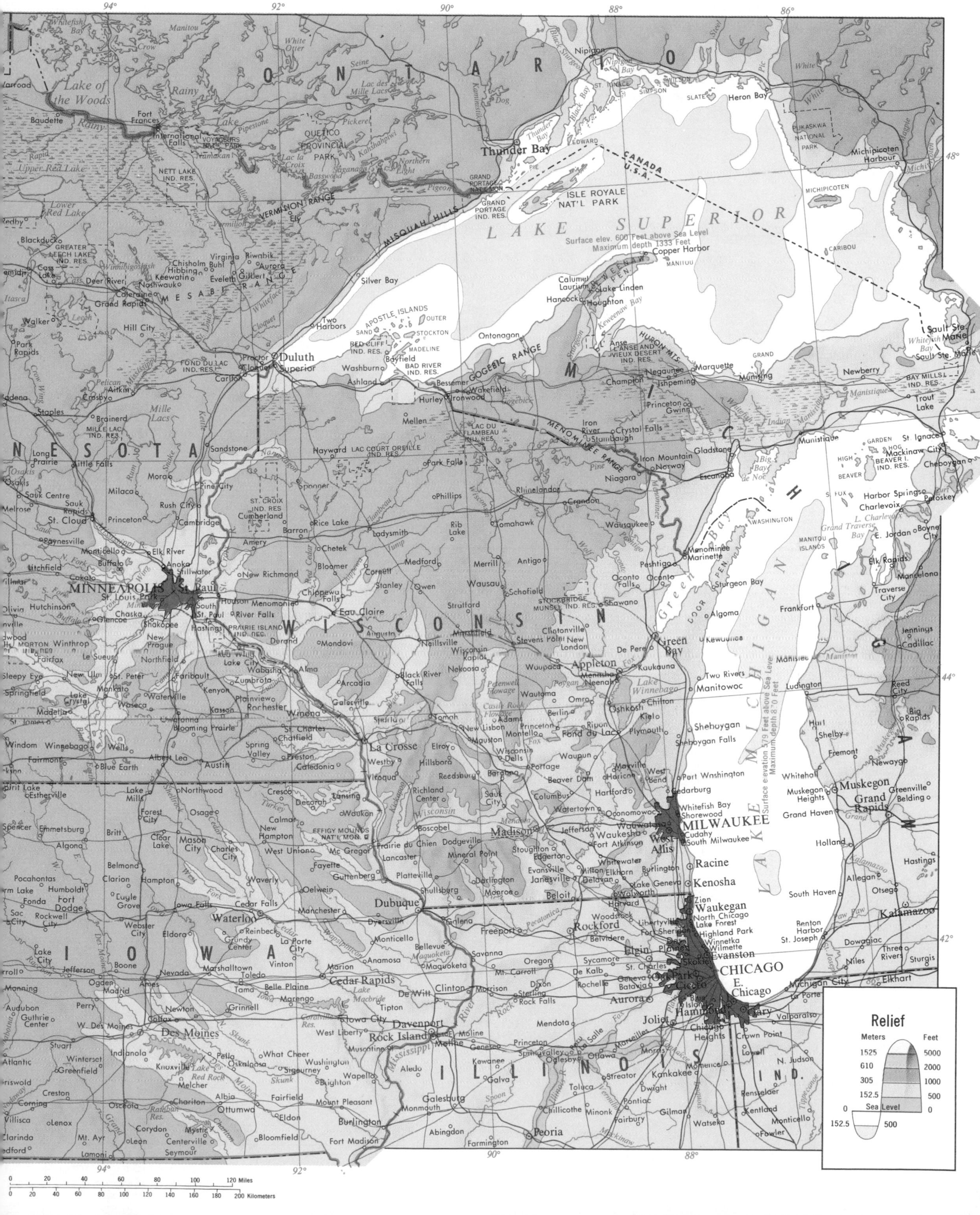
ONTARIO
LAKE SUPERIOR
Surface elev. 600 Feet above Sea Level
Maximum depth 1333 Feet
ISLE ROYALE NAT'L PARK
CANADA
U.S.A.
Thunder Bay
Nipigon
Heron Bay
PUKASKWA NATIONAL PARK
Michipicoten Harbour
QUETICO PROVINCIAL PARK
Lake of the Woods
Fort Frances
International Falls
VOYAGEURS NAT'L PARK
Baudette
NETT LAKE IND. RES.
GRAND PORTAGE IND. RES.
VERMILION RANGE
MISQUAH HILLS
MESABI RANGE
Virginia
Hibbing
Chisholm
Eveleth
Grand Rapids
Duluth
Superior
Two Harbors
Silver Bay
APOSTLE ISLANDS
Bayfield
Ashland
Washburn
BAD RIVER IND. RES.
GOGEBIC RANGE
Ironwood
Hurley
Bessemer
Ontonagon
Houghton
Hancock
Copper Harbor
HURON MTS.
Marquette
Ishpeming
Negaunee
Munising
Newberry
Sault Ste. Marie
MENOMINEE RANGE
Iron Mountain
Escanaba
Gladstone
Manistique
St. Ignace
Mackinaw City
Cheboygan
Petoskey
Charlevoix
Traverse City
Grand Traverse Bay
Frankfort
Cadillac
Manistee
Ludington
Muskegon
Grand Rapids
Grand Haven
Holland
Kalamazoo
Benton Harbor
St. Joseph
Niles
Elkhart
Michigan City
Gary
LAKE MICHIGAN
Surface elevation 579 Feet above Sea Level
Maximum depth 870 Feet
MICHIGAN
MINNESOTA
MINNEAPOLIS
St. Paul
St. Cloud
Brainerd
Mille Lacs
Rochester
Winona
Mankato
Austin
Albert Lea
WISCONSIN
Eau Claire
La Crosse
Wausau
Green Bay
Appleton
Oshkosh
Fond du Lac
Lake Winnebago
Sheboygan
Manitowoc
Madison
MILWAUKEE
Racine
Kenosha
Janesville
Beloit
IOWA
Mason City
Waterloo
Cedar Falls
Dubuque
Cedar Rapids
Iowa City
Davenport
Des Moines
Burlington
Ottumwa
ILLINOIS
Rockford
Waukegan
Evanston
CHICAGO
Joliet
Aurora
Elgin
Rock Island
Moline
Galesburg
Peoria
Kankakee
IND.
Relief
Meters
Feet
1525
610
305
152.5
0
Sea Level
5000
2000
1000
500
0
152.5
500
Miles
Kilometers

Longitude West of Greenwich

Cities and Towns

0 to 50,000	◦	500,000 to 1,000,000	◎
50,000 to 500,000	⊙	1,000,000 and over	

Scale 1:4 000 000; one inch to 64 miles. Conic Projection
Elevations and depressions are given in feet

QUEBEC
MONTREAL
Ottawa
Hull
ONTARIO
ALGONQUIN PROVINCIAL PARK
CANADA
U.S.A.
LAKE ONTARIO
Surface 245 Feet above Sea Level
maximum depth 802 Feet
TORONTO
Hamilton
St. Catharines
Niagara Falls
BUFFALO
Rochester
Syracuse
Utica
Schenectady
Albany
Troy
Kingston
Peterborough
Oshawa
ADIRONDACK MTS.
CATSKILL MTS.
NEW YORK
VERMONT
NEW HAMPSHIRE
MAINE
WHITE MTS.
GREEN MTS.
TACONIC RANGE
Portland
Portsmouth
Manchester
Concord
Lawrence
Lowell
BOSTON
Cambridge
Somerville
Quincy
Brockton
Worcester
Springfield
Holyoke
Chicopee
Hartford
New Britain
Providence
Pawtucket
Cranston
Warwick
Fall River
New Bedford
New Haven
Bridgeport
Stamford
Norwalk
Waterbury
LONG ISLAND SOUND
NEW YORK
Paterson
Newark
Jersey City
Elizabeth
Yonkers
New Rochelle
Binghamton
Elmira
Scranton
Wilkes-Barre
Allentown
Bethlehem
Reading
Harrisburg
Lancaster
York
PHILADELPHIA
Camden
Trenton
Chester
Wilmington
Atlantic City
Cape May
PENNSYLVANIA
POCONO MTS.
APPALACHIAN MOUNTAINS
ALLEGHENY FRONT
PITTSBURGH
McKeesport
Altoona
Johnstown
Erie
NEW JERSEY
DEL.
MARYLAND
BALTIMORE
Dundalk
Annapolis
WASHINGTON D.C.
Arlington
Alexandria
Silver Spr.
Wheaton
Bethesda
VIRGINIA
BLUE RIDGE
Richmond
Lynchburg
Charlottesville
Fredericksburg
Norfolk
Portsmouth
Newport News
Hampton
Virginia Beach
CHESAPEAKE BAY
Delaware Bay
CAPE HENLOPEN
C. CHARLES
SANDY HOOK
MONTAUK PT.
MARTHAS VINEYARD
BLOCK I.
C. COD
C. ANN
ATLANTIC OCEAN
Relief
Meters
Feet
1525
610
305
152.5
0
Sea Level
152.5
1525
3050
5000
2000
1000
500
0
500
5000
10 000
A-520596-76 -5-13
COPYRIGHT BY RAND McNALLY & COMPANY MADE IN U.S.A.
0 20 40 60 80 100 120 Miles
0 20 40 60 80 100 120 140 160 180 200 Kilometers
80°
78°
76°
74°
72°
70°
44°
42°
40°
38°

Scale 1:4 000 000; one inch to 64 miles. Conic Projection
Elevations and depressions are given in feet

Relief
Meters
Feet
1525
610
305
152.5
0
152.5
1525
5000
2000
1000
500
Sea Level
0
500
5000
W. VA.
VIRGINIA
NORTH CAROLINA
SOUTH CAROLINA
FLORIDA
ATLANTIC OCEAN
SEA ISLANDS
GULF OF MEXICO
Richmond
Lynchburg
Roanoke
Petersburg
Newport News
Hampton
Norfolk
Virginia Beach
Portsmouth
Danville
Winston-Salem
Greensboro
Burlington
Durham
Raleigh
Charlotte
Fayetteville
Wilmington
Asheville
Columbia
Augusta
Charleston
Savannah
Jacksonville
Jacksonville Beach
Orlando
Tampa
St. Petersburg
MIAMI
Miami Beach
Fort Lauderdale
Hollywood
W. Palm Beach
Key West
FLORIDA KEYS
CAPE CHARLES
CAPE HENRY
CAPE HATTERAS
CAPE LOOKOUT
CAPE FEAR
CAPE CANAVERAL
CAPE ROMANO
CAPE SABLE
Pamlico Sound
Albemarle Sound
Onslow Bay
Long Bay
Florida Bay
Lake Okeechobee
THE EVERGLADES
EVERGLADES NATIONAL PARK
DRY TORTUGAS N.P.
FORT SUMTER NAT'L MON.
FORT PULASKI NAT'L MON.
FORT FREDERICA NAT'L MON.
CASTILLO DE SAN MARCOS NAT'L MON.
FORT MATANZAS NAT'L MON.
Same scale as main map
a
©RMcN.
0 20 40 60 80 100 120 Miles
0 20 40 60 80 100 120 140 160 180 200 Kilometers

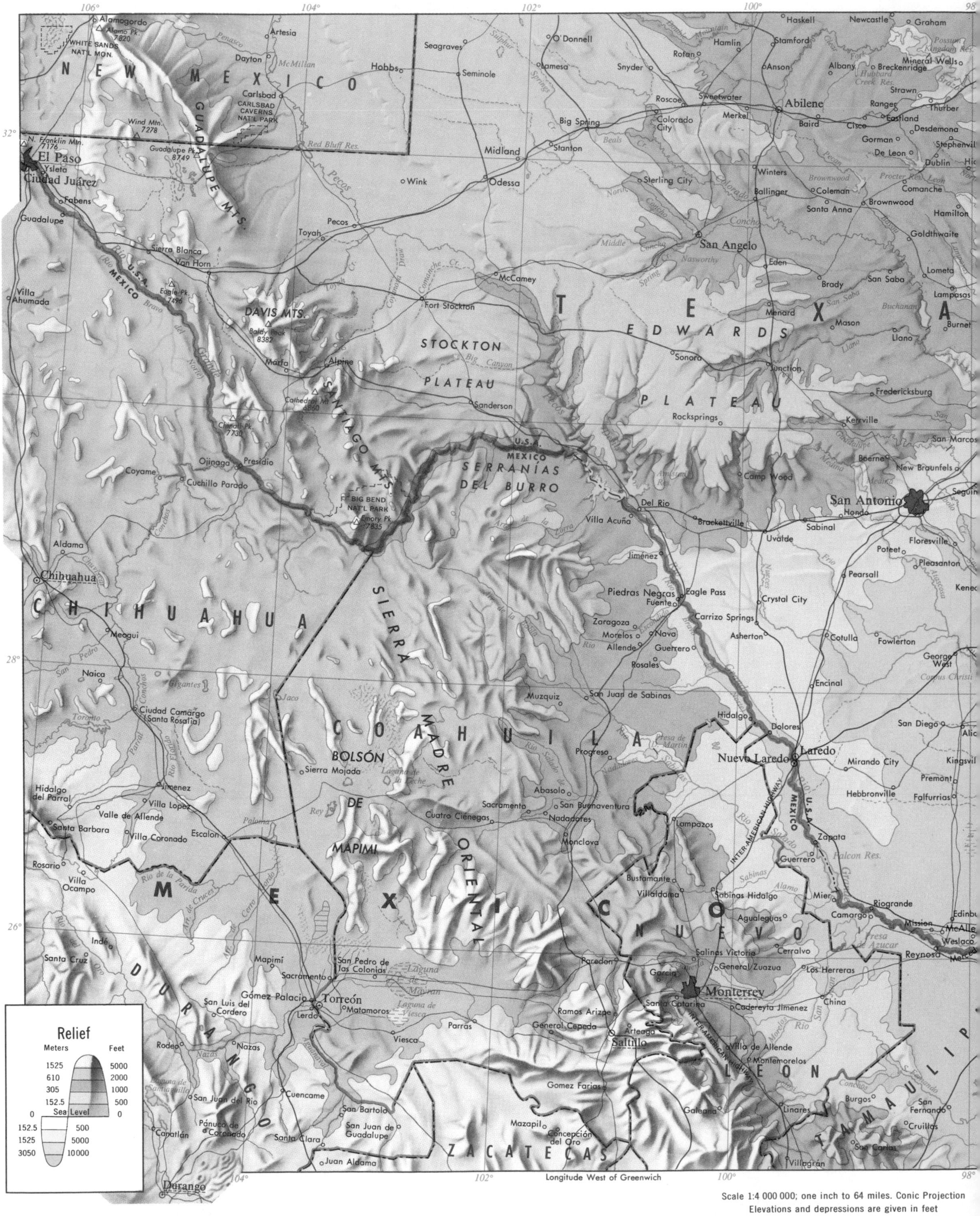

Scale 1:4 000 000; one inch to 64 miles. Conic Projection
Elevations and depressions are given in feet

0 20 40 60 80 100 120 Miles
0 20 40 60 80 100 120 140 160 180 200 Kilometers

Cities and Towns

0 to 50,000	○	500,000 to 1,000,000	⊚
50,000 to 500,000	⊙	1,000,000 and over	

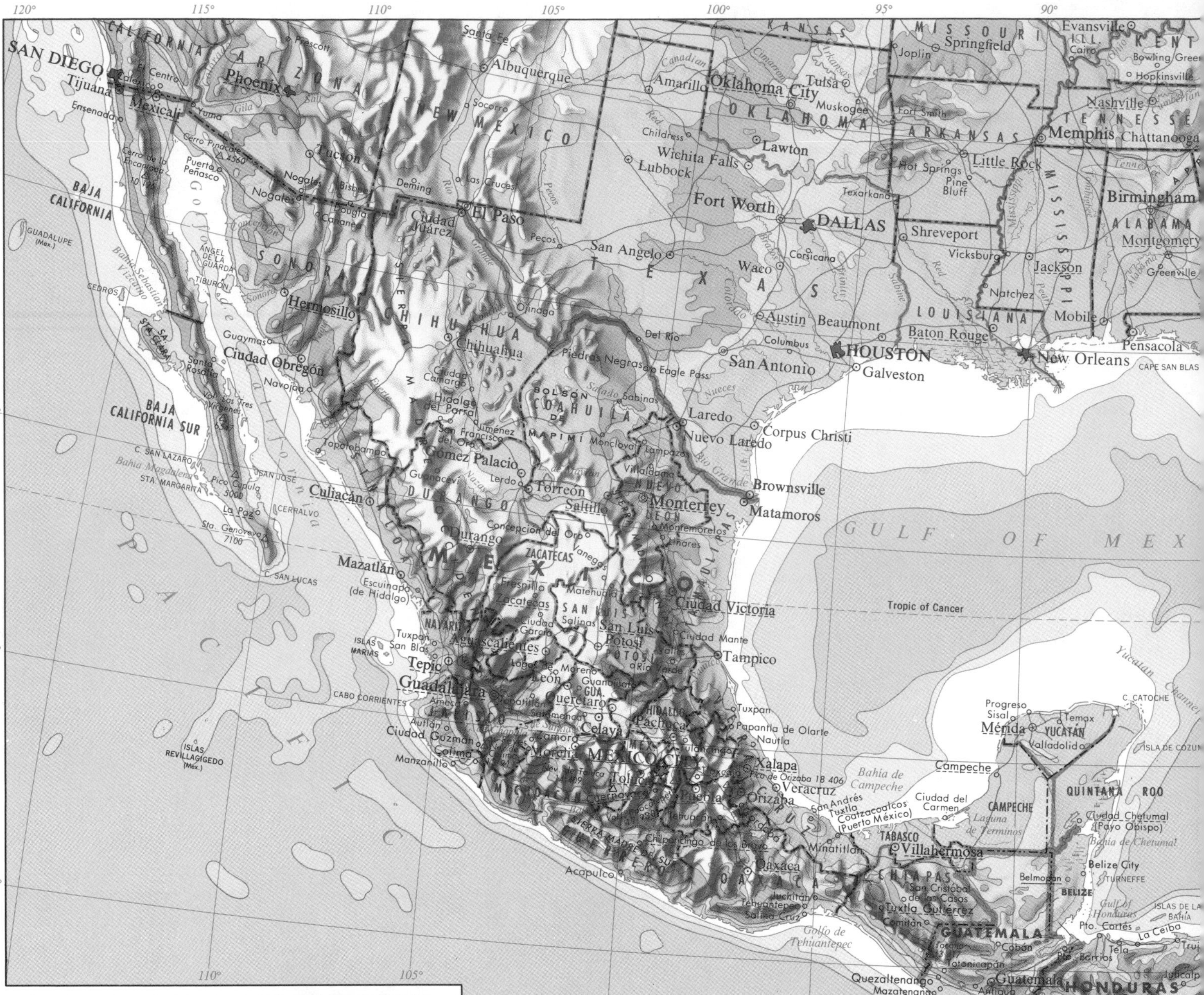

a

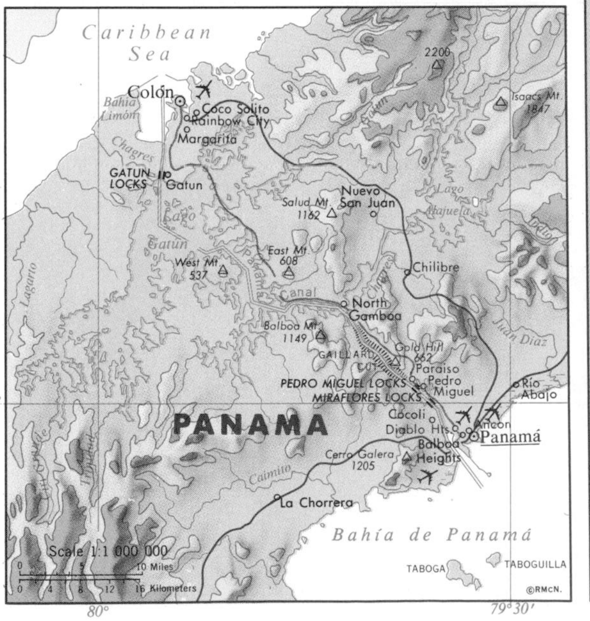

Scale 1:16 000 000; one inch to 250 miles. Polyconic Projection
Elevations and depressions are given in feet

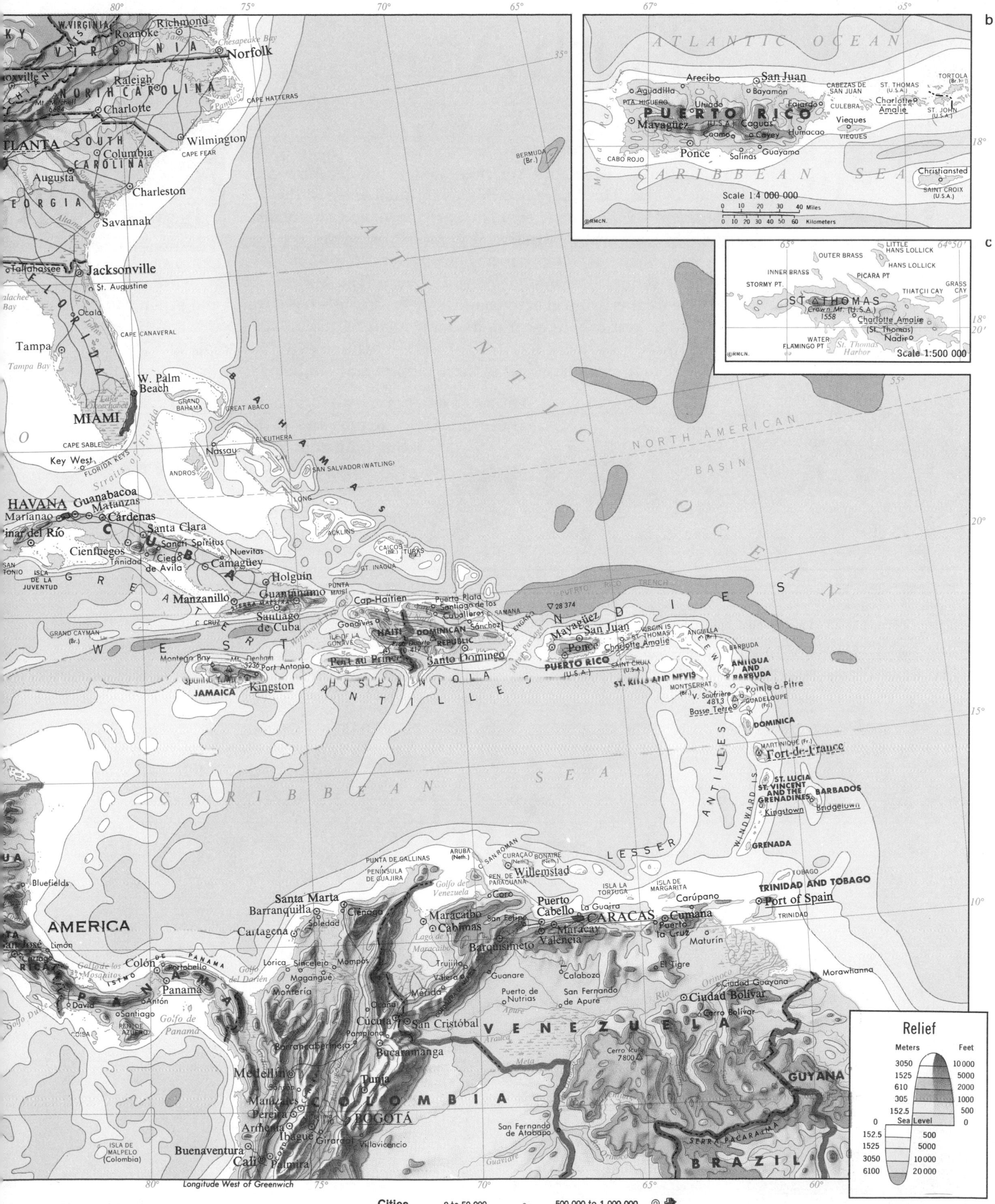
b
ATLANTIC OCEAN
PUERTO RICO
San Juan
Arecibo
Bayamon
Aguadilla
PTA. HIGUERO
Mayagüez
Utuado
Caguas
Fajardo
Humacao
Coamo
Cayey
Ponce
Salinas
Guayama
CABO ROJO
CABEZAS DE SAN JUAN
CULEBRA
Vieques
VIEQUES
ST. THOMAS (U.S.A.)
Charlotte Amalie
TORTOLA (Br.)
ST. JOHN (U.S.A.)
Christiansted
SAINT CROIX (U.S.A.)
CARIBBEAN SEA
Scale 1:4 000 000
Miles
Kilometers
c
OUTER BRASS
LITTLE HANS LOLLICK
HANS LOLLICK
INNER BRASS
PICARA PT
STORMY PT.
THATCH CAY
GRASS CAY
ST. THOMAS
Crown Mt. (U.S.A.) 1558
Charlotte Amalie (St. Thomas)
Nadir
WATER
FLAMINGO PT
St. Thomas Harbor
Scale 1:500 000
VIRGINIA
W. VIRGINIA
Richmond
Roanoke
Norfolk
NORTH CAROLINA
Raleigh
Charlotte
CAPE HATTERAS
SOUTH CAROLINA
Columbia
Wilmington
CAPE FEAR
ATLANTA
Augusta
Charleston
GEORGIA
Savannah
BERMUDA (Br.)
ATLANTIC OCEAN
Tallahassee
Jacksonville
St. Augustine
FLORIDA
Ocala
CAPE CANAVERAL
Tampa
Tampa Bay
W. Palm Beach
MIAMI
CAPE SABLE
Key West
Straits of Florida
BAHAMAS
GRAND BAHAMA
GREAT ABACO
ELEUTHERA
Nassau
ANDROS
SAN SALVADOR (WATLING)
LONG
ACKLINS
CAICOS (Br.)
TURKS (Br.)
GT. INAGUA
NORTH AMERICAN BASIN
HAVANA
Guanabacoa
Matanzas
Marianao
Cárdenas
Pinar del Río
CUBA
Santa Clara
Cienfuegos
Sancti Spíritus
Trinidad
Ciego de Avila
Nuevitas
Camagüey
ISLA DE LA JUVENTUD
Holguín
Manzanillo
Guantánamo
PUNTA MAISI
Santiago de Cuba
C. CRUZ
GRAND CAYMAN (Br.)
WEST INDIES
GREATER ANTILLES
Cap-Haïtien
Puerto Plata
Santiago de los Caballeros
SAMANA
Gonaïves
HAITI
DOMINICAN REPUBLIC
Port-au-Prince
Santo Domingo
HISPANIOLA
PUERTO RICO TRENCH
28 374
Mayagüez
San Juan
Ponce
Charlotte Amalie
PUERTO RICO (U.S.A.)
SAINT CROIX (U.S.A.)
VIRGIN IS.
ANGUILLA (Br.)
BARBUDA
ANTIGUA AND BARBUDA
ST. KITTS AND NEVIS
MONTSERRAT (Br.)
Pointe-à-Pitre
V. Soufrière 4813
GUADELOUPE (Fr.)
Basse Terre
DOMINICA
MARTINIQUE (Fr.)
Fort-de-France
ST. LUCIA
ST. VINCENT AND THE GRENADINES
Kingstown
BARBADOS
Bridgetown
GRENADA
LEEWARD IS.
WINDWARD IS.
LESSER ANTILLES
Montego Bay
Port Antonio
JAMAICA
Kingston
CARIBBEAN SEA
ARUBA (Neth.)
CURAÇAO (Neth.)
BONAIRE (Neth.)
Willemstad
PUNTA DE GALLINAS
PENÍNSULA DE GUAJIRA
Golfo de Venezuela
ISLA LA TORTUGA
ISLA DE MARGARITA
TOBAGO
TRINIDAD AND TOBAGO
Port of Spain
TRINIDAD
Bluefields
AMERICA
Santa Marta
Barranquilla
Ciénaga
Cartagena
Maracaibo
Cabimas
Coro
Puerto Cabello
La Guaira
CARACAS
Cumaná
Carúpano
Puerto la Cruz
Maracay
Valencia
Barquisimeto
Maturín
Limón
San José
Colón
Portobelo
Panamá
PANAMA
Golfo de Panamá
Santiago
David
Golfo del Darién
Lorica
Sincelejo
Mompós
Magangué
Montería
Trujillo
Valera
Mérida
Guanare
Calabozo
El Tigre
Ciudad Guayana
Ciudad Bolívar
Cerro Bolívar
Morawhanna
Puerto de Nutrias
San Fernando de Apure
Cúcuta
San Cristóbal
Pamplona
VENEZUELA
Barrancabermeja
Bucaramanga
Cerro Icutú 7800
GUYANA
Medellín
Tunja
COLOMBIA
Manizales
Pereira
Armenia
Ibagué
Girardot
BOGOTÁ
Villavicencio
San Fernando de Atabapo
SERRA PACARAIMA
BRAZIL
ISLA DE MALPELO (Colombia)
Buenaventura
Cali
Palmira
Longitude West of Greenwich
Relief
Meters
Feet
Sea Level

0 50 100 200 300 400 500 Miles

0 100 200 400 600 800 Kilometers

Cities and Towns			
0 to 50,000	○	500,000 to 1,000,000	◎
50,000 to 500,000	⊙	1,000,000 and over	

South America

Floodplain of the Amazon River, Brazil

With an area of 6.9 million square miles (17.8 million sq km), triangular-shaped South America is fourth among the continents in size. The Andes, which pass through seven of the continent's 13 mainland countries, are the longest mountain chain in the world. The mighty Amazon River carries a greater volume of water than any other river: 46 million gallons per second flow into the Atlantic Ocean. The Amazon basin contains an estimated one-fifth of the world's fresh water and is home to the world's largest rain forest with its countless plant and animal species. Angel Falls, in a remote Venezuelan forest, is the world's highest waterfall, dropping 3,212 feet (979 m), or almost the height of three Empire State Buildings.

One of South America's other great wonders is manmade. High in the Peruvian Andes lie the ruins of the sacred city of Machu Picchu, built centuries ago by the Incas. The city has an exquisite design and was built with remarkable skill. The Inca population, like most of South America's other native peoples, declined rapidly after the arrival of Europeans in the early 16th century.

South America at a glance

Land area: 6,900,000 square miles (17,800,000 sq km)

Estimated population: 352,960,000

Population density: 51/square mile (20/sq km)

Mean elevation: 1,800 feet (550 m)

Highest point: Aconcagua, Argentina, 22,831 feet (6,959 m)

Lowest point: Salinas Chicas, Argentina, 138 feet (42 m) below sea level

Longest river: Amazon-Ucayali, 4,000 mi (6,400 km)

Number of countries (incl. dependencies): 15

Largest independent country: Brazil, 3,300,172 square miles (8,547,404 sq km)

Smallest independent country: Suriname, 63,251 square miles (163,820 sq km)

Most populous independent country: Brazil, 175,260,000

Least populous independent country: Suriname, 435,000

Largest city: São Paulo, pop. 9,713,692

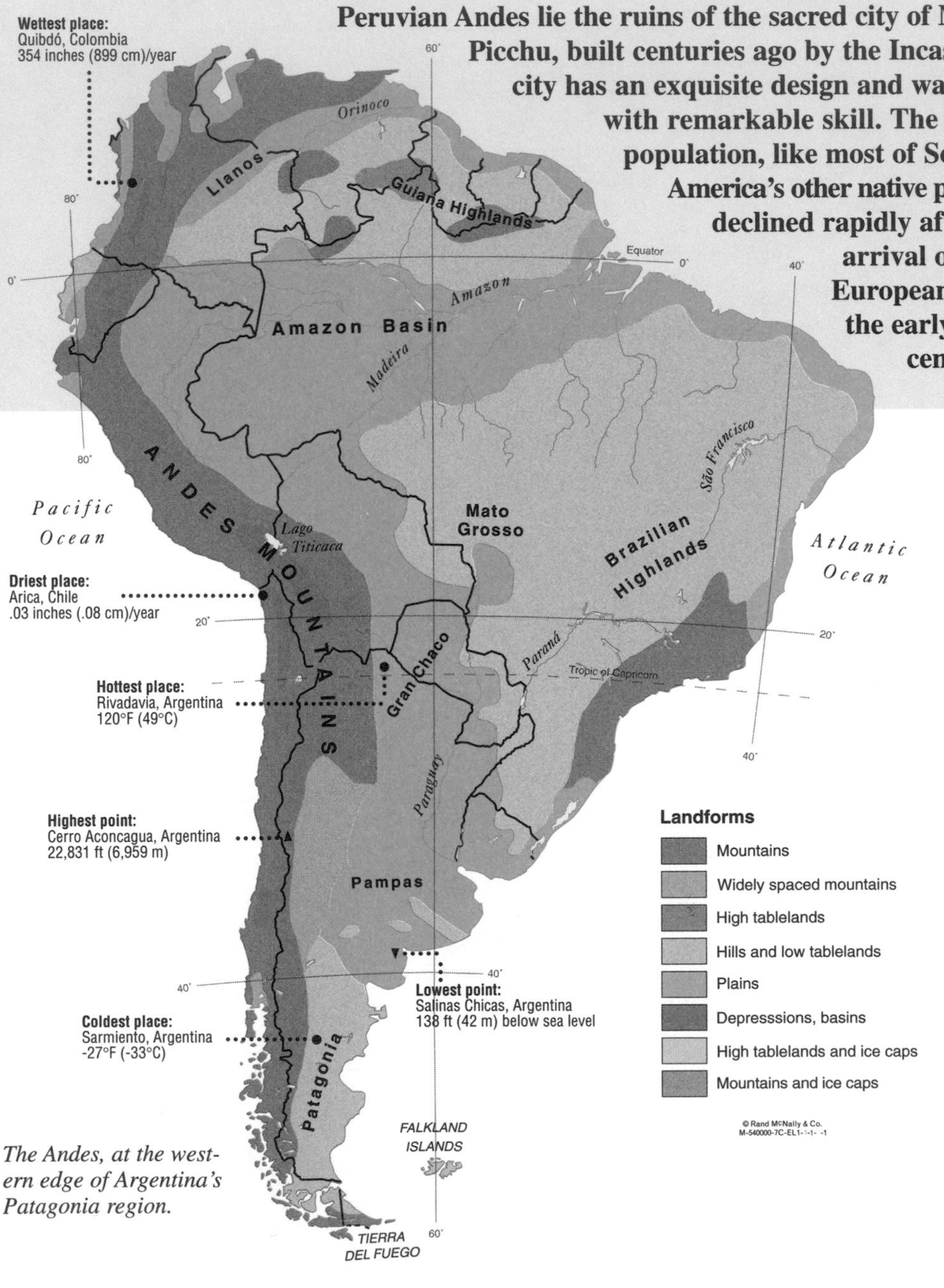

The Andes, at the western edge of Argentina's Patagonia region.

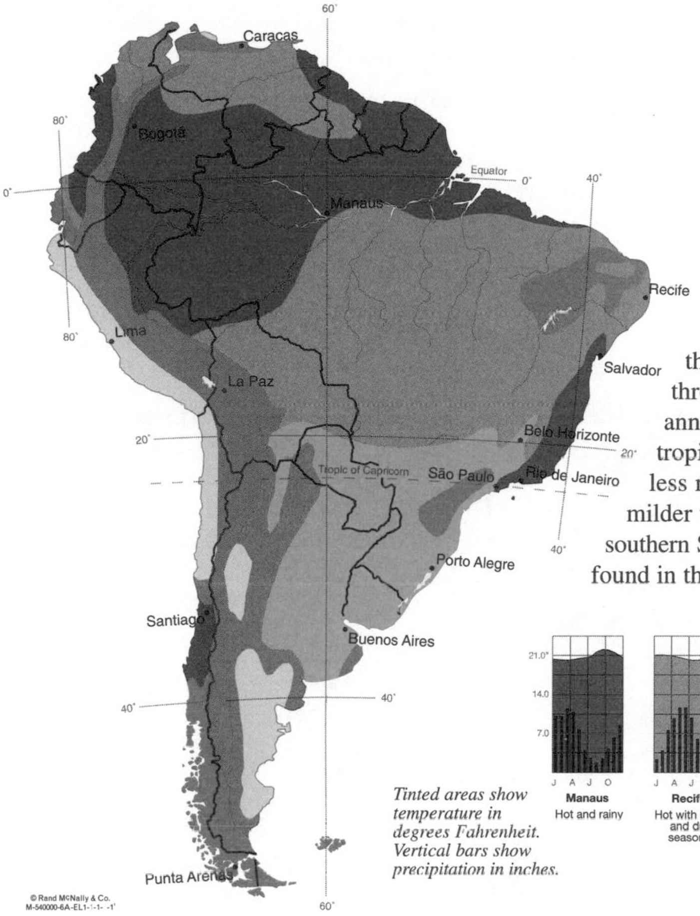

Climate

South America's most predominant climate zones are the vast tropical rain forests and tropical savannas which cover most of the northern half of the continent. In the rain forests, rain falls throughout the year, averaging 60 to 80 inches (152 to 203 cm) annually. Daytime temperatures usually exceed 80° F (27° C). The tropical savanna regions experience the same high temperatures but less rainfall, with a dry season in winter. A temperate climate, with milder temperatures and moderate rainfall, prevails throughout much of southern South America, east of the Andes. Arid to semiarid conditions are found in the far south and at Brazil's eastern tip.

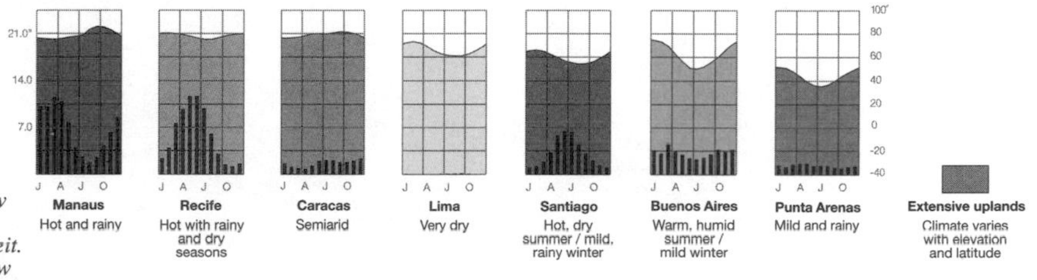

Tinted areas show temperature in degrees Fahrenheit. Vertical bars show precipitation in inches.

Population

South America shares the rank of fourth most-densely populated continent with North America, with 51 people per square mile (20 per sq km). Despite this relatively low figure, the continent is intensely urban because the Andes and the Amazon rain forest render most of it either inaccessible or unsuitable for farming. More than 90% of South America's 353 million people live within 150 miles (240 km) of the coast. São Paulo, Brazil, with a metropolitan population of more than 17 million, is the world's sixth-largest metropolitan area. Most South Americans are *mestizo*—of mixed European and Indian descent. Spanish is the predominant language, followed by Portuguese. More than 90% of the people are Roman Catholics.

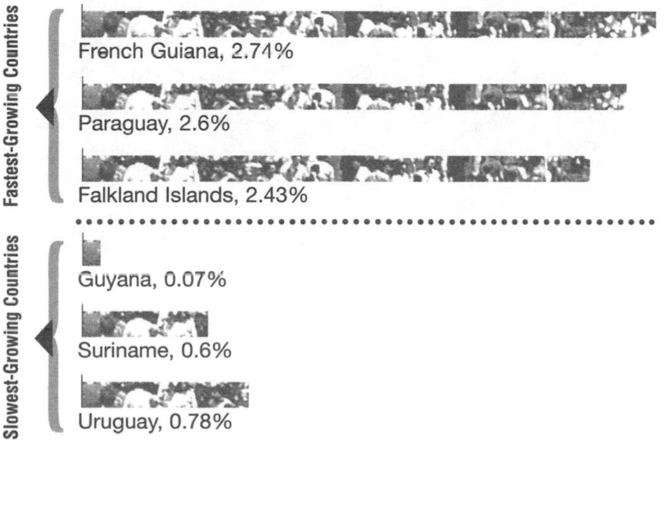

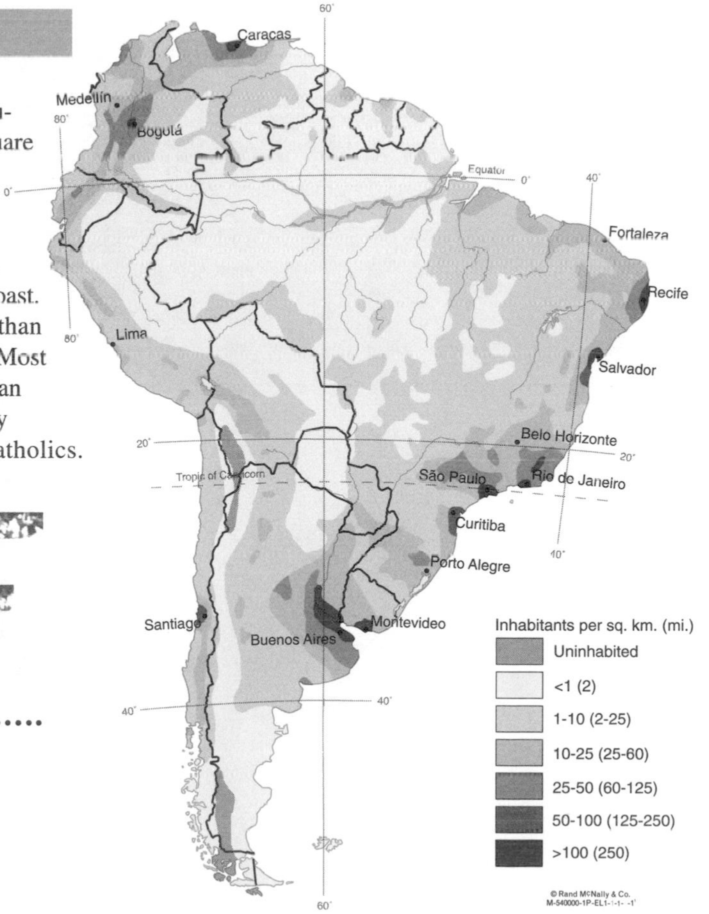

Environments and Land Use

Land suitable for farming is very limited in South America, covering only about 6% of the continent. Small, family-run subsistence farms are common, and typical crops are maize, wheat, and potatoes. Despite the scarcity of arable land, commercial agriculture for export is a major part of the economies of several countries. Ecuador is the world's leading exporter of bananas, while Brazil and Colombia grow almost 40% of the world's coffee beans. Brazil is also a major exporter of sugar. Chile has developed a large trade in produce—such as tomatoes and grapes—that is exported to North America during its winter months (South America's summer months). Production of coca, the basis for illicit drugs, has become a part of the rural economies of Colombia, Bolivia, and Peru.

Cattle ranching is centered on the vast, grassy Pampas region, which extends through northern Argentina, Uruguay, and southern Brazil. Sheep, raised both for meat and wool, are important throughout the Andes and southern Argentina. About 25% of the continent is suitable for grazing.

As South America's population grows, pressure builds to clear more land for farming. Much expansion has taken place in the Amazon basin at the cost of millions of acres of rain forest, which are cleared of trees and drained. Balancing the demands of the population with the need to preserve the rain forest is one of the continent's most pressing issues.

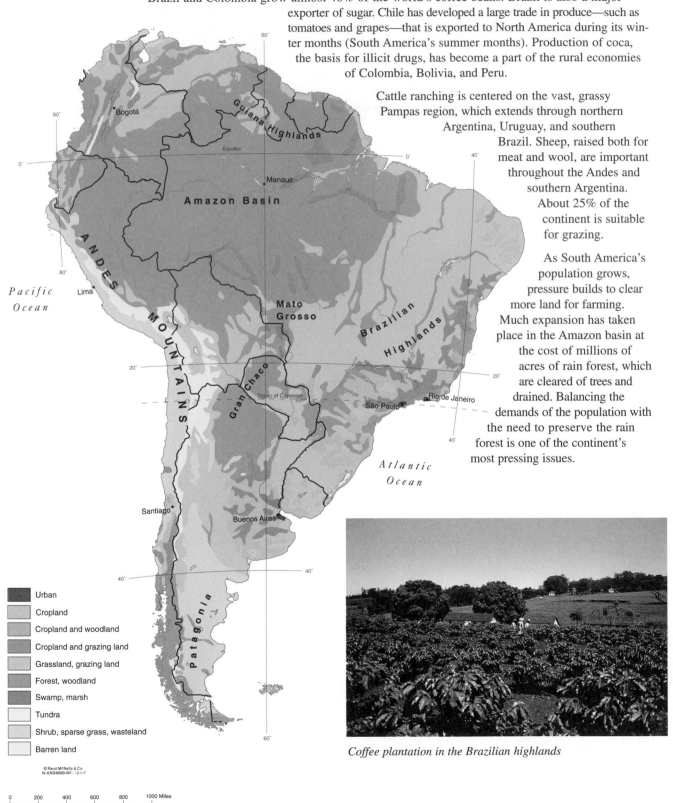

Coffee plantation in the Brazilian highlands

Destruction of the Rain Forest

The Amazonian rain forest contains an abundance and diversity of life that is matched by few places in the world. In fact, it has been estimated that the plant and animal species of Amazonia account for nearly one-half of those found on Earth. New plants and animals are constantly being discovered, and scientists have found in Amazonian plants a treasure trove of new substances, some of which are now being used to produce life-saving medicines. It is thought that cures for many more diseases could be found in the plants yet to be studied.

In recent decades, nearly 10% of the rain forest's original 1.58 million square miles (4.09 million sq km) has been cleared (see map below) for farming, cattle ranching, mining, and commercial logging. The most effective way to clear the land is the "slash-and-burn" method, which has been practiced by indigenous peoples on an insignificant scale for centuries. Today, widespread usage of this method is destroying vast areas of the rain forest, and smoke from the fires is polluting the atmosphere and possibly contributing to global warming. The destruction also imperils the Indians living within the forest; their numbers have shrunk by more than half in this century alone.

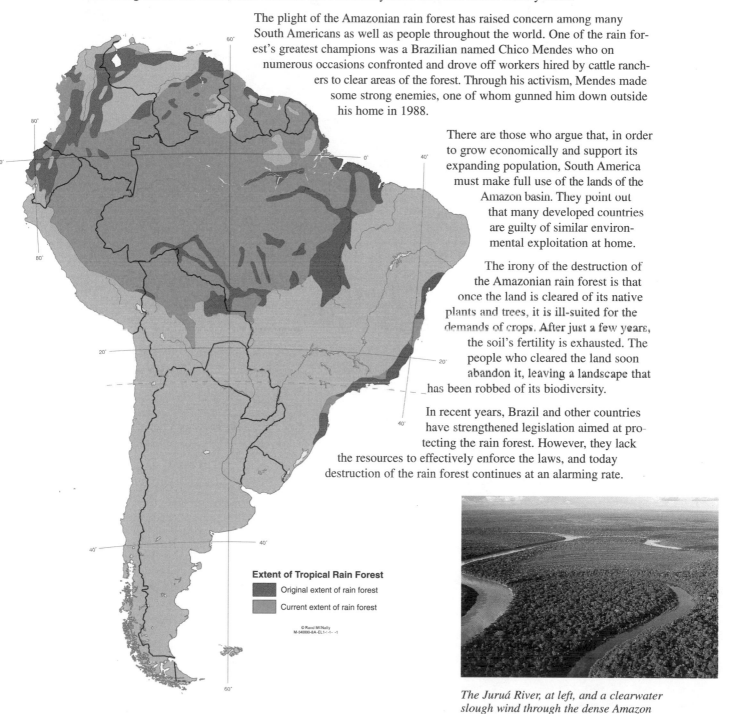

The plight of the Amazonian rain forest has raised concern among many South Americans as well as people throughout the world. One of the rain forest's greatest champions was a Brazilian named Chico Mendes who on numerous occasions confronted and drove off workers hired by cattle ranchers to clear areas of the forest. Through his activism, Mendes made some strong enemies, one of whom gunned him down outside his home in 1988.

There are those who argue that, in order to grow economically and support its expanding population, South America must make full use of the lands of the Amazon basin. They point out that many developed countries are guilty of similar environmental exploitation at home.

The irony of the destruction of the Amazonian rain forest is that once the land is cleared of its native plants and trees, it is ill-suited for the demands of crops. After just a few years, the soil's fertility is exhausted. The people who cleared the land soon abandon it, leaving a landscape that has been robbed of its biodiversity.

In recent years, Brazil and other countries have strengthened legislation aimed at protecting the rain forest. However, they lack the resources to effectively enforce the laws, and today destruction of the rain forest continues at an alarming rate.

The Juruá River, at left, and a clearwater slough wind through the dense Amazon rain forest near Eirunepé, Brazil.

Scale 1:40 000 000; one inch to 630 miles. Lambert's Azimuthal, Equal Area Projection
Elevations and depressions are given in feet

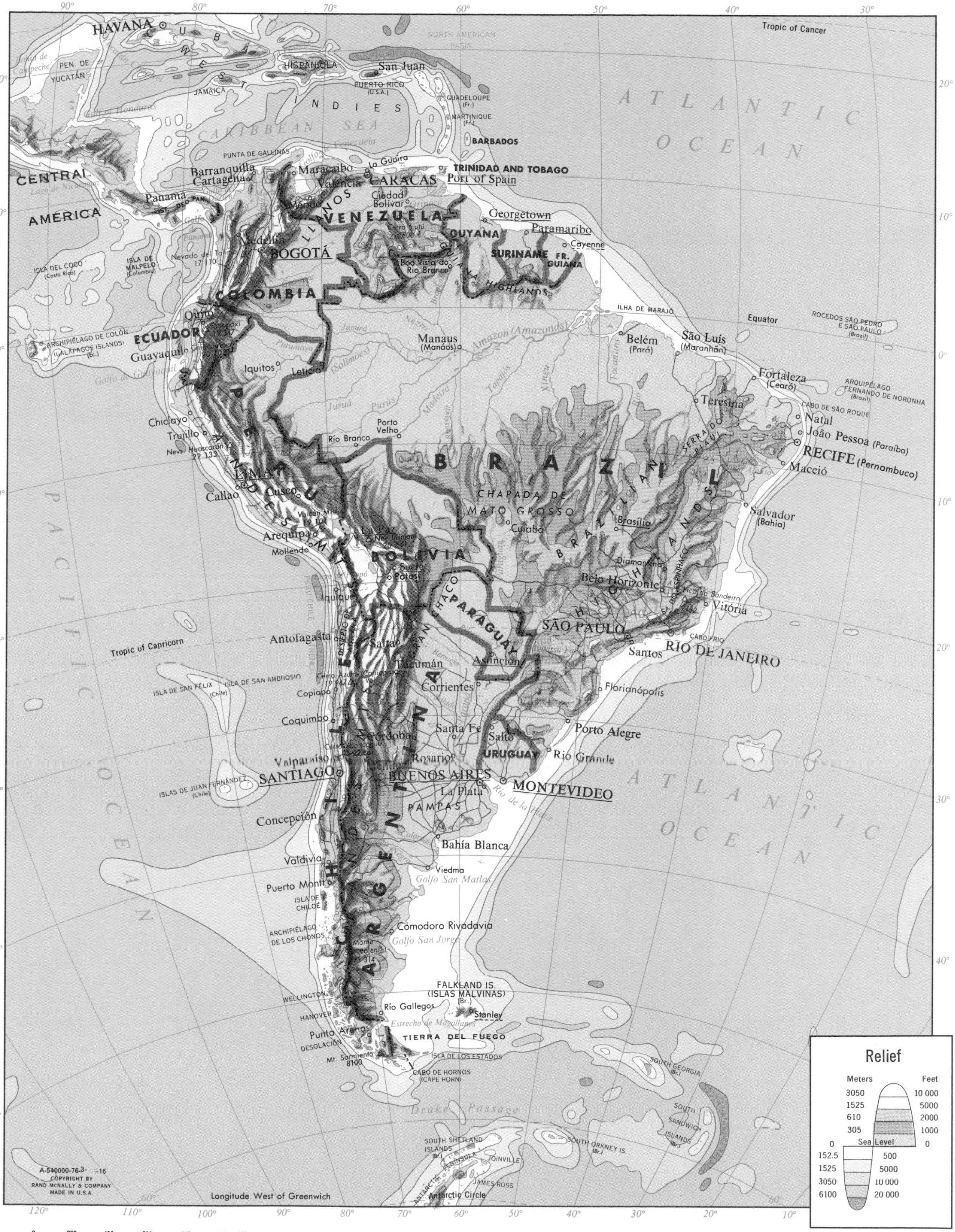

0 200 400 600 800 1000 Miles

0 400 800 1200 1600 Kilometers

Scale 1:40 000 000; one inch to 630 miles. Lambert's Azimuthal, Equal Area Projection

Elevations and depressions are given in feet

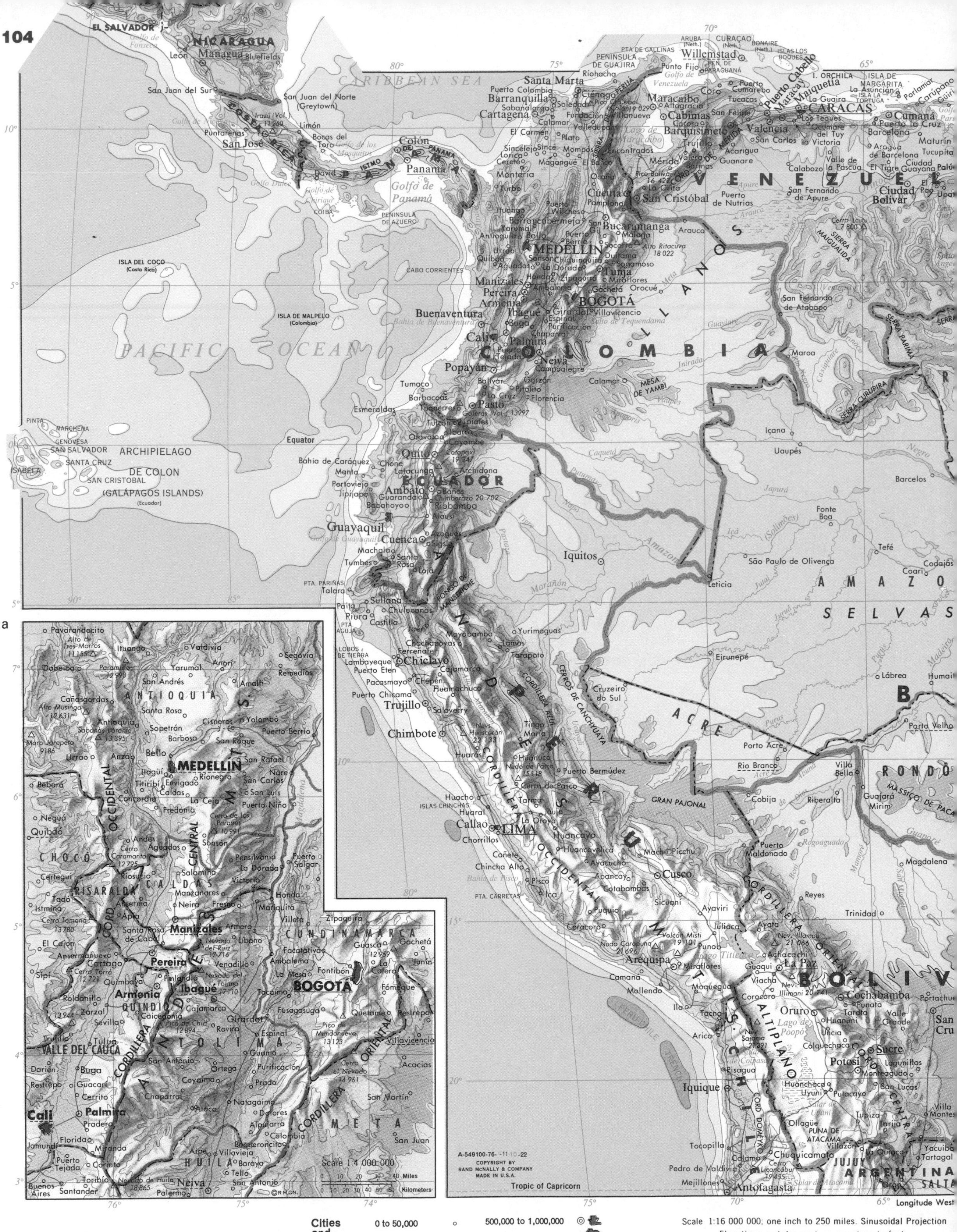

Cities and Towns: 0 to 50,000 ○ · 50,000 to 500,000 ⊙ · 500,000 to 1,000,000 · 1,000,000 and over

Scale 1:16 000 000; one inch to 250 miles. Sinusoidal Projection
Elevations and depressions are given in feet

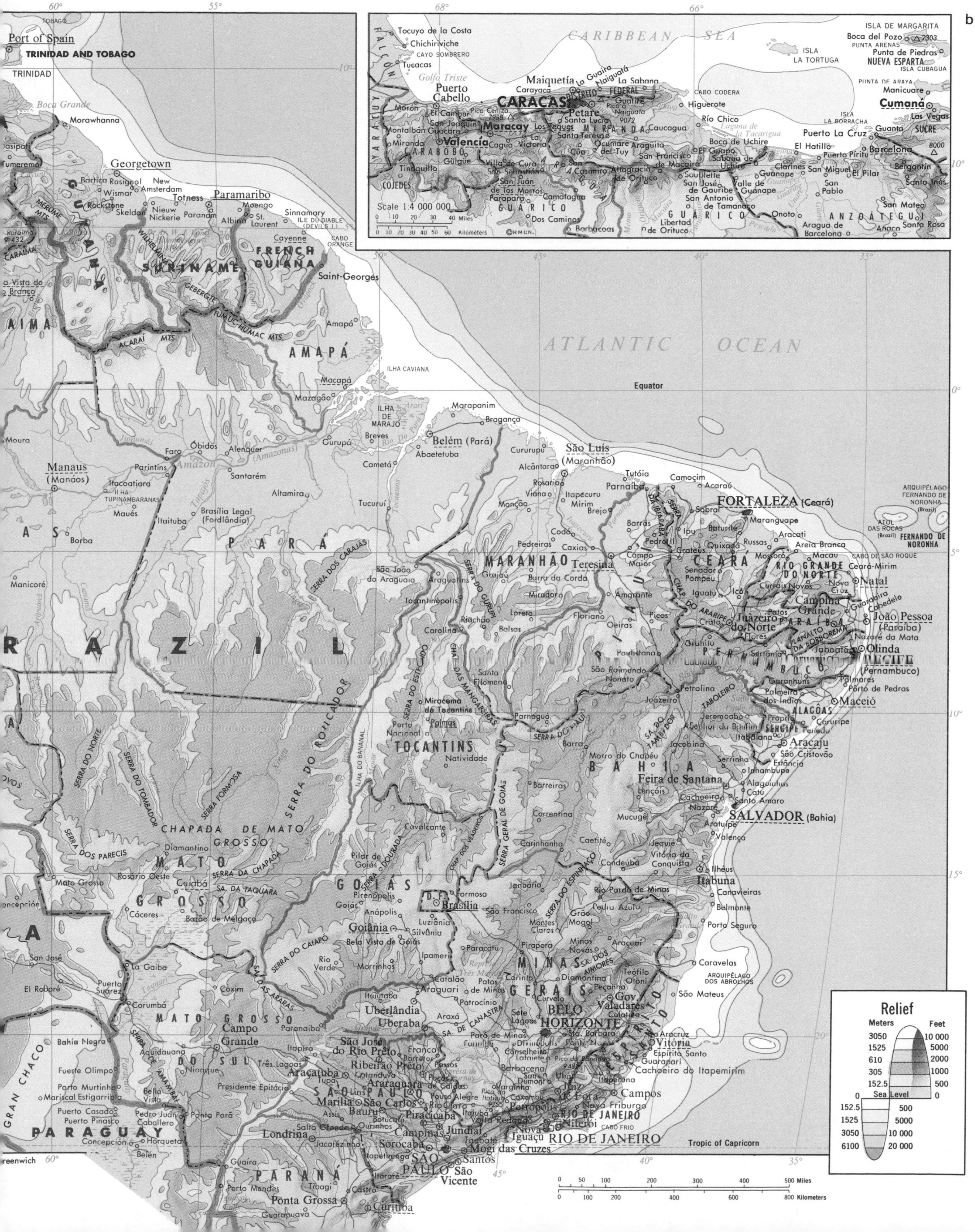
b
CARIBBEAN SEA
ISLA DE MARGARITA
ISLA LA TORTUGA
NUEVA ESPARTA
CARACAS
Maracay
Valencia
Cumaná
Barcelona
Puerto La Cruz
CARABOBO
MIRANDA
GUÁRICO
ANZOÁTEGUI
SUCRE
FALCÓN
COJEDES
Scale 1:4 000 000
0 10 20 30 40 Miles
0 10 20 30 40 50 60 Kilometers
Port of Spain
TRINIDAD AND TOBAGO
Georgetown
Paramaribo
Cayenne
FRENCH GUIANA
SURINAME
AMAPÁ
ATLANTIC OCEAN
Equator
Macapá
Belém (Pará)
São Luís (Maranhão)
Manaus (Manáos)
FORTALEZA (Ceará)
Teresina
Natal
João Pessoa (Paraíba)
Olinda
RECIFE (Pernambuco)
Maceió
Aracaju
SALVADOR (Bahia)
BRAZIL
PARÁ
MARANHÃO
PIAUÍ
CEARÁ
RIO GRANDE DO NORTE
PARAÍBA
PERNAMBUCO
ALAGOAS
SERGIPE
BAHIA
TOCANTINS
MATO GROSSO
GOIÁS
MINAS GERAIS
ESPÍRITO SANTO
MATO GROSSO DO SUL
SÃO PAULO
PARANÁ
RIO DE JANEIRO
PARAGUAY
GRAN CHACO
Brasília
Goiânia
BELO HORIZONTE
Vitória
Campo Grande
Cuiabá
Curitiba
SÃO PAULO
RIO DE JANEIRO
Tropic of Capricorn
ARQUIPÉLAGO FERNANDO DE NORONHA
Relief
Meters Feet
3050 10 000
1525 5000
610 2000
305 1000
152.5 500
0 Sea Level 0
152.5 500
1525 5000
3050 10 000
6100 20 000
0 50 100 200 300 400 500 Miles
0 100 200 400 600 800 Kilometers

0 50 100 200 300 400 500 Miles
0 100 200 400 600 800 Kilometers

Scale 1:16 000 000; one inch to 250 miles. Sinusoidal Projection
Elevations and depressions are given in feet

a

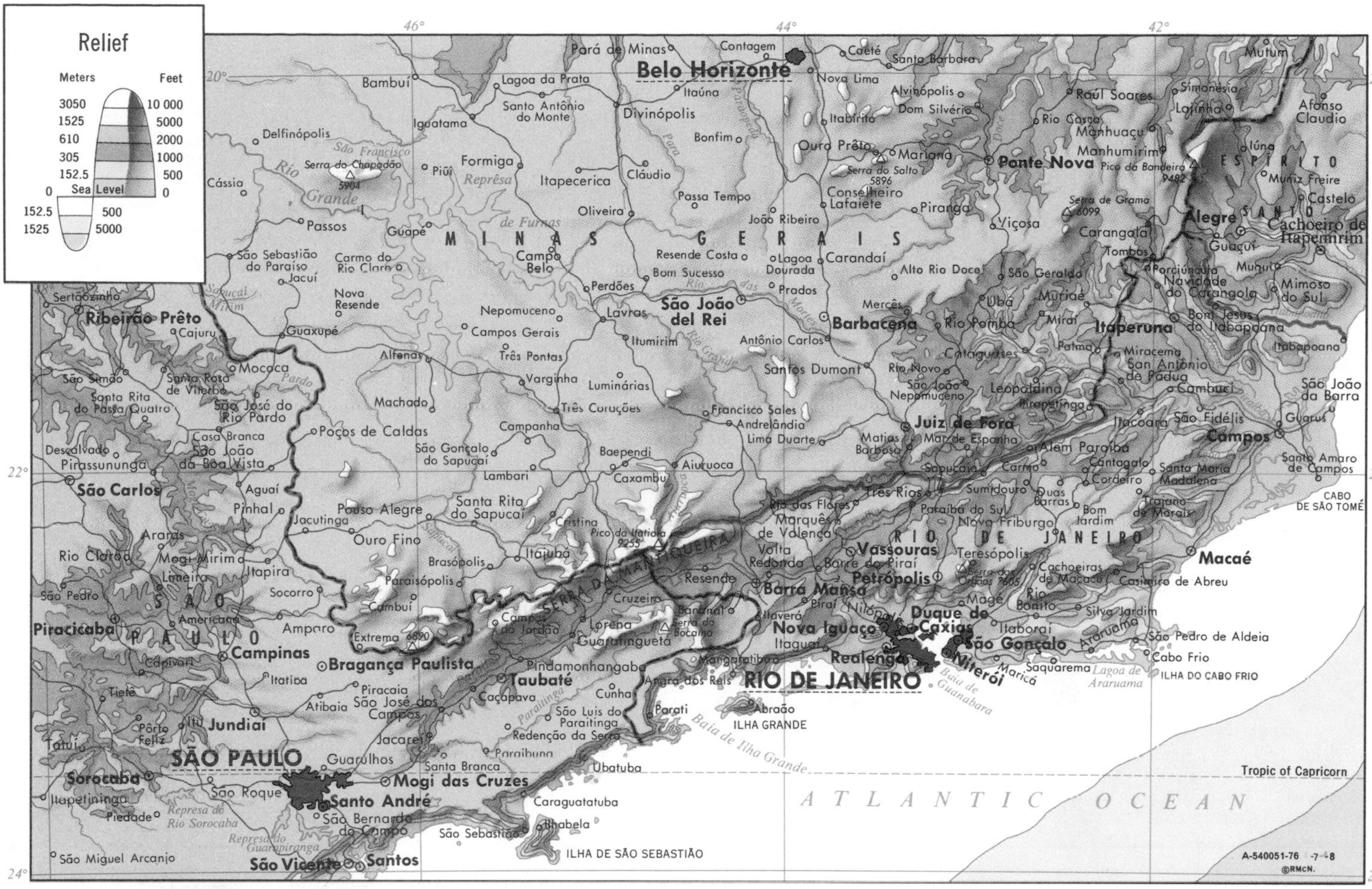

b

c

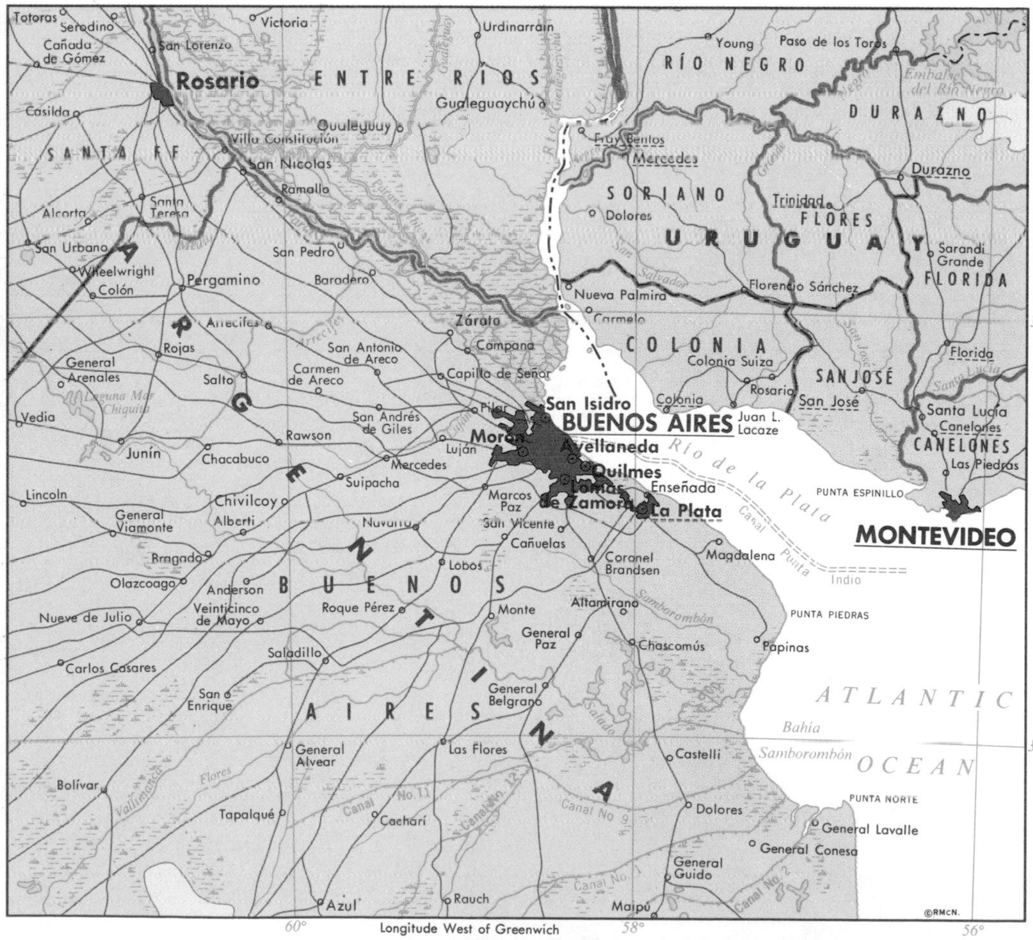

Longitude West of Greenwich

Miles	0	10	20	30	40	50	60	70	80	90	100	110	120

Kilometers	0	20	40	60	80	100	120	140	160	180	200

Cities and Towns

0 to 50,000 ○	500,000 to 1,000,000
50,000 to 500,000 ⊙	1,000,000 and over

Scale 1:4 000 000; one inch to 64 miles.
Elevations and depressions are given in feet.

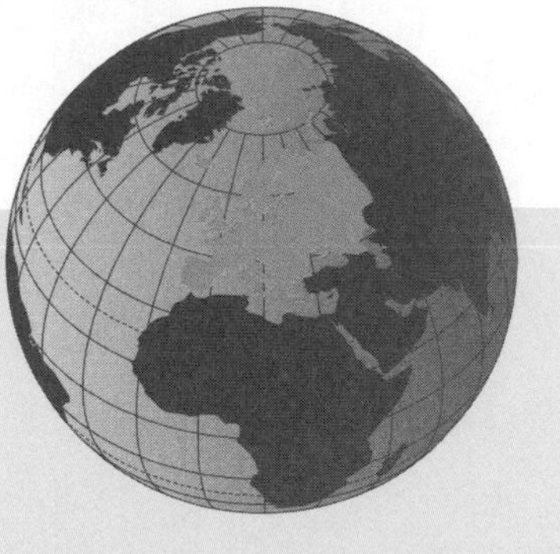

Europe

Europe is smaller than every other continent except Australia. In a sense, Europe is not really a continent at all, since it is part of the same vast landmass as Asia. Geographers sometimes refer to this landmass as a single continent, Eurasia. Europe occupies only about 18% of the land area of Eurasia.

Europe can be described as an enormous peninsula, stretching from the Ural Mountains, Ural River, and Caspian Sea in the east, to the Atlantic Ocean in the west; and from the Arctic Ocean in the north to the Mediterranean Sea, Black Sea, and Caucasus mountains in the south. The British Isles, Iceland, Corsica, Crete, and thousands of smaller islands that lie off the European mainland are usually considered as part of the continent.

A sweep of mountain ranges, including the Pyrenees, Alps and Carpathians, divides the colder, wetter north from the sun-drenched south.

Europe at a glance

Land area: 3,800,000 square miles (9,900,000 sq km)

Estimated population: 728,975,000

Population density: 192/square mile (74/sq km)

Mean elevation: 980 feet (300 m)

Highest point: Gora El' brus, Russia, 18,510 feet (5,642 m)

Lowest point: Caspian Sea, Asia-Europe, 92 feet (28 m) below sea level

Longest river: Volga, 2,194 mi (3,531 km)

Number of countries (incl. dependencies): 49

Largest independent country: Russia (Europe/Asia), 6,592,849 square miles (17,075,400 sq km)

Smallest independent country: Vatican City, 0.2 square miles (0.4 sq km)

Most populous independent country: Russia (Europe/Asia), 145,215,000

Least populous independent country: Vatican City, 1,000

Largest city: Moscow, pop. 8,368,449

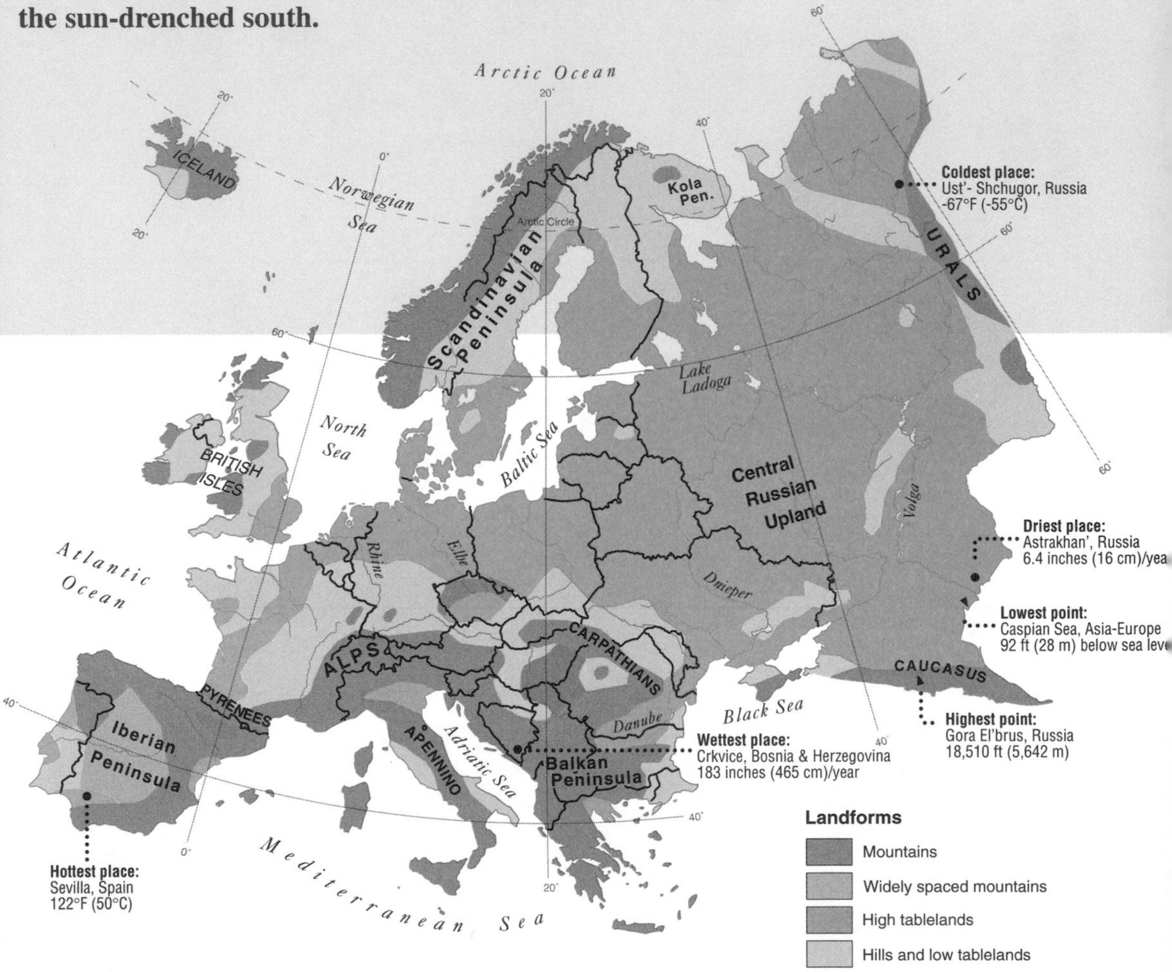

The Alps tower above a village in the Virgen Tal valley of western Austria.

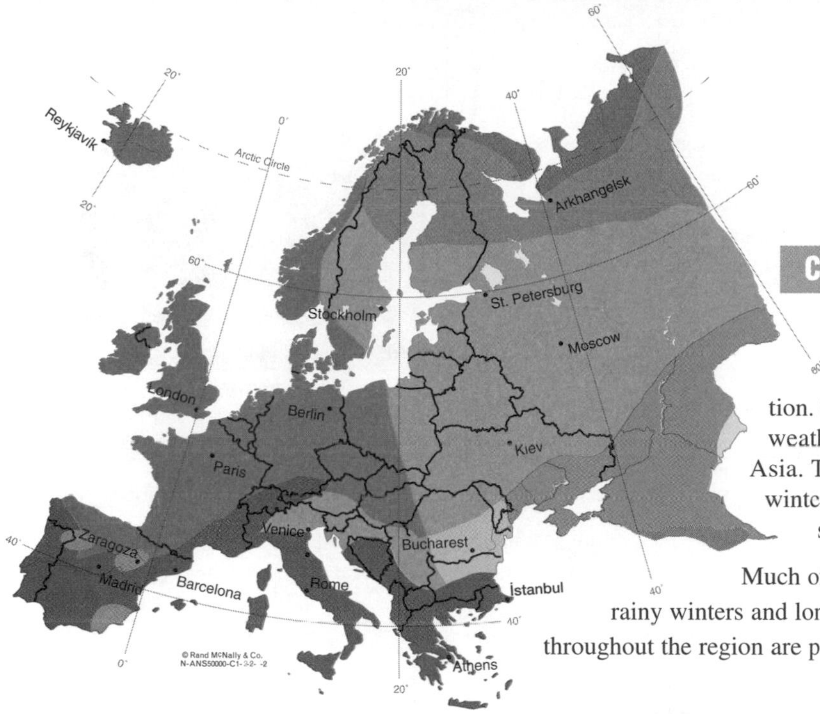

Climate

Warm, moist air masses flowing in from the Atlantic Ocean give much of Europe a mild climate and abundant precipitation. Cities like London, Paris and Rome all enjoy warmer weather than cities at similar latitudes in North America and Asia. The moderate winds don't reach eastern Europe, where the winters are long and cold and the summers short and cool. The same is true in the northern regions of Scandinavia.

Much of the south enjoys a Mediterranean climate, marked by short, rainy winters and long, dry summers. Indeed, the many beaches and islands found throughout the region are popular with vacationers year-round.

Tinted areas show temperature in degrees Fahrenheit. Vertical bars show precipitation in inches.

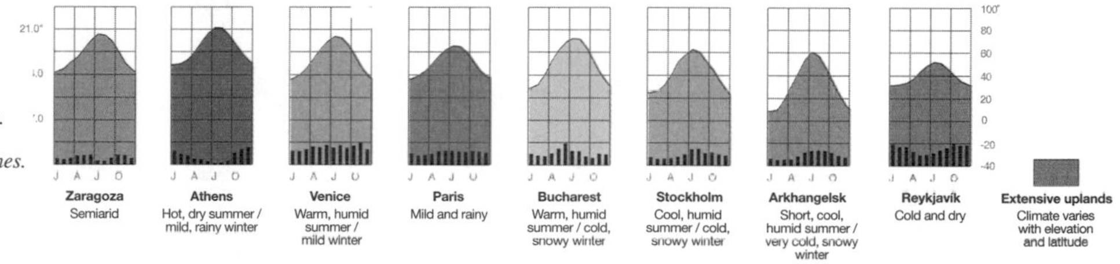

Population

Europe is the second most densely populated continent. Only Asia has a greater population density. However, Europe's density varies dramatically from country to country. The Netherlands, for instance, has a density of 991 people per square mile (383 per sq km), making it one of the most densely populated countries in the world. In contrast, Norway has only 30 people per square mile (12 per sq km).

A vast array of ethnic groups and cultures can be found in Europe's relatively small area. Throughout the centuries, this diversity has enriched European culture while also leading to many hostilities. Of the 60 languages spoken, the majority are derived from Latin, Germanic or Slavic roots. Most Europeans are Christian, either Protestant or Roman Catholic.

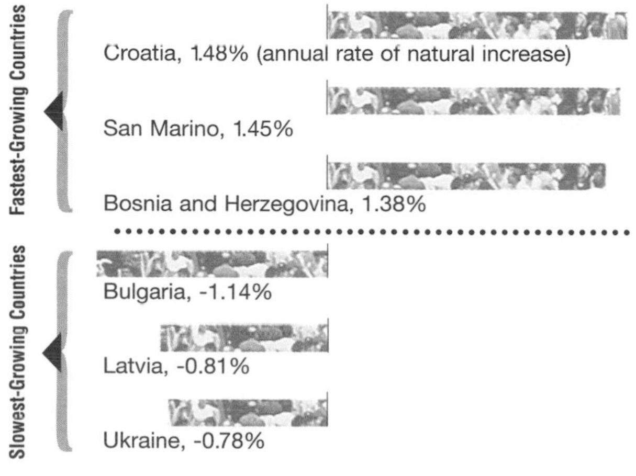

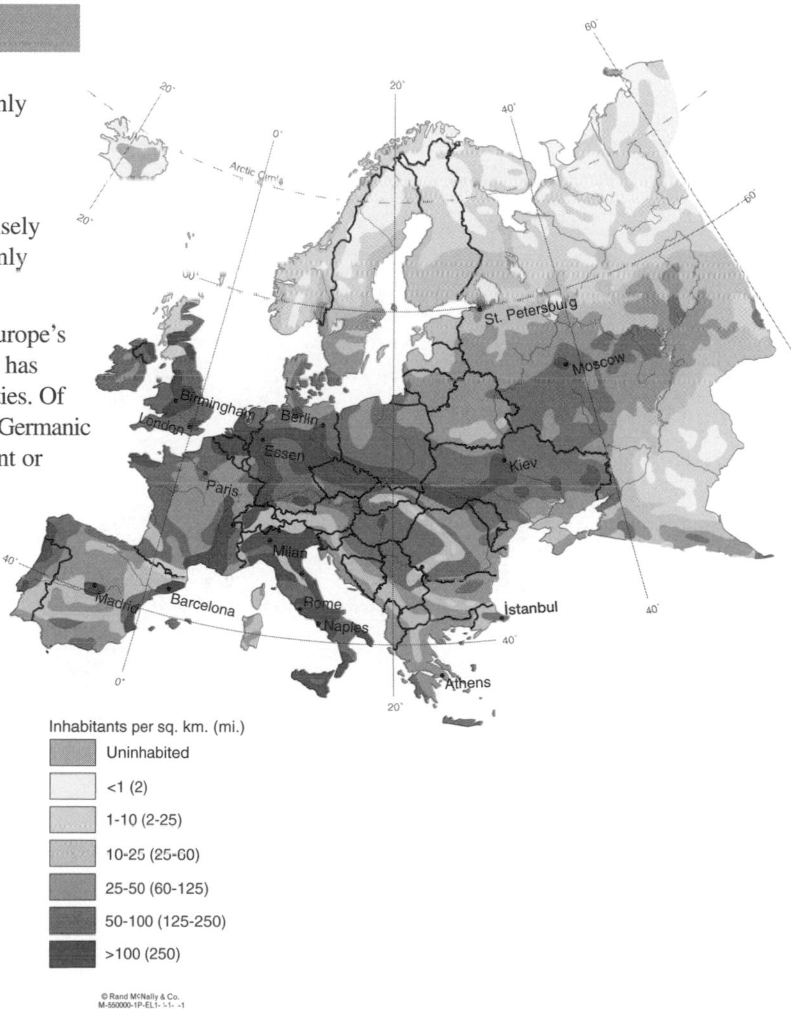

Environments and Land Use

Harvesting grapes from vineyards in Burgundy, France

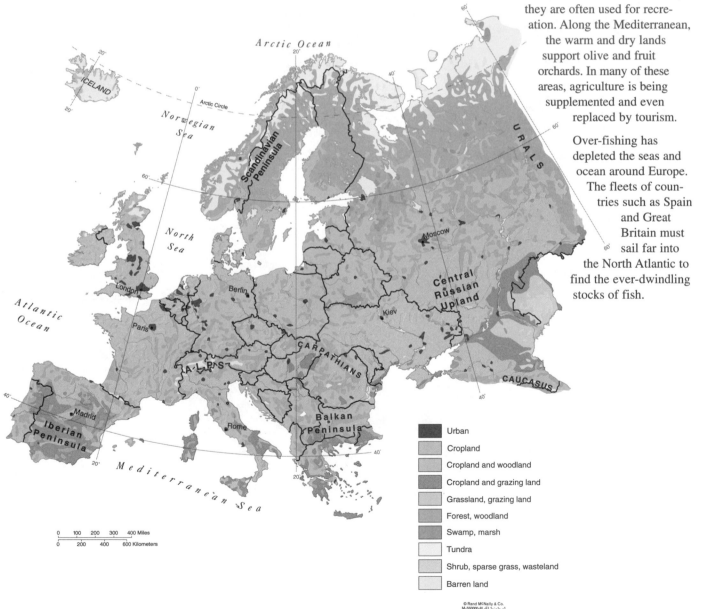

Given the high population density of Europe, it is not surprising that evidence of human development can be seen in every part of the continent, with the exception of the northern reaches of Scandinavia. In Western Europe, small farms are surrounded by towns, cities and industrial areas. Only in the east, in areas such as the vast rolling steppes of the Ukraine, can large farms and unbroken natural vistas be found.

The heavily industrialized countries of Western Europe boast rich economies and high standards of living. Switzerland has a per capita Gross Domestic Product (GDP) approaching U.S. $22,000, the highest in the world. The figures are generally much lower in Eastern Europe. One of the continent's poorest countries is the tiny former Communist state of Albania, which has a per capita GDP of only U.S. $998.

Pollution is an unfortunate by-product of the continent's industry. One example is the scenic Rhine River: in the 1980s, large stretches were found to be so polluted that they were devoid of life. These findings sparked a 20-year program to clean up the river. In general, the countries of Eastern Europe suffer from the worst pollution, as economic development has in the past taken precedence over environmental policies.

The vast forests of Scandinavia support a large paper and wood-products economy. Where forests survive in countries farther to the south, they are often used for recreation. Along the Mediterranean, the warm and dry lands support olive and fruit orchards. In many of these areas, agriculture is being supplemented and even replaced by tourism.

Over-fishing has depleted the seas and ocean around Europe. The fleets of countries such as Spain and Great Britain must sail far into the North Atlantic to find the ever-dwindling stocks of fish.

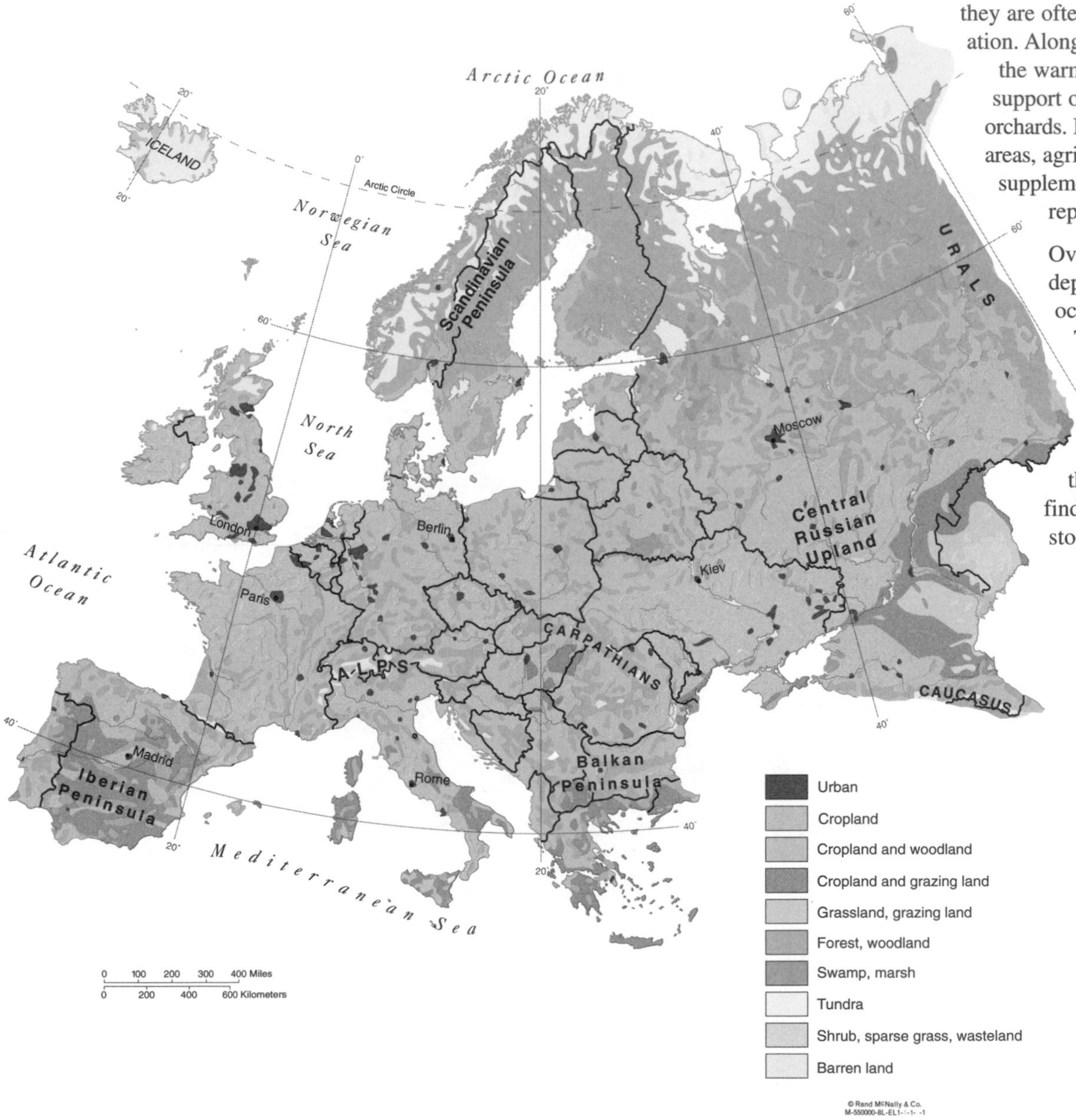

Political Changes Since 1989

Much of Europe lay in economic and physical ruin after World War II ended in 1945. Germany's cities and industrial centers had been ravaged by aerial bombardment and assaults by the Allied armies. Many other countries, such as Russia, Poland, Belgium, and the Netherlands suffered gravely from Nazi invasions and occupation.

After 1945, tensions among the victorious Allies grew, specifically between the western powers—the United States, Great Britain and France—and the Soviet Union. It became clear that the two sides had vastly different visions for post-war Europe. In 1946, former British prime minister Winston Churchill observed that an "Iron Curtain" had gone down across Europe. It was to stay in place for almost 45 years.

Germany and the city of Berlin were divided between the western powers and the Soviet Union. West Germany quickly joined the other countries of Western Europe in building a stable, affluent democratic society. East Germany became part of a bloc of Eastern European countries dominated by the Soviet Union. These included Poland, Czechoslovakia, Hungary, Romania, Albania, and Bulgaria (see map at right). The economies in these countries were tightly controlled and personal freedoms were severely limited by the Communist governments in power.

The two blocs faced each other in a tense, generally non-military standoff called "The Cold War," which lasted for four decades. However, in 1985 winds of reform began sweeping through Eastern Europe. In 1989, Hungary relaxed its borders with Austria, setting off a flow of refugees from the east who had been forbidden to travel to the west. Thus began a dizzying period of change: the next two years saw the collapse of the Soviet Union, the reunification of Germany, independence for the former Soviet republics, and freedom from Soviet influence for the former bloc countries.

Although much of the old east seems intent on adopting western ideals of democracy and freedom, the process is not without problems. Switching from communism to market economies has meant hardship for millions. It has also led to ethnic tensions that resulted in the peaceful break-up of Czechoslovakia and the violent civil wars in the former Yugoslavia.

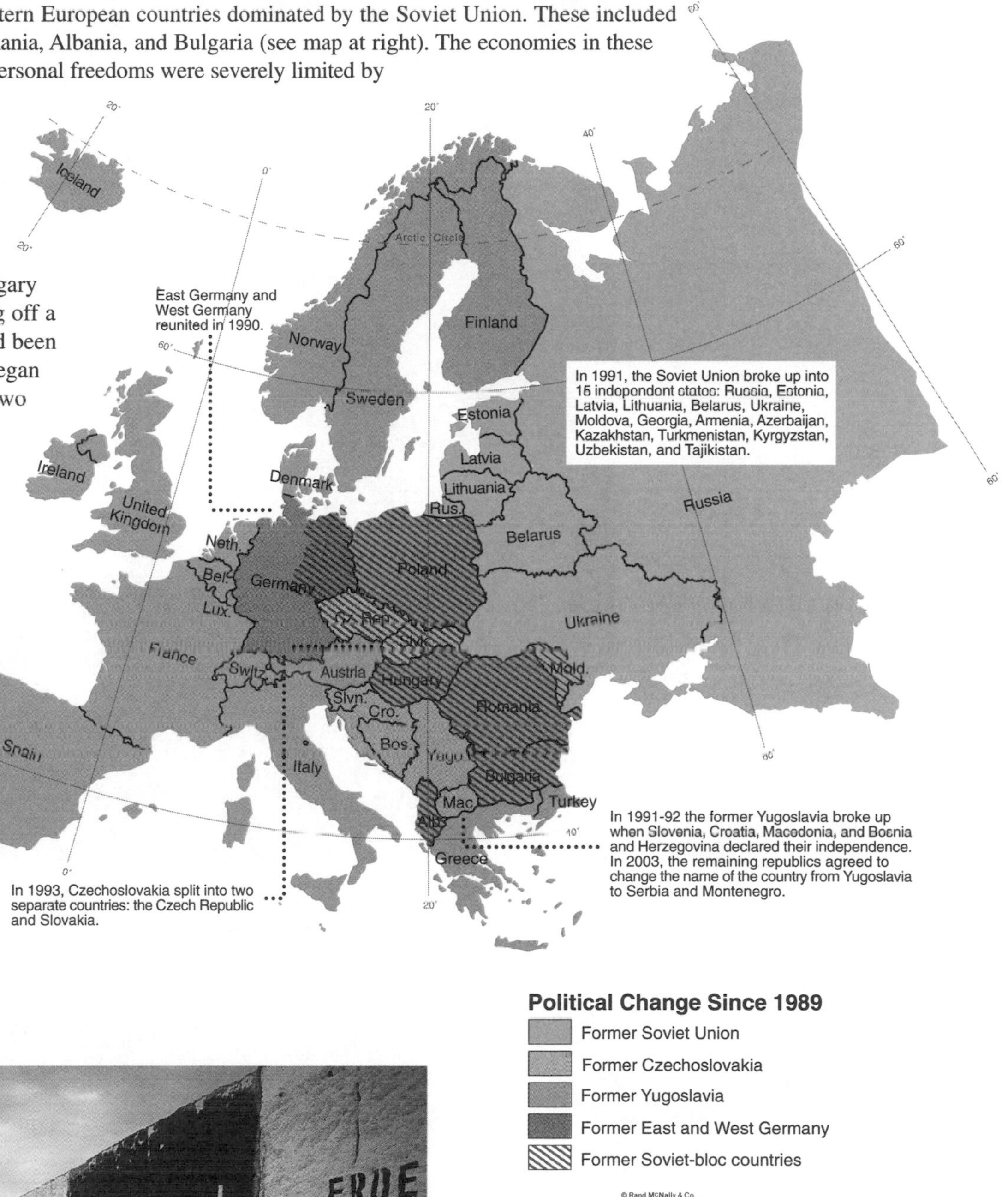
East Germany and West Germany reunited in 1990.
In 1991, the Soviet Union broke up into 15 independent states: Russia, Estonia, Latvia, Lithuania, Belarus, Ukraine, Moldova, Georgia, Armenia, Azerbaijan, Kazakhstan, Turkmenistan, Kyrgyzstan, Uzbekistan, and Tajikistan.
In 1991-92 the former Yugoslavia broke up when Slovenia, Croatia, Macedonia, and Bosnia and Herzegovina declared their independence. In 2003, the remaining republics agreed to change the name of the country from Yugoslavia to Serbia and Montenegro.
In 1993, Czechoslovakia split into two separate countries: the Czech Republic and Slovakia.
Iceland
Arctic Circle
Finland
Norway
Sweden
Estonia
Latvia
Lithuania
Rus.
Russia
Ireland
United Kingdom
Denmark
Neth.
Bel.
Lux.
Germany
Poland
Belarus
Ukraine
Cz. Rep.
Slvk.
Mold.
France
Switz.
Austria
Hungary
Romania
Slvn.
Cro.
Bos.
Yugo.
Bulgaria
Portugal
Spain
Italy
Mac.
Alb.
Turkey
Greece
0°
20°
40°
60°
Political Change Since 1989
Former Soviet Union
Former Czechoslovakia
Former Yugoslavia
Former East and West Germany
Former Soviet-bloc countries
© Rand McNally & Co.

ERDE
WERDE
ERDE

Berlin Wall memorial

Scale 1: 16 000 000; one inch to 250 miles. Conic Projection

Elevations and depressions are given in feet

0 50 100 200 300 400 500 Miles

0 100 200 400 600 800 Kilometers

RUSSIA
KAZAKHSTAN
UZBEKISTAN
TURKMENISTAN
TURKEY
IRAN (PERSIA)
SYRIA
IRAQ
UKRAINE
GEORGIA
AZERBAIJAN
ARMENIA
AFGHANISTAN
NORTH CYPRUS
CYPRUS
LEBANON
WHITE SEA
BLACK SEA
SEA OF AZOV
CASPIAN SEA
ARAL SEA
Surface -92 ft. Below Sea Level
CASPIAN DEPRESSION
MANYCH DEPRESSION
USTYURT PLATEAU
KYZYL-KUM (DESERT)
KARA-KUM (DESERT)
DASHT-E-KAVIR (DESERT)
KAVIR-E-LUT (DESERT)
TURKESTAN
MOYYNQUM
URAL MTS.
ELBURZ MTS.
ZAGROS MTS.
CAUCASUS
TRANSCAUCASIA
KURDISTAN
ASIA MINOR
KUZEY ANADOLU DAĞLARI
TOROS DAĞLARI
VALDAI HILLS
KOLGUYEV
P-OV KANIN
Nar'yan-Mar
Mezen'
Arkhangel'sk (Archangel)
Onega
Syktyvkar
Kotlas
Petrozavodsk
Vologda
Cherepovets
Rybinsk
Kostroma
Yaroslavl'
Kineshma
Ivanovo
Kovrov
NIZHNIY NOVGOROD
Dzerzhinsk
Vladimir
Tver'
Vyshniy Volochëk
Rzhev
MOSCOW (Moskva)
Noginsk
Kolomna
Serpukhov
Ryazan'
Kaluga
Tula
Novomoskovsk
Smolensk
Bryansk
Orël
Yelets
Lipetsk
Michurinsk
Tambov
Morshansk
Penza
Syzran'
Saransk
Ul'yanovsk
SAMARA
Chapayevsk
Kazan'
Cheboksary
Yoshkar-Ola
Izhevsk
Votkinsk
Sarapul
Naberezhnyye Chelny
Kirov
Krasnokamsk
Perm'
Berezniki
Solikamsk
Chusovoy
Lys'va
Serov
Krasnoural'sk
Nizhniy Tagil
YEKATERINBURG
Asbest
Kamensk-Ural'skiy
CHELYABINSK
Kyshtym
Zlatoust
Ufa
Beloretsk
Sterlitamak
Magnitogorsk
Orenburg
Orsk
Troitsk
Kurgan
Tyumen'
Tobol'sk
Ishim
Petropavlovsk
Omsk
Tara
Tatarsk
Barabinsk
Kuybyshev
NOVOSIBIRSK
Leninsk-Kuznetskiy
Novokuznetsk
Barnaul
Biysk
Slavgorod
Pavlodar
Semey
Kökshetau
Qostanay
Astana (Aqmola)
Atbasar
Temirtau
Qaraghandy
Balqash
Surgut
Berëzovo
Saratov
Engel's
Vol'sk
Balashov
Borisoglebsk
Voronezh
Kursk
Kamyshin
VOLGOGRAD
Astrakhan
Atyrau
Oral
Aqtöbe
Torghay
Yrghyz
Aral
Shalqar
Zhangaqazaly
Qyzylorda
Türkistan
Shymkent
Zhambyl
TASHKENT
Samarqand
Bukhara
Chimbay
Kungrad
Urgench
Turtkul'
Dashhowuz
Khiva
Charjew
Mary
Ashgabat
Gyzylarbat
Nebitdag
Turkmenbashy
Fort Shevchenko
Aqtau
Makhachkala
Derbent
BAKU (Bakı)
Gäncä
Groznyy
Vladikavkaz
Pyatigorsk
Stavropol'
Armavir
Maykop
Krasnodar
Novorossiysk
Sochi
Sukhumi
Kutaisi
Poti
TBILISI
Batumi
Gyumri
Kars
Yerevan
Chernihiv
Nizhyn
Sumy
KIEV (Kyïv)
KHARKIV
Poltava
Kremenchuk
DNIPROPETROVS'K
Dniprodzerzhyns'k
Zaporizhzhia
Kryvyi Rih
Nikopol'
Mykolaïv
Kherson
Odesa
Melitopol'
Berdyans'k
Mariupol'
DONETS'K
Makiïvka
Horlivka
Luhans'k
Shakhty
Novocherkassk
Rostov-na-Donu
Taganrog
Kerch
Simferopol'
Sevastopol'
Yalta
Constanța
Sinop
Samsun
Trabzon (Trebizond)
Erzurum
Zonguldak
ISTANBUL
Ankara (Angora)
Bursa
Eskişehir
Afyon
Konya
Kayseri
Sivas
Diyarbakır
Gaziantep
Adana
İçel
Antalya
İskenderun
Aleppo
Homs
Palmyre
Nicosia
Beirut
Al Mawşil
Nineveh (Ruins)
Karkūk
BAGHDAD
Babylon (Ruins)
Basra
Khorramshahr
Ābādān
Tabrīz
Rasht
Bābol
Gorgān
TEHRAN
Hamadān
Kāshān
Eşfahān
Shushtar
Yazd
Kermān
Shīrāz
Persepolis (Ruins)
Mashhad
Herāt
Zāhedān
Farāh
Maimana
Qolleh-ye Damāvand
Mt. Ararat 16854
Gora El'brus 18510
G. Kazbek 16512
G. Narodnaya 6217
G. Tel'pos-Iz 5305
Balqash költ
Bayqongyr
A-519697-26
COPYRIGHT BY RAND MCNALLY & COMPANY
MADE IN U.S.A.

Scale 1: 16 000 000; one inch to 250 miles. Conic Projection

Elevations and depressions are given in feet

0 50 100 200 300 400 500 Miles

0 100 200 400 600 800 Kilometers

RUSSIA
KAZAKHSTAN
UZBEKISTAN
TURKMENISTAN
TURKEY
IRAN
(PERSIA)
IRAQ
SYRIA
UKRAINE
GEORGIA
AFGHANISTAN
LEBANON
NORTH CYPRUS
CYPRUS
MOSCOW
(Moskva)
NIZHNIY NOVGOROD
SAMARA
YEKATERINBURG
CHELYABINSK
NOVOSIBIRSK
VOLGOGRAD
KIEV
(Kyiv)
KHARKIV
DNIPROPETROVS'K
DONETS'K
TBILISI
BAKU
(Bakı)
TEHRAN
BAGHDAD
TASHKENT
Astana
(Aqmola)
Ashgabat
Yerevan
Ankara
(Angora)
ISTANBUL
Nicosia
Beirut
Arkhangelsk
(Archangel)
Petrozavodsk
Cherepovets
Vologda
Kotlas
Syktyvkar
Kirov
Perm
Ufa
Kazan'
Izhevsk
Orenburg
Orsk
Saratov
Astrakhan
Atyrau
Makhachkala
Rostov-na-Donu
Krasnodar
Odesa
Sevastopol'
Simferopol'
Yalta
Kerch
Sochi
Batumi
Trabzon
Samsun
Erzurum
Tabriz
Rasht
Mashhad
Esfahan
Kerman
Yazd
Hamadan
Basra
Aleppo
Homs
Adana
Konya
Kayseri
Diyarbakir
Al Mawsil
Kirkuk
Omsk
Tyumen'
Tobol'sk
Petropavlovsk
Pavlodar
Semey
Barnaul
Balqash
Qaraghandy
Qyzylorda
Shymkent
Zhambyl
Samarkand
Bukhara
Urgench
Charjew
Mary
WHITE SEA
BLACK SEA
SEA OF AZOV
CASPIAN SEA
Surface—92 Ft. Below Sea Level
ARAL SEA
CASPIAN DEPRESSION
URAL MTS.
KARA-KUM (DESERT)
KYZYL-KUM (DESERT)
DASHT-E-KAVIR (DESERT)
KAVIR-E-LUT (DESERT)
ELBURZ MTS.
ZAGROS MTS.
CAUCASUS
TRANSCAUCASIA
ASIA MINOR
KURDISTAN
UST-URT PLATEAU
MANYCH DEPRESSION
VALDAI HILLS
MOYYNQUM
A-519697-76 -13-10-35-
COPYRIGHT BY
RAND McNALLY & COMPANY
MADE IN U.S.A.

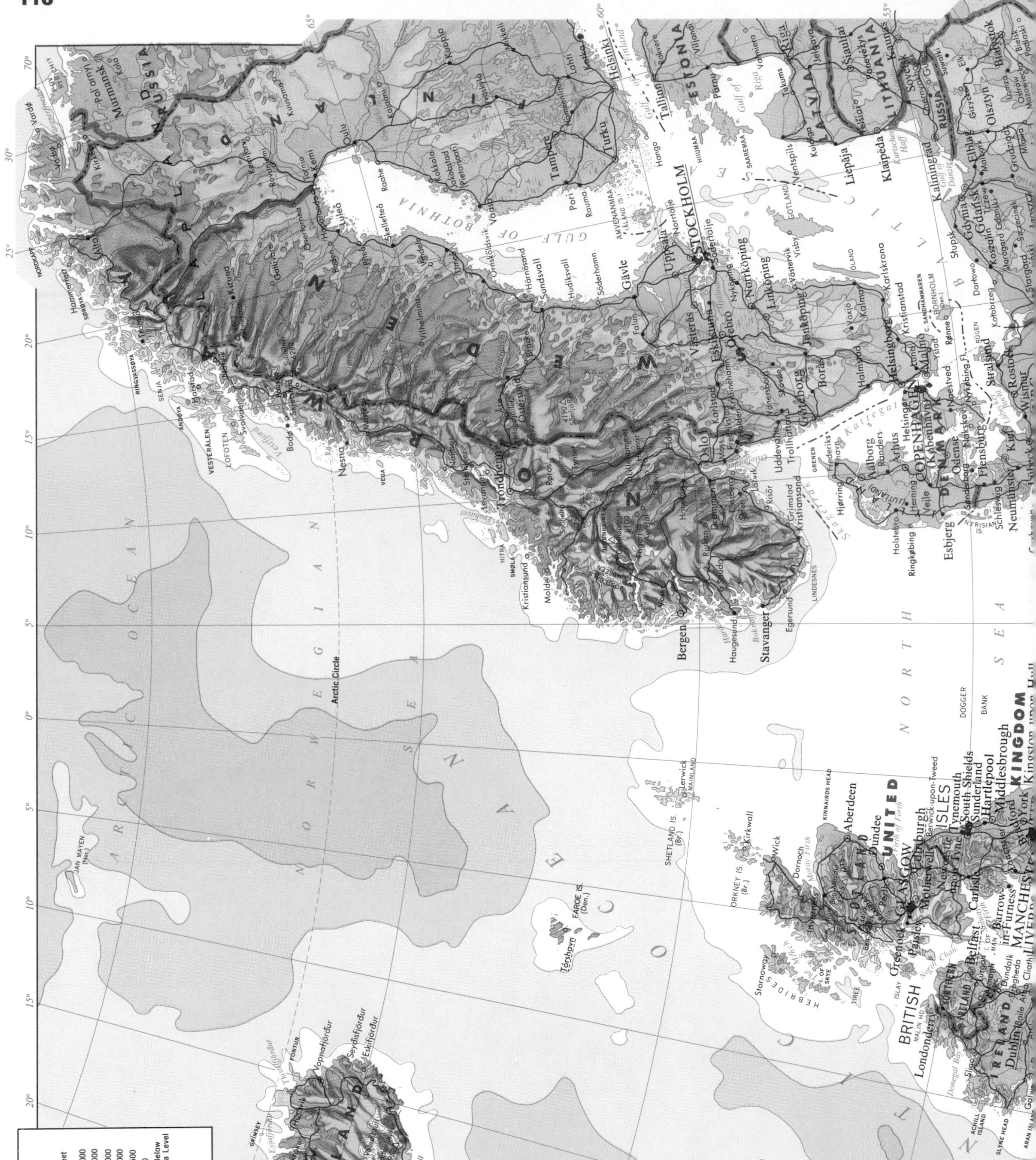

Scale 1: 10 000 000; one inch to 160 miles. Conic Projection

Elevations and depressions are given in feet

Longitude West of Greenwich
Longitude East of Greenwich
0 50 100 150 200 250 300 Miles
0 100 200 300 400 500 Kilometers
A-559400-76 -13-10-28
COPYRIGHT BY RAND McNALLY & COMPANY
MADE IN U.S.A.
LONDON
PARIS
MADRID
ROME
BERLIN
AMSTERDAM
BRUSSELS
LISBON
BARCELONA
NAPLES
MUNICH
PRAGUE
BUDAPEST
WARSAW
FRANCE
SPAIN
ITALY
GERMANY
TUNISIA
MOROCCO
CORSICA (Fr.)
SARDINIA (It.)
TYRRHENIAN SEA
IONIAN SEA
LIGURIAN SEA
BAY OF BISCAY
ENGLISH CHANNEL
Algiers
Tunis
Marseille
Lyon
Bordeaux
Toulouse
Milan
Venice
Palermo
Valencia
Sevilla
Porto

Cities and Towns

0 to 50,000 ○ — 50,000 to 500,000 ⊙ — 500,000 to 1,000,000 ◎ — 1,000,000 and over

Scale 1:10 000 000; one inch to 160 miles. Conic Projection

Elevations and depressions are given in feet.

Scale 1:10 000 000; one inch to 160 miles. Bonne's Projection
Elevations and depressions are given in feet

UKRAINE
Vinnytsia
Smila
Kremenchuk
Pavlohrad
DONETS'K
Novocherkassk
Rostov-na-Donu
Dniprodzerzhyns'k
DNIPROPETROVS'K
Zaporizhzhia
Taganrog
Mariupol'
Kirovohrad
Kryvyi Rih
Nikopol'
Melitopol'
Berdians'k
Yeysk
RUSSIA
Tikhoretsk
Kropotkin
Stavropol'
Armavir
Labinsk
Maykop
Krasnodar
Timashevskaya
Temryuk
Primorsko-Akhtarskaya
SEA OF AZOV
Kerch
Anapa
Novorossiysk
Feodosiia
Tuapse
Sochi
Sukhumi
GEORGIA
Mykolaïv
Kherson
Odesa
Tiraspol
Chişinău
MOLDOVA
Bălţi
Chernivtsi
Ternopil'
L'viv
Zhmerynka
Khmel'nyts'kyi
Kamianets-Podil's'kyi
Ivano-Frankivs'k
Uzhhorod
Mukacheve
Uman'
Voznesens'k
Ievpatoriia
Simferopol'
Sevastopol'
Yalta
KRYMS'KYI PIVOSTRIV (CRIMEAN PEN.)
Karkinits'ka zatoka
BLACK SEA
KATOWICE
Zabrze
Kraków
Tarnów
Rzeszów
POLAND
BESKID MTS.
CARPATHIAN MTS.
Ostrava
Olomouc
Brno
Znojmo
Hradec Králové
Žilina
Košice
Prešov
SLOVAKIA
VIENNA
Bratislava
Nové Zámky
Miskolc
Nyíregyháza
Debrecen
Győr
Pápa
BUDAPEST
Székesfehérvár
Szombathely
Kecskemét
HUNGARY
Nagykanizsa
Szekszárd
Pécs
Szeged
Maribor
Varaždin
Zagreb
CROATIA
Osijek
Sisak
Našice
Subotica
Sombor
Novi Sad
Senta
Arad
Oradea
Cluj-Napoca
Satu Mare
Baia Mare
Botoşani
Iaşi
Bacău
Piatra-Neamţ
Târgu Mureş
Sibiu
Braşov
Bârlad
Galaţi
Brăila
Buzău
Ploieşti
Târgovişte
Piteşti
BUCHAREST
Constanţa
Călăraşi
Timişoara
ROMANIA
TRANSYLVANIAN ALPS
Tulcea
Izmail
Bolgrad
Vylkova
Sulina
Bilhorod-Dnistrovs'kyy
Chornomors'ke
Craiova
Drobeta-Turnu Severin
Vršac
Pančevo
Belgrade (Beograd)
Zemun
Šabac
Loznica
Tuzla
Banja Luka
BOSNIA AND HERZEGOVINA
Sarajevo
Mostar
Split
Dubrovnik
Kragujevac
Kraljevo
SERBIA AND MONTENEGRO
Niš
Novi Pazar
Priština
Peć
Podgorica
Cetinje
Ulcinj
Shkodër
Tiranë
Durrës
Elbasan
ALBANIA
Korçë
Vlorë (Vlonë)
Gjirokastër
Skopje
MACEDONIA
Prilep
Bitola
Vidin
Lom
Ruse
Razgrad
Dobrich
Varna (Stalin)
Shumen
Pleven
Veliko Tŭrnovo
Sofia (Sofiya)
STARA PLANINA (BALKAN MTS.)
BULGARIA
Sliven
Yambol
Burgas
Stara Zagora
Plovdiv
Pazardzhik
Kyustendil
Pernik
RHODOPE MTS.
Edirne
Kırklareli
Tekirdağ
İSTANBUL
İzmit
Adapazarı
Zonguldak
Ereğli
Bolu
Bartın
Kastamonu
Sinop
Inebolu
Samsun
Ordu
Giresun
Trabzon
Rize
Çorum
Amasya
Tokat
Sivas
Erzincan
Yozgat
Çankırı
Ankara (Angora)
Kırşehir
Kayseri
Malatya
Elazığ
Eskişehir
Bursa
Bilecik
Gelibolu
Çanakkale
Balıkesir
Kütahya
Afyon
Uşak
Manisa
İzmir
Aydın
Denizli
Burdur
Isparta
Konya
Aksaray
Niğde
Ereğli
Karaman
Adana
Tarsus
İçel
İskenderun
Osmaniye
Kahramanmaraş
Gaziantep
Şanlıurfa
Kilis
TURKEY
ASIA MINOR
TOROS DAĞLARI
Antalya
Alanya
Silifke
Fethiye
Muğla
Antalya Körfezi
Marmara Denizi
Kavála
Thessaloníki
Sérres
Komotiní
Alexandroúpoli
Kozáni
Kastoriá
Flórina
Édessa
Kérkyra
Ioánnina
Tríkala
Lárisa
Vólos
Lamía
Agrínio
Khalkída
Thíva (Thebes)
ATHENS (Athínai)
Peiraiás
Pátra
Pýrgos
Kyparissía
Kalamáta
Spárti
Trípoli
Kórinthos
GREECE
AEGEAN SEA
IONIAN ISLANDS
THÁSOS
SAMOTHRÁKI
LIMNOS
AGIOS EFSTRATIOS
LESVOS
Mytilíni
SKYROS
EVVOIA
CHIOS
SÁMOS
ÁNDROS
TÍNOS
SÝROS
PÁROS
NÁXOS
AMORGÓS
MÍLOS
ASTYPÁLAIA
Ródos
RÓDOS
KÁRPATHOS
KÁSOS
KÝTHIRA
ANTIKYTHIRA
ÁKRA TAÍNARO
ÁKRA MALEAS
Chaniá
Iráklein
CRETE
GÁVDOS
KEFALLINÍA
ZÁKYNTHOS
LEFKADA
IONIAN SEA
Monte Sant'Angelo
Barletta
Molfetta
Bari
Altamura
Brindisi
Lecce
Taranto
Potenza
Golfo di Taranto
Rossano
Nicastro
Catanzaro
Reggio di Calabria
C. S. MARIA DI LEUCA
SAZANIT
Str. of Otranto
TOCI PALAGRUŽA (Cro.)
VIS
LASTOVO
MLJET
The Turkish Republic of Northern Cyprus unilaterally declared its independence on Nov. 15, 1983.
NORTH CYPRUS
CYPRUS
Nicosia
Famagusta
Larnaka
Limassol
SYRIA
Aleppo
Antakya
Al Lādhiqīyah (Latakia)
Hamāh
Homs
Tarţūs
Ţarābulus (Tripoli)
LEBANON
Beirut
Zahlah
Şaydā (Sidon)
Şūr (Tyre)
Damascus (Dimashq)
As Suwaydā'
Acre
Haifa
Nazareth
Nābulus
Amman
ISRAEL
Tel Aviv-Yafo
Jerusalem
Bethlehem
Hebron
Gaza
JORDAN
Areas occupied by Israel since 1967.
Ma'ān
Al 'Aqabah
SAUDI ARABIA
SINAI PEN.
Jabal Kātrīnā 8668
Gulf of Suez
G. of Aqaba
RED SEA
Dumyāt
Port Said (Būr Sa'īd)
Rashīd
ALEXANDRIA (Al Iskandarīyah)
Al Maḩallah al Kubrá
Al Manşūrah
Al Ismā'īlīyah
Ţanţā
Damanhūr
Az Zaqāzīq
Shibīn al Kawm
CAIRO (Al Qāhirah)
Suez (As Suways)
Al Jīzah
Ḩulwān
Al Wāsiţah
Banī Suwayf
Al Fayyūm
Al Fashn
Banī Mazār
Al Minyā
Mallawī
EGYPT
MUNKHAFAD AL QAŢŢĀRAH 436
LIBYAN PLATEAU
LIBYAN DESERT
Marsá Maţrūḩ
Al 'Alamayn
As Sallūm
Sīdī Barrānī
Tubruq (Tobruk)
Darnah
Shaḩḩāt
Tulmaythah
Tūkrah
Sulūntah
AL JABAL AL AKHDAR
Banghāzī
Sulūq
BARQAH (CYRENAICA)
Khalīj Surt
Surt
An Nawfalīyah
Ajdābiyah
Qaşr al Burayqah
Al 'Uqaylah
Al Jaghbūb
Awjilah
Jālū (Oasis)
Marādah
LIBYA
MEDITERRANEAN SEA
0 50 100 150 200 250 300 Miles
0 100 200 300 400 500 Kilometers

Africa

The Drakensberg Mountains in southern South Africa.

Africa, the second-largest continent, comprises about one-fifth of the world's land area. From the Equator, Africa extends roughly the same distance to the north as it does to the south.

A high plateau covers much of the continent. The edges of the plateau are marked by steep slopes, called escarpments, where the land angles sharply downward onto narrow coastal plains or into the sea. Many of the continent's great rivers plunge over these escarpments in falls or rapids, and therefore cannot be used as transportation routes from the coast into the continent's interior.

Among Africa's most significant mountain systems are the Atlas range in the far north and the Drakensberg range in the far south. A long string of mountain ranges and highlands running north-south through eastern Africa marks the course of the Great Rift Valley.

Africa at a glance

Land area: 11,700,000 square miles (30,300,000 sq km)

Estimated population: 832,590,000

Population density: 71/ square mile (27/sq km)

Mean elevation: 1,900 feet (580 m)

Highest point: Kilimanjaro, Tanzania, 19,340 feet (5,895 m)

Lowest point: Lac Assal, Djibouti, 515 feet (157 m) below sea level

Longest river: Nile, 4,145 mi (6,671 km)

Number of countries (incl. dependencies): 61

Largest independent country: Sudan, 967,500 square miles (2,505,813 sq km)

Smallest independent country: Seychelles, 176 square miles (455 sq km)

Most populous independent country: Nigeria, 128,285,000

Least populous independent country: Seychelles, 80,000

Largest city: Cairo, pop. 6,801,000

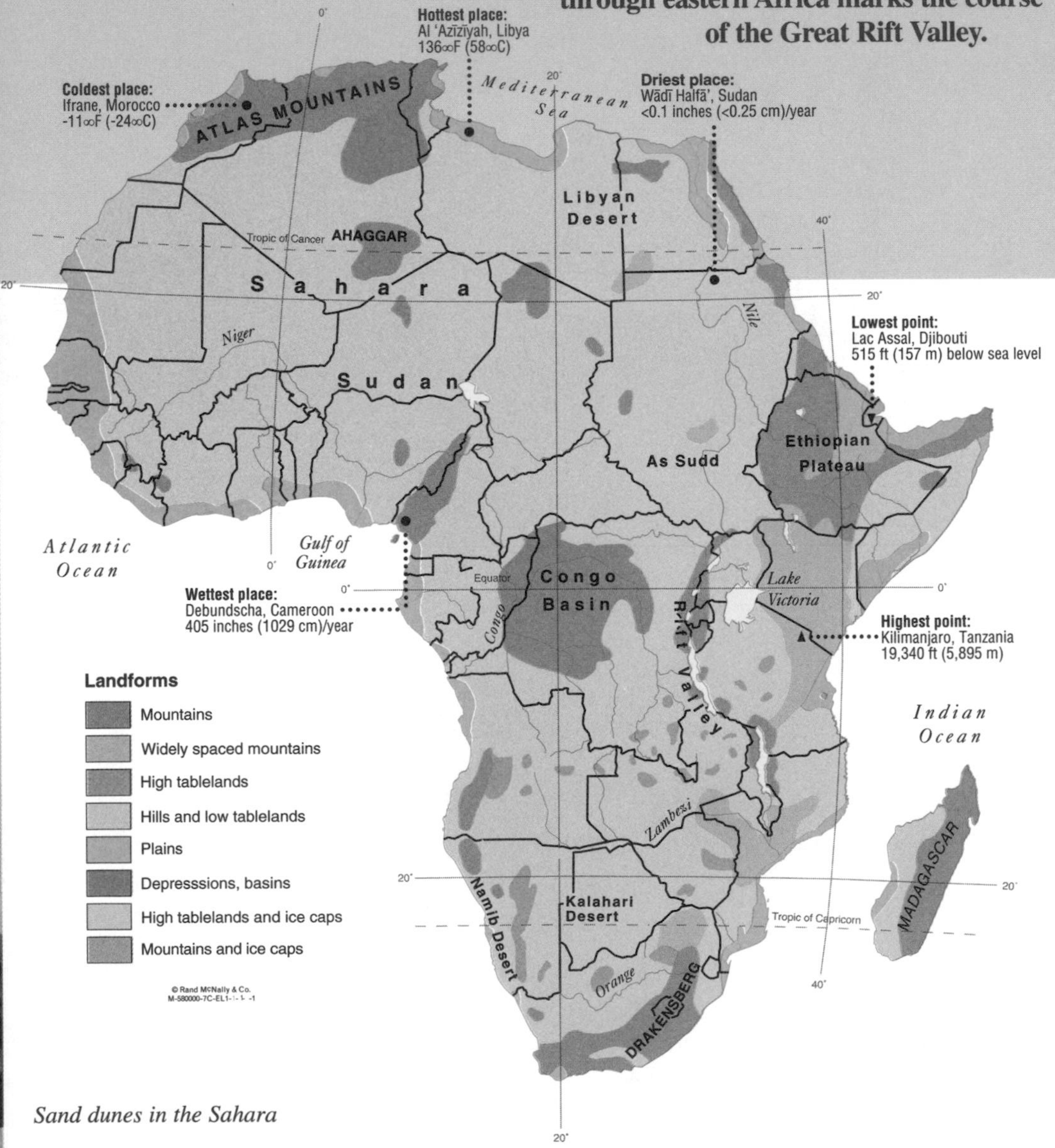

Sand dunes in the Sahara

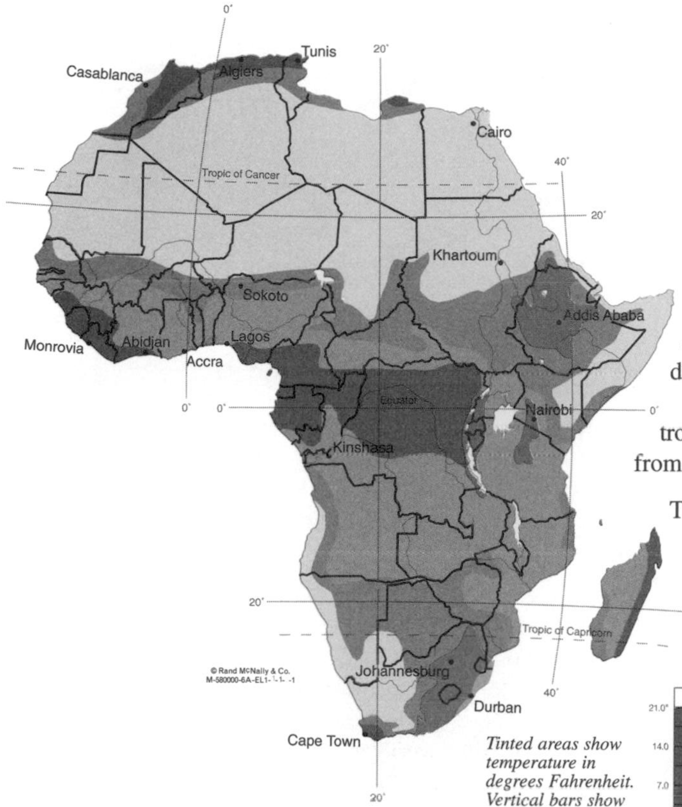

Climate

Africa's most prominent climatic region is the vast Sahara desert which spreads over much of the northern half of the continent. The Sahara experiences scorching daytime temperatures, minimal rainfall, and hot, dry, dust-laden winds that blow nearly continuously. South of the Sahara, the climate becomes increasingly humid, moving through zones of semiarid steppe and tropical savanna to the tropical rain forest that stretches across equatorial Africa from the Atlantic Ocean to the Rift Valley.

The climate patterns of northern Africa are repeated in reverse south of the Equator. The rain forest gives way to zones of decreasing humidity, and desert regions cover western South Africa and Namibia. Africa's mildest, most temperate climates are found along its Mediterranean coast, at its southwestern tip, and in eastern South Africa.

Tinted areas show temperature in degrees Fahrenheit. Vertical bars show precipitation in inches.

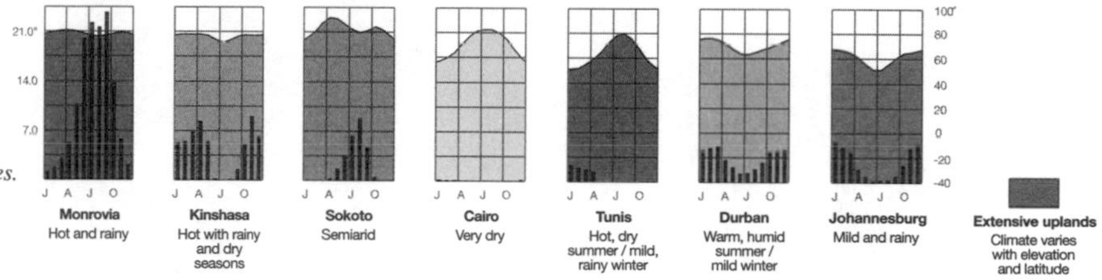

Population

About one-seventh of the world's people live in Africa. It is the second most populous continent. The population is almost evenly divided between the sub-Saharan countries and those bordering the Mediterranean. Large tracts of the Sahara are uninhabited. Despite recurring famines, disease, and warfare, the population is rapidly increasing.

The largest concentrations of people are generally found in regions in which one or more of the following conditions exist: moderate temperatures, ample water supply, and arable land. These regions include Egypt's fertile Nile Valley, the northern coast of the Gulf of Guinea, the highlands of East Africa, and the coastal regions of Morocco, Algeria, and Tunisia, north of the Atlas Mountains.

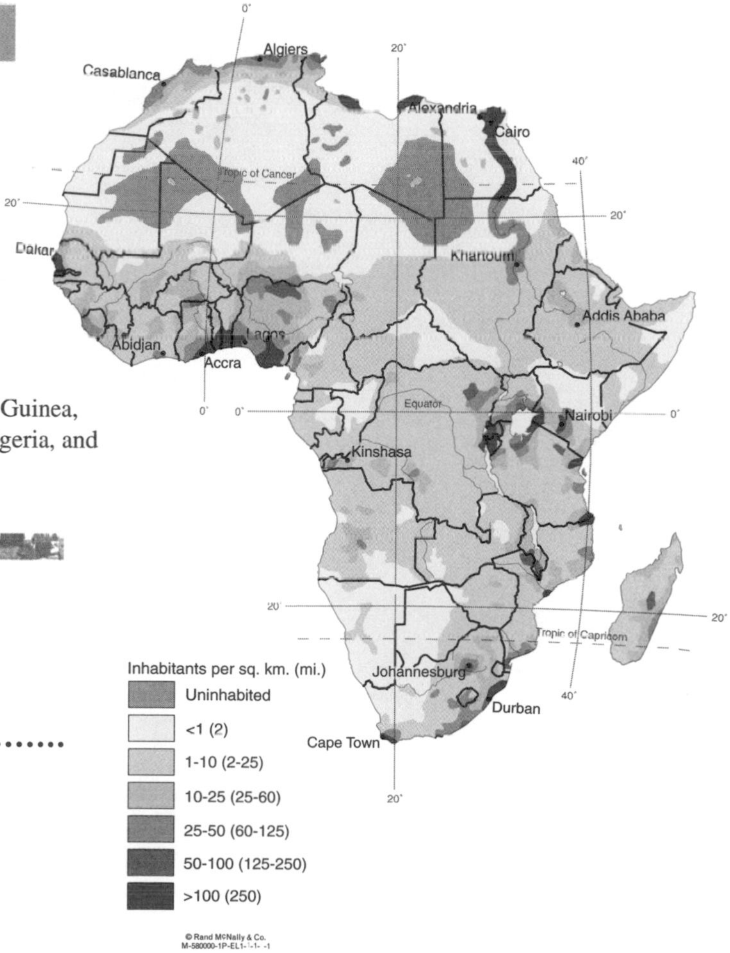

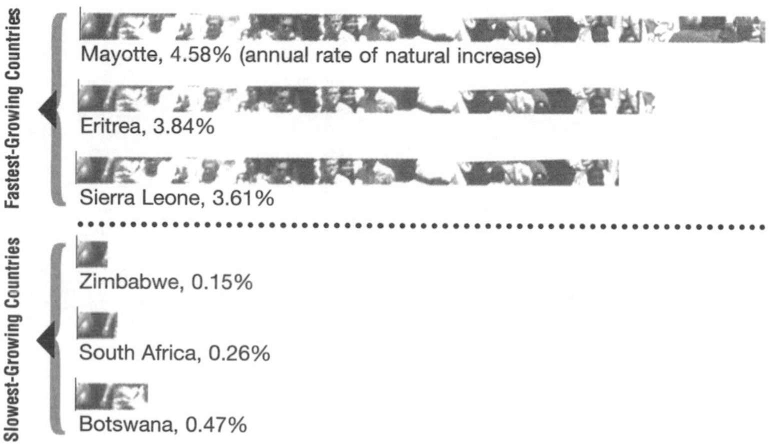

Environments and Land Use

Shepherd with goats in the Sahel (Sudan)

Deserts account for one-third of Africa's land area, and they claim new land every year. Drought, over-farming, and over-grazing can quickly turn marginal land, such as that of the Sahel region (also known as the Sudan), into barren wasteland. The huge Sahara desert has itself only existed a short time, in geological terms: cave paintings and other archeological evidence indicate that green pastureland covered the area just a few thousand years ago.

Most Africans are subsistence farmers, growing sorghum, corn, millet, sweet potatoes, and other starchy foods. Commercial farms, most of which date from the colonial period, can be found throughout central and southern Africa, producing cash crops such as coffee, bananas, tobacco and cacao. One-quarter of the continent's land is suitable for grazing, but disease and drought have made raising animals difficult. Although three out of four Africans work in agriculture, Africa is the only continent that is not self-sufficient for food.

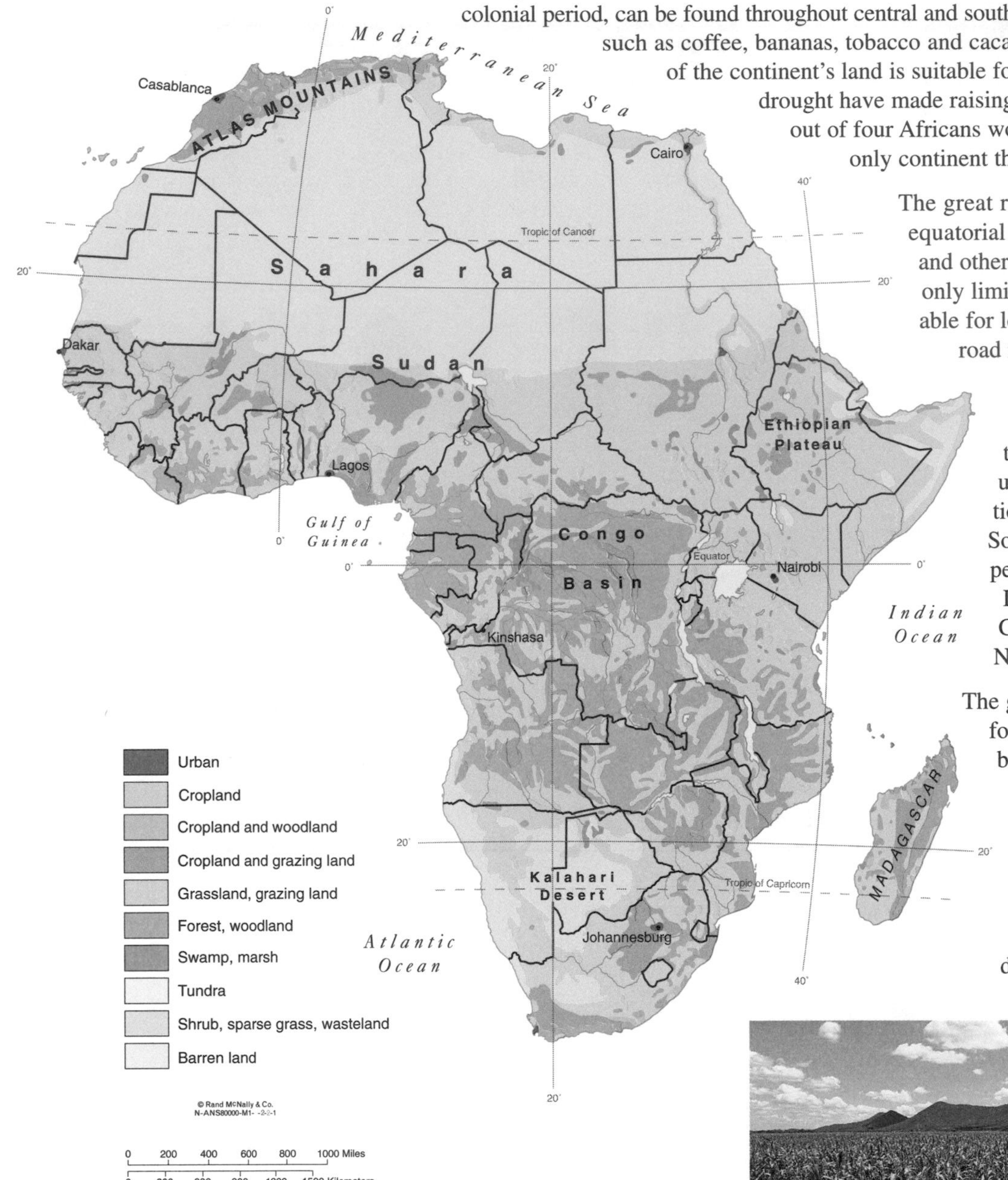

The great rain forests that cover much of equatorial Africa produce mahogany, ebony, and other valuable hardwoods. However, only limited areas of the forests are suitable for logging, and the lack of developed road networks makes it difficult and costly to transport the wood.

Vast mineral reserves are spread throughout the continent. Most are unexploited, but notable exceptions include the diamond mines of South Africa and Namibia, the copper mines of Zambia and Democratic Republic of the Congo, and the oil fields of Nigeria, Libya, and Algeria.

The great concentrations of wildlife for which Africa is famous can still be found in places such as Tanzania's Serengeti Plain and Botswana's Kalahari Desert. In many other parts of the continent, however, wildlife is quickly disappearing as humans encroach on habitat and poachers decimate entire species.

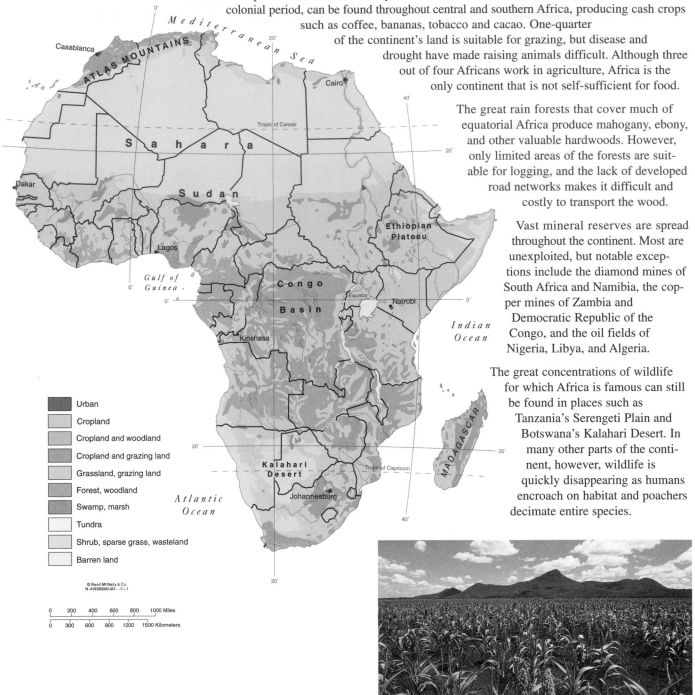

Field of sorghum in Zimbabwe

Africa: from Colonial Rule to Independence

The origins of Europe's colonization of Africa can be traced back to the 1500s, when a lucrative slave trade developed to supply European settlers in the New World with laborers. Africa became the primary source for slaves: between the mid-1500s and the mid-1800s, 11 million Africans were captured and sold into slavery.

When the slave trade was banned across Europe in the early 1800s, commercial trade with Africa continued. In the second half of the century, competition for Africa's minerals and other raw materials intensified, and between 1880 and 1914, France, Britain, Italy, Portugal, Belgium, Spain, and Germany annexed large areas of Africa. Colonial rule was often characterized by racial prejudice and segregation.

In the late 19th and early 20th centuries, Egypt, Ethiopia, and South Africa began to break free from colonial influence. For most or Africa, however, colonial rule persisted through the mid-1900s, although it faced growing bitterness and nationalist sentiment. As the colonial powers struggled through two world wars, and as their international dominance declined, it became increasingly difficult for them to maintain their empires.

In 1951, Libya gained its independence, following a UN resolution that ended British and French control. Sudan peacefully won independence from Britain and Egypt in 1956. A year later, Britain granted independence to the Gold Coast, which became the new country of Ghana. Guinea separated from France in 1958, followed by all of the other French colonies in 1960. Anti-colonial movements gathered strength across Africa, and by the end of the 1970s, a total of 43 countries had become independent.

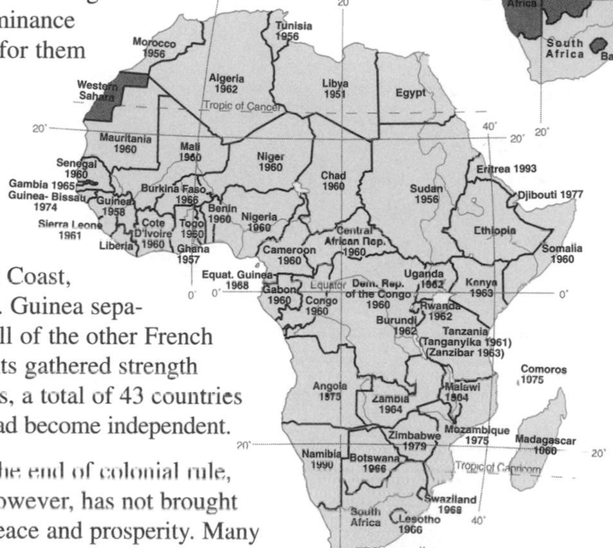

People of the Samburu tribe

The end of colonial rule, however, has not brought peace and prosperity. Many of the newly freed countries were ill-prepared for independence. Their economics were oriented to fit the needs of the now-departed colonists, few transportation networks existed, and dictators and rival despots fought for power in civil wars.

Further, most Africans identify themselves primarily with the tribe to which they belong. The political delineations established by the European powers have little meaning and often conflict with traditional tribal boundaries. In some cases, enemy tribes found themselves pushed together in a single country; in others, single tribes were divided among several countries. These conditions have already brought much warfare and hardship. Still, Africa is a land of promise and opportunity. The rich diversity of its people and abundance of its resources should inevitably enable the continent to realize its potential.

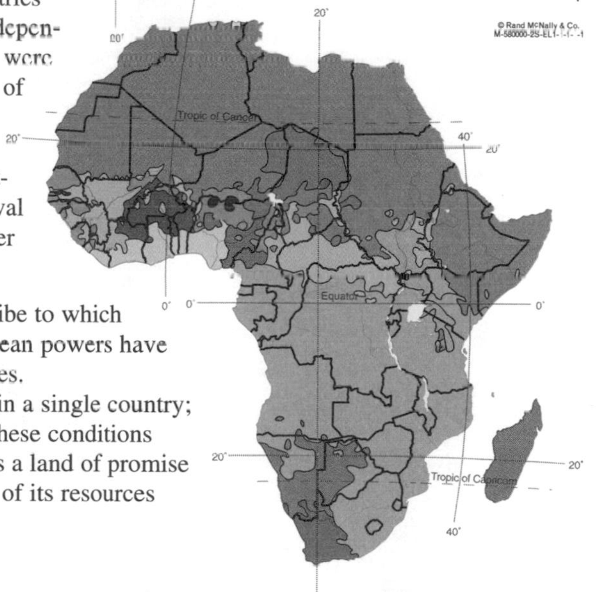

Ethno-linguistic Groups

- Semitic-Hamitic
- Mande
- Guinean
- Hausa
- Bantu
- Central Bantoid
- Eastern Bantoid
- Western Bantoid
- Indo-European
- Kanuri
- Songhai
- Khoisan
- Nilotic
- Malay-Polynesian
- Kanuri, Semitic-Hamitic
- Hausa, Western Bantoid
- Central/Eastern Sudanese, Bantu
- Indo-European, Semitic-Hamitic
- Central/Eastern Sudanese, Semitic-Hamitic
- Central/Eastern Sudanese

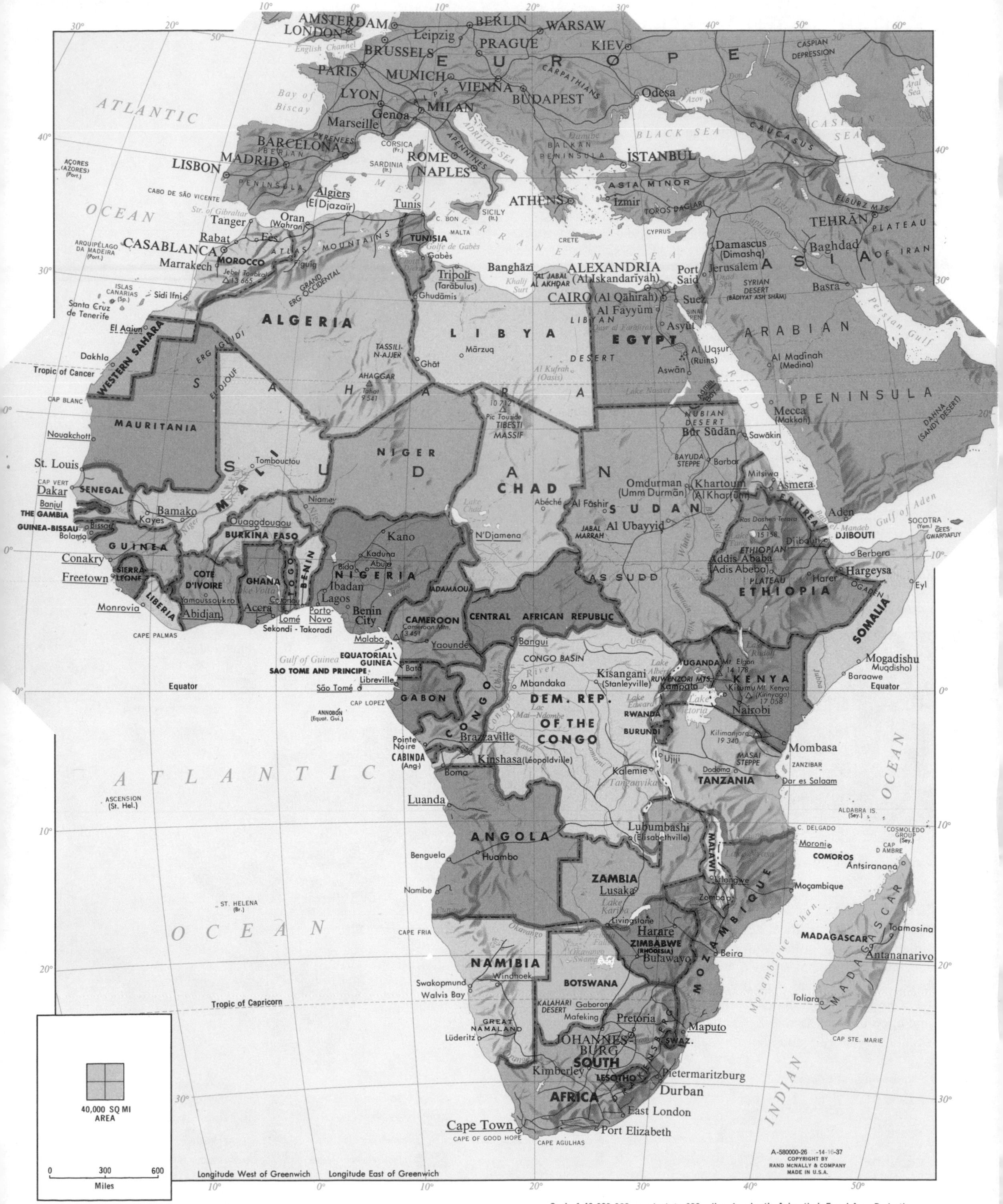

0 200 400 600 800 1000 Miles
0 400 800 1200 1600 Kilometers

Scale 1:40 000 000; one inch to 630 miles. Lambert's Azimuthal, Equal Area Projection

Elevations and depressions are given in feet.

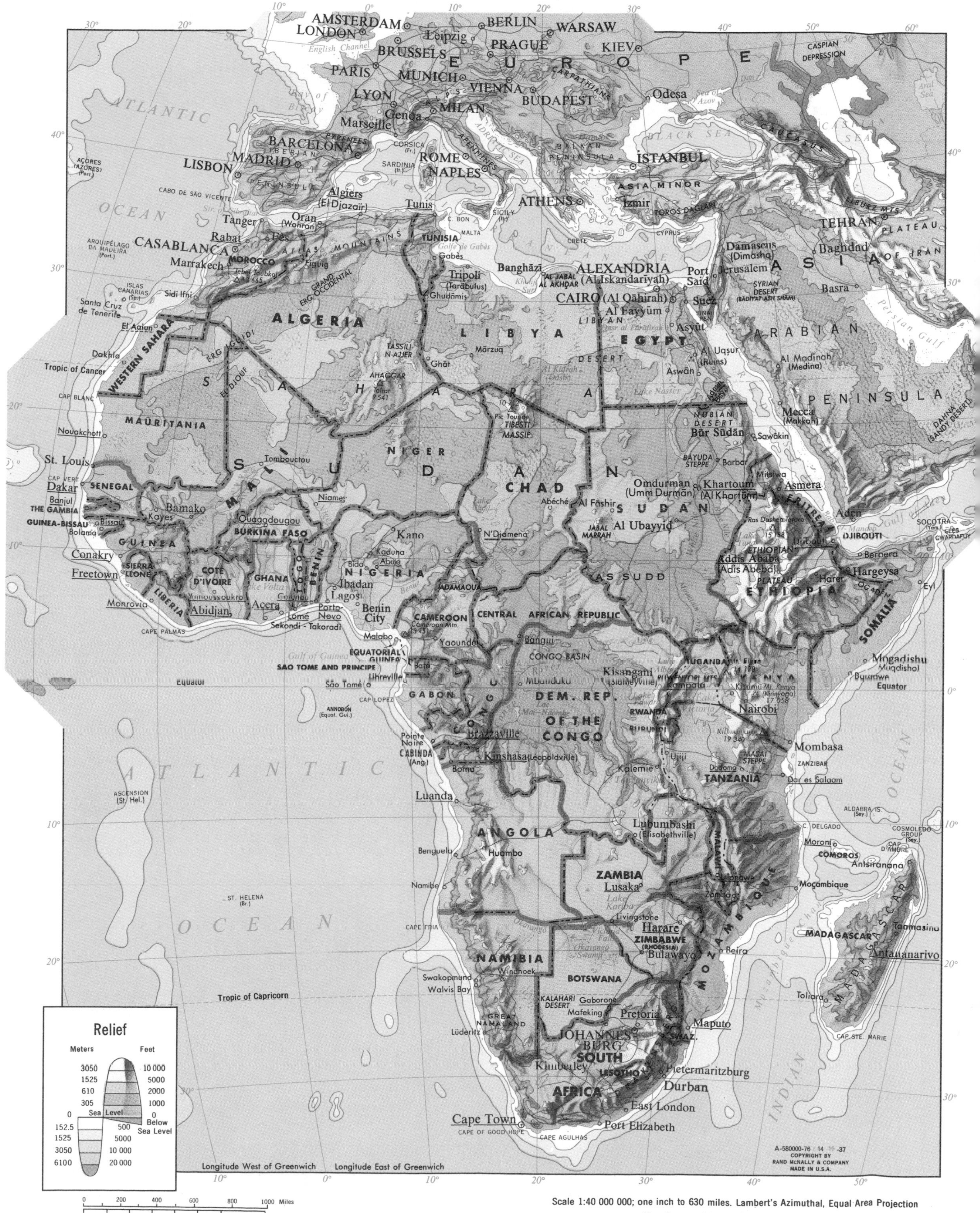

0 200 400 600 800 1000 Miles
0 400 800 1200 1600 Kilometers

Scale 1:40 000 000; one inch to 630 miles. Lambert's Azimuthal, Equal Area Projection
Elevations and depressions are given in feet.

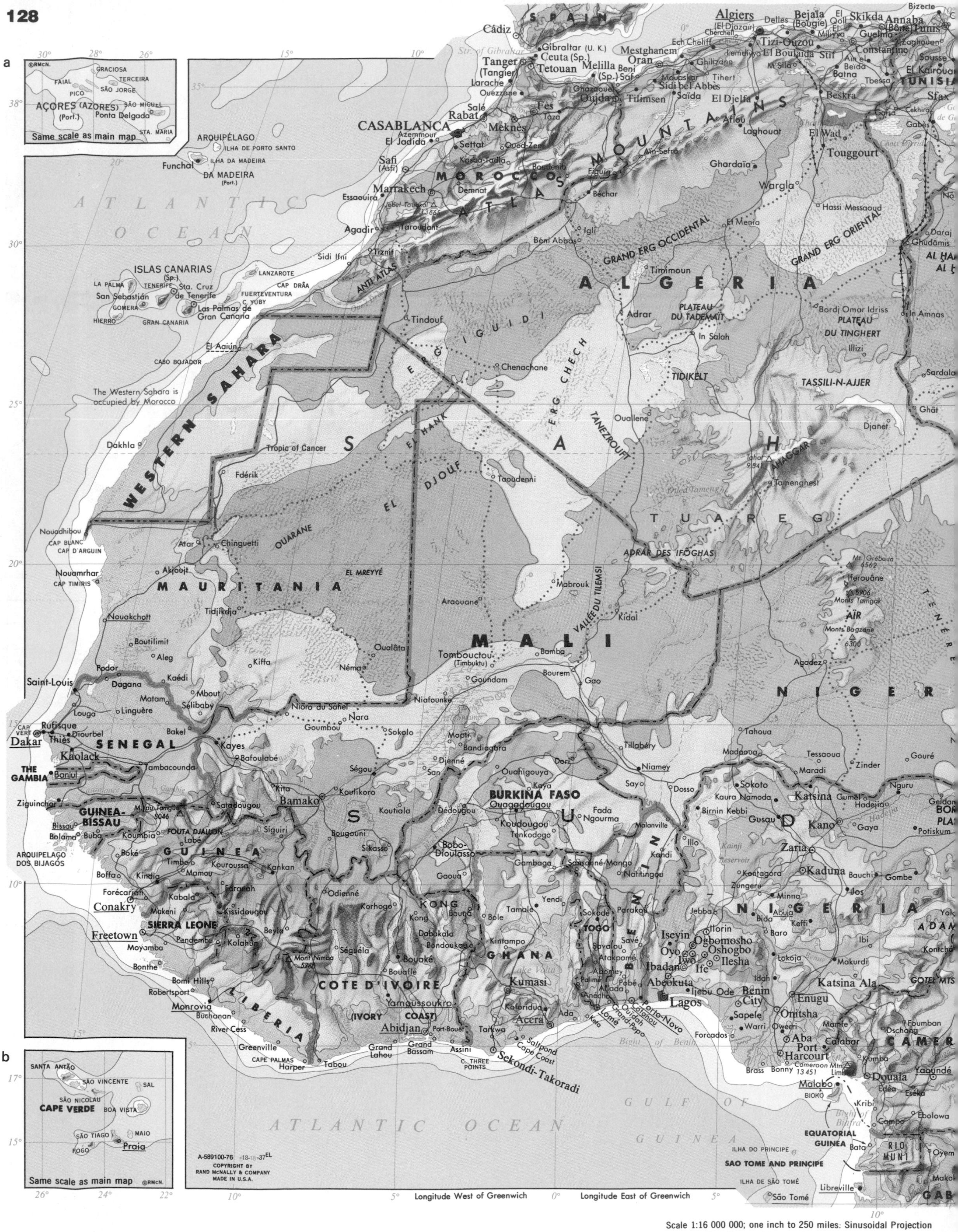

Scale 1:16 000 000; one inch to 250 miles. Sinusoidal Projection

Elevations and depressions are given in feet

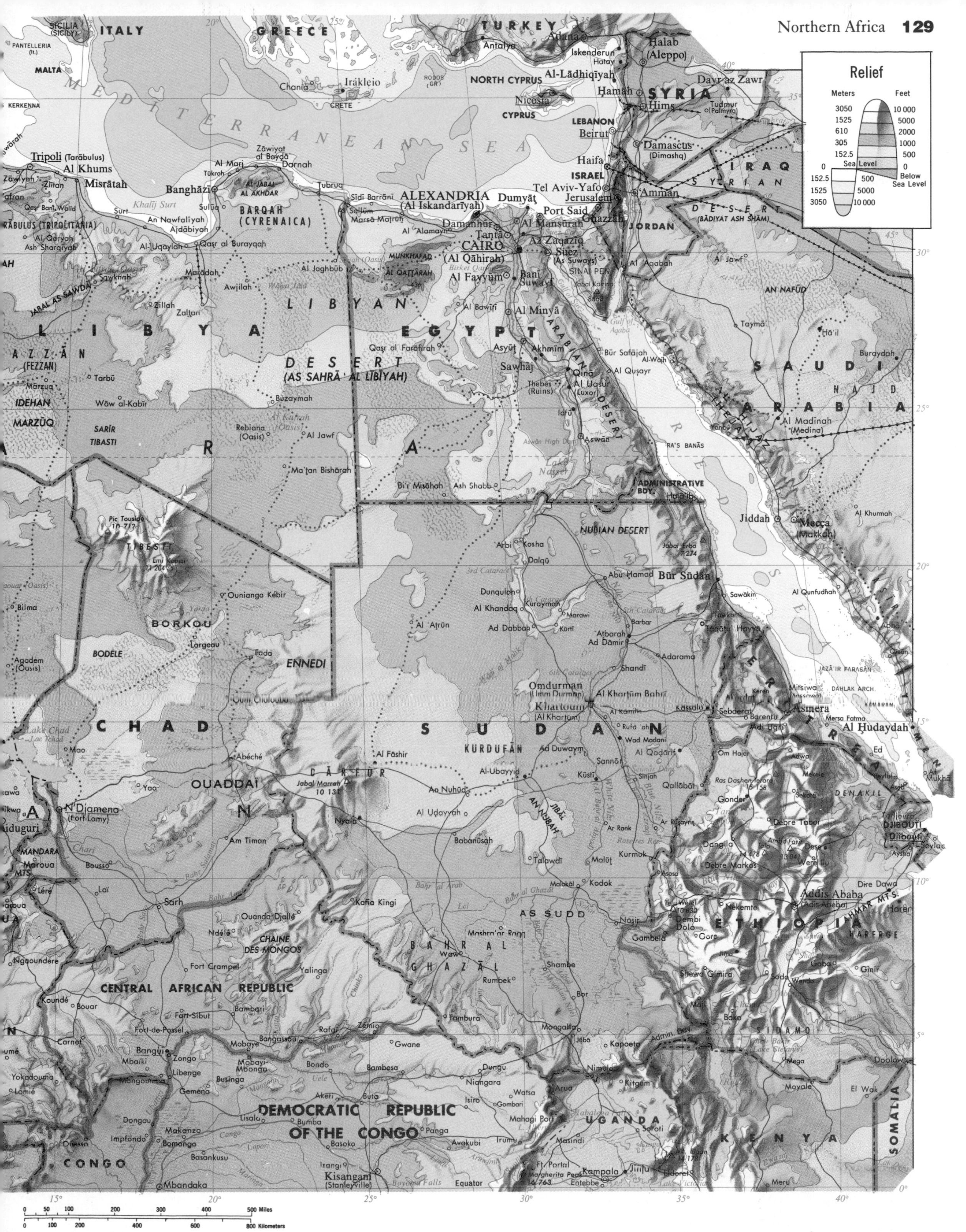
Relief
Meters
Feet
3050
1525
610
305
152.5
0
Sea Level
152.5
1525
3050
10 000
5000
2000
1000
500
0
Below Sea Level
500
5000
10 000
ITALY
GREECE
TURKEY
SICILIA (SICILY)
PANTELLERIA (It.)
MALTA
KERKENNA
MEDITERRANEAN SEA
Iráklein
Chania
CRETE
RODOS (GR.)
NORTH CYPRUS
Nicosia
CYPRUS
Antalya
Adana
Iskenderun
Hatay
Ḥalab (Aleppo)
Al-Lādhiqīyah
Ḥamāh
SYRIA
Ḥimṣ
Tudmur (Palmyra)
Dayr az Zawr
LEBANON
Beirut
Damascus (Dimashq)
Haifa
ISRAEL
Tel Aviv-Yafo
Jerusalem
Amman
JORDAN
IRAQ
SYRIAN DESERT (BĀDIYAT ASH SHĀM)
Ghazzah
Port Said
Dumyāṭ
ALEXANDRIA (Al Iskandarīyah)
Damanhūr
Al Manṣūrah
Ṭanṭā
Az Zaqāzīq
CAIRO (Al Qāhirah)
Suez (As Suways)
SINAI PEN.
Al 'Aqabah
Al Jawf
AN NAFŪD
Tripoli (Ṭarābulus)
Al Khums
Misrātah
Zāwiyah
Zlītan
ṬARĀBULUS (TRIPOLITANIA)
Al Qaryah Ash Sharqīyah
Surt
Khalīj Surt
Banghāzī
Al Marj
Ṭūkrah
Zāwiyat al Bayḍā
Darnah
AL JABAL AL AKHḌAR
BARQAH (CYRENAICA)
Sulūq
An Nawfalīyah
Ajdābiyah
Al-'Uqaylah
Qaṣr al Burayqah
Ṭubruq
Sīdī Barrānī
As Sallūm
Marsā Maṭrūḥ
Al 'Alamayn
MUNKHAFAḌ AL QAṬṬĀRAH
Al Jaghbūb
Al Fayyūm
Banī Suwayf
Birket Qarun
Marādah
Awjilah
Sawknah
JABAL AS SAWDĀ'
Zillah
Zaltan
LIBYA
LIBYAN DESERT (AS SAHRĀ' AL LĪBĪYAH)
EGYPT
Al Bawīṭī
Al Minyā
Asyūṭ
Akhmīm
Sawhāj
Qinā
Al Uqṣur (Luxor)
Thebes (Ruins)
Idfū
Aswān
Aswān High Dam
Lake Nasser
ARABIAN DESERT
Qaṣr al Farāfirah
Gulf of Suez
Jabal Katrīnā 8668
Gulf of Aqaba
Būr Safājah
Al Quṣayr
Al-Wajh
Taymā'
Ḥā'il
Buraydah
SAUDI ARABIA
NAJD
AL ḤIJĀZ
Yanbu'
Al Madīnah (Medina)
RA'S BANĀS
RED SEA
FAZZĀN (FEZZAN)
Tarbū
Murzuq
IDEHAN MARZŪQ
Wāw al-Kabīr
SARĪR TIBASTĪ
Buzaymah
Al Kufrah (Oasis)
Rebiana (Oasis)
Al Jawf
Ma'ṭan Bishārah
Bi'r Misāḥah
Ash Shabb
ADMINISTRATIVE BDY.
Halā'ib
NUBIAN DESERT
Jabal Erba 7274
Arbi
Kosha
Dalqū
3rd Cataract
Abū Ḥamad
Būr Sūdān
Jiddah
Mecca (Makkah)
Al Khurmah
Al Qunfudhah
Sawākin
Pic Toussidé 10 712
TIBESTI
Emi Koussi 11 204
Ounianga Kébir
Bilma
BORKOU
BODÉLÉ
Largeau
Fada
ENNEDI
Agadem (Oasis)
Dunqulah
Al Khandaq
Kuraymah
Marawi
Al 'Aṭrūn
Ad Dabbah
Kūrtī
Barbar
'Aṭbarah
Ad Dāmir
Adarama
Shandī
Ṭawkar
Tagātu Hayyā
Omdurman (Umm Durmān)
Khartoum (Al Kharṭūm)
Al Kharṭūm Baḥrī
Al Kāmilīn
Kassalā
ERITREA
Keren
Asmera
Mitsiwa (Massawa)
DAHLAK ARCH.
JAZĀ'IR FARASĀN
Sebderat
Barentu
Adi Ugri
Mersa Fatma
Al Ḥudaydah
YEMEN
CHAD
SUDAN
Lake Chad
Mao
Abéché
Al Fāshir
KURDUFĀN
DĀRFŪR
Jabal Marrah 10 131
Ad Duwaym
Rufā'ah
Wad Madanī
Al Qaḍārif
Om Hajer
Sannār
Kūstī
Sinjah
Al-Ubayyiḍ
An Nuhūd
Al Udayyah
JIBĀL AN NŪBAH
White Nile
Blue Nile
Qallābāt
Gonder
Ras Dashen Terara 15 158
Mekele
DENAKIL
Yao
OUADDAÏ
N'Djamena (Fort-Lamy)
Maiduguri
MANDARA MTS.
Maroua
Am Timan
Nyala
Babanūsah
Ar Rank
Ar Ruṣayriṣ
Roseires Res.
Talawdī
Malūṭ
Kurmuk
Dangila
Debre Tabor
Debre Markos
Dese
Djibouti
DJIBOUTI
Zeylac
Lac Ibl
Bousso
Léré
Laï
Sarh
Kafia Kingi
Malakal
Kodok
AS SUDD
Nāṣir
Gambela
Dembi Dolo
Gore
Nekemte
Addis Ababa (Adis Abeba)
Dire Dawa
Harer
AHMAR MTS.
HARERGE
ETHIOPIA
Ouanda Djallé
Ndélé
CHAINE DES MONGOS
Mashra' ar Raqq
BAHR AL GHAZĀL
Wāw
Rumbek
Shambe
Bor
Jīma
Gimira
Shewa Gimira
Gaba
Ginir
Ngaoundéré
Fort Crampel
Yalinga
CENTRAL AFRICAN REPUBLIC
Koundé
Bouar
Bambari
Fort-Sibut
Fort-de-Possel
Rafai
Zemio
Tambura
Mongalla
Maji
Bako
SIDAMO
Carnot
Bangui
Zongo
Mobaye
Bangassou
Gwane
Jūbā
Kapoeta
Admin. Bdy.
Lake Stefanie
Mega
Dolow
Mbaïki
Libenge
Mobayi-Mbongo
Bondo
Bambesa
Dungu
Nimule
Yokadouma
Lomié
Mongoumba
Businga
Gemena
Aketi
Buta
Niangara
Isiro
Watsa
Gombari
Arua
Kitgum
Moyale
El Wak
SOMALIA
Dongou
Impfondo
Makanzo
Bomongo
Lisala
Bumba
DEMOCRATIC REPUBLIC OF THE CONGO
Panga
Basoko
Avakubi
Mahagi Port
UGANDA
Soroti
KENYA
Ouesso
CONGO
Basankusu
Isangi
Kisangani (Stanleyville)
Boyoma Falls
Equator
Irumu
Masindi
Ft. Portal
Margherita Peak 16 763
Kampala
Entebbe
Jinja
Eldoret
Lake Victoria
Meru
Mbandaka
15°
20°
25°
30°
35°
40°
45°
0
50
100
200
300
400
500 Miles
0
100
200
400
600
800 Kilometers

Scale 1:16 000 000; one inch to 250 miles. Sinusoidal Projection
Elevations and depressions are given in feet

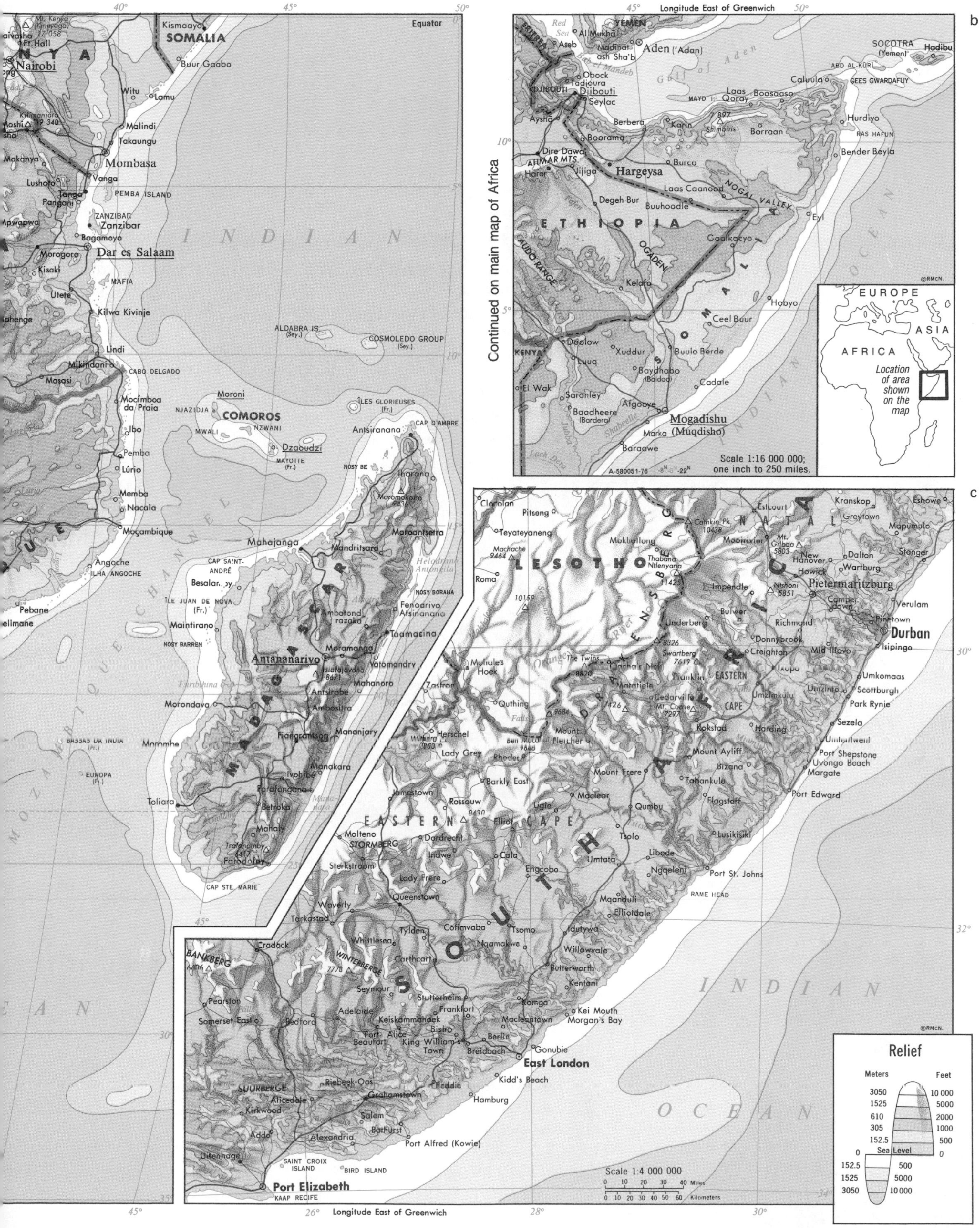
b
c
Longitude East of Greenwich
Equator
Continued on main map of Africa
SOMALIA
Kismaayo
Buur Gaabo
Nairobi
Witu
Lamu
Malindi
Takaungu
Mombasa
Vanga
Lushoto
Tanga
Pangani
PEMBA ISLAND
ZANZIBAR
Zanzibar
Bagamoyo
Morogoro
Dar es Salaam
Kisaki
MAFIA
Utete
Kilwa Kivinje
Lindi
Mikindani
Masasi
CABO DELGADO
Mocímboa da Praia
Ibo
Pemba
Lúrio
Memba
Nacala
Moçambique
Angoche
ILHA ANGOCHE
Pebane
I N D I A N
ALDABRA IS. (Sey.)
COSMOLEDO GROUP (Sey.)
Moroni
NJAZIDJA
COMOROS
MWALI
NZWANI
Dzaoudzi
MAYOTTE (Fr.)
ÎLES GLORIEUSES (Fr.)
CAP D'AMBRE
Antsiranana
NOSY BE
Iharana
Maroantsetra
Mahajanga
Mandritsara
CAP SAINT-ANDRÉ
Besalampy
ÎLE JUAN DE NOVA (Fr.)
Maintirano
NOSY BARREN
NOSY BORAHA
Fenoarivo Atsinanana
Ambatondrazaka
Toamasina
Moramanga
Antananarivo
Vatomandry
Mahanoro
Antsirabe
Ambositra
Morondava
Fianarantsoa
Mananjary
Manakara
Ivohibe
Farafangana
Toliara
Betroka
Mahaly
Taolanaro
CAP STE. MARIE
MADAGASCAR
MOZAMBIQUE CHANNEL
BASSAS DA INDIA (Fr.)
Morombe
EUROPA (Fr.)
YEMEN
Red Sea
Al Mukha
Aseb
ERITREA
Madinat ash Sha'b
Aden ('Adan)
Gulf of Aden
Obock
Tadjoura
DJIBOUTI
Djibouti
Seylac
Aysha
Berbera
Laas Qoray
Boosaaso
Caluula
SOCOTRA (Yemen)
Hadibu
'ABD AL-KURI
GEES GWARDAFUY
Hurdiyo
RAS HAFUN
Bender Beyla
Borraan
Dire Dawa
AHMAR MTS.
Harer
Jijiga
Hargeysa
Burco
Laas Caanood
NOGAL VALLEY
Eyl
Degeh Bur
Buuhoodle
ETHIOPIA
Gaalkacyo
OGADEN
Kelafo
Hobyo
Ceel Buur
SOMALIA
KENYA
Doolow
Xuddur
Luuq
Buulo Berde
Baydhabo (Baidoa)
Cadale
El Wak
Sarahley
Baadheere (Bardera)
Afgooye
Mogadishu (Muqdisho)
Marka
Baraawe
Scale 1:16 000 000; one inch to 250 miles.
EUROPE
ASIA
AFRICA
Location of area shown on the map
LESOTHO
Teyateyaneng
Maseru
Roma
Mokhotlong
Thabana Ntlenyana 11425
NATAL
Estcourt
Kranskop
Greytown
Mapumulo
Stanger
New Hanover
Dalton
Wartburg
Howick
Pietermaritzburg
Verulam
Pinetown
Durban
Isipingo
Richmond
Bulwer
Impendle
Underberg
Donnybrook
Creighton
Ixopo
Umkomaas
Scottburgh
Park Rynie
Sezela
Harding
Kokstad
Umzinto
Port Shepstone
Uvongo Beach
Margate
Port Edward
Bizana
Flagstaff
Lusikisiki
Port St. Johns
RAME HEAD
Mount Frere
Mount Fletcher
Maclear
Qumbu
Tsolo
Umtata
Libode
Ngqeleni
Mqanduli
Elliotdale
Idutywa
Willowvale
Butterworth
Kentani
Kei Mouth
Morgan's Bay
Komga
Macleantown
Gonubie
East London
Kidd's Beach
Hamburg
Berlin
King William's Town
Bisho
Breidbach
EASTERN CAPE
SOUTH AFRICA
Barkly East
Lady Grey
Herschel
Rhodes
Elliot
Ugie
Jamestown
Rossouw
Molteno
STORMBERG
Dordrecht
Indwe
Cala
Engcobo
Sterkstroom
Lady Frere
Queenstown
Tarkastad
Cofimvaba
Tsomo
Tylden
Whittlesea
Cathcart
Seymour
Stutterheim
Frankfort
Keiskammahoek
Adelaide
Fort Beaufort
Alice
Bedford
Somerset East
Pearston
Cradock
BANKBERG
WINTERBERGE
SUURBERGE
Riebeek-Oos
Grahamstown
Peddie
Alicedale
Kirkwood
Salem
Bathurst
Port Alfred (Kowie)
Addo
Alexandria
Uitenhage
SAINT CROIX ISLAND
BIRD ISLAND
Port Elizabeth
KAAP RECIFE
Zastron
Quthing
Cedarville
Matatiele
Franklin
EASTERN CAPE
Umzimkulu
INDIAN OCEAN
Scale 1:4 000 000
Miles
Kilometers
Relief
Meters
Feet
3050
1525
610
305
152.5
0
Sea Level
10 000
5000
2000
1000
500
©RMCN.

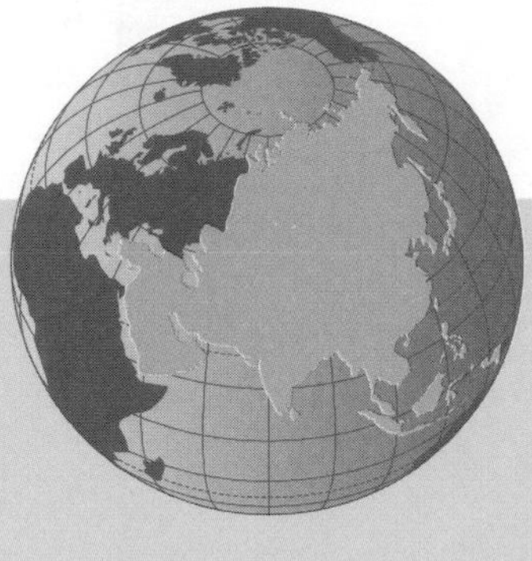

Asia

Covering nearly one-third of the Earth's land surface, Asia is by far the largest of the seven continents. It is a land of extremes and dramatic physical contrasts, containing nearly every type of landform, and many of them on a vast scale. It boasts the world's lowest point (the Dead Sea), its highest point (Mt. Everest), its highest and largest plateau (the Plateau of Tibet), and its largest inland body of water (the Caspian Sea).

Wide belts of mountain systems cover much of Asia. The Himalayas, which form a great 1,500-mile (2,400-km) arc south of Tibet, are the highest mountains in the world: more than 90 Himalayan peaks rise above 24,000 feet (7,320 m).

The beginnings of civilization can be traced to three distinct areas of Asia: Mesopotamia, around 4000 BC; the Indus River valley, around 3000 BC; and China, around 2000 BC. Eight of the world's major religions—Buddhism, Christianity, Confucianism, Hinduism, Islam, Judaism, Shinto, and Taoism—originated in Asia.

Asia at a glance

Land area: 17,300,000 square miles (44,900,000 sq km)

Estimated population: 3,761,165,000

Population density: 217/square mile (84/sq km)

Mean elevation: 3,000 feet (910 m)

Highest point: Mt. Everest, China (Tibet)-Nepal, 29,028 feet (8,848 m)

Lowest point: Dead Sea, Israel-Jordan, 1,339 feet (408 m) below sea level

Longest river: Yangtze (Chang), 3,900 mi (6,300 km)

Number of countries (incl. dependencies): 50

Largest independent country: Russia (Europe/Asia), 6,592,849 square miles (17,075,400 sq km)

Smallest independent country: Maldives, 115 square miles (298 sq km)

Most populous independent country: China, 1,278,720,000

Least populous independent country: Maldives, 315,000

Largest city: Mumbai, India, pop. 11,914,398

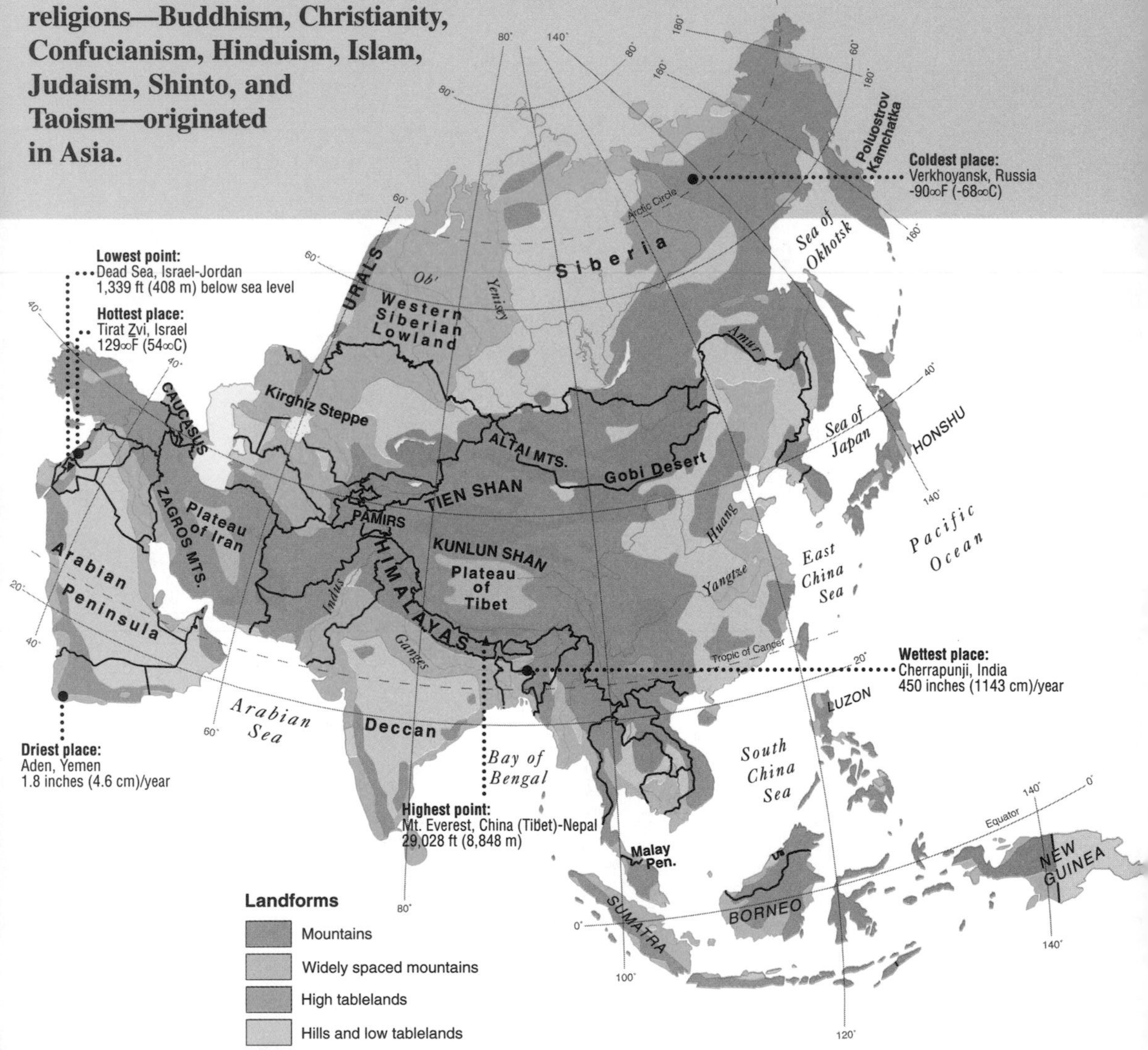

Annapurna, one of the highest mountains in the Himalayas

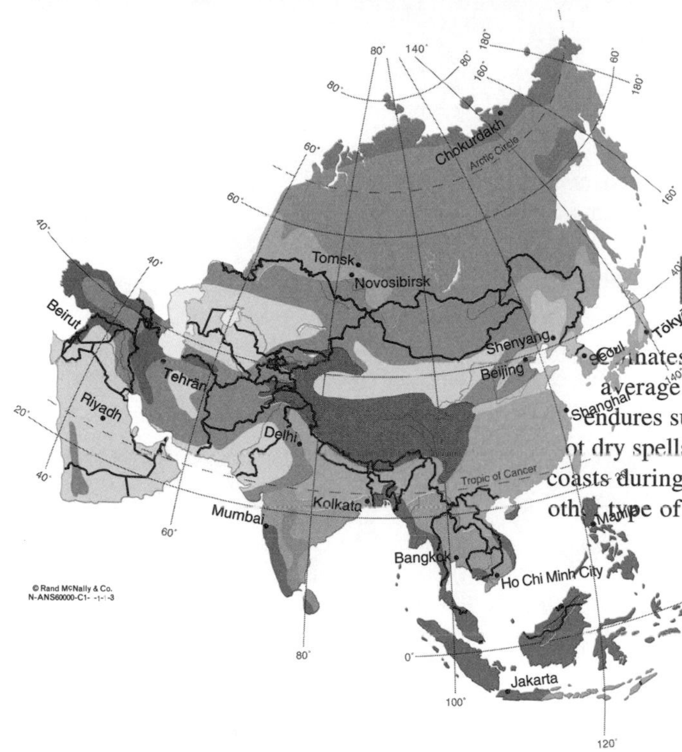

Climate

Climates vary greatly across Asia. In much of Siberia, temperatures average below -5°F (-20°C) in January, while the Persian Gulf region endures summer temperatures as high as 122°F (50°C). Monsoons interrupt hot dry spells with much-needed rain along the southeast and Indian Ocean coasts during the summer months. Between these extremes, almost every other type of climate on Earth can be found in Asia.

This climatic diversity can be explained by the continent's great expanse, from the Arctic to the tropics, and its great range in elevations.

Tinted areas show temperature in degrees Fahrenheit. Vertical bars show precipitation in inches.

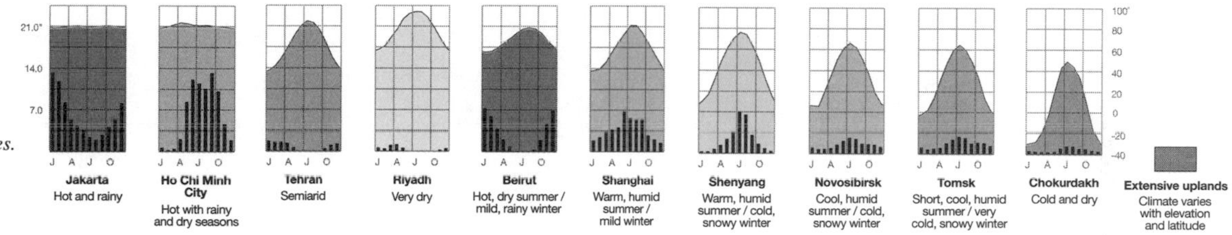

Population

With 3.8 billion people, Asia is nearly five times as populous as any other continent and is home to more than one out of every two people in the world. If its current annual growth rate continues, Asia's population will double by the year 2030. The continent contains the two most populous countries in the world, China and India, as well as the most populous metropolitan area, Tōkyō-Yokohama, Japan.

Great concentrations of people are found in India, eastern China, Japan, Vietnam, and on the Indonesian island of Java. In contrast, vast stretches of northern Siberia, Mongolia, western China, and the Arabian Peninsula are only sparsely populated. Numerous desert regions, including Arabia's Rub' al Khālī and China's Takla Makān, are uninhabited.

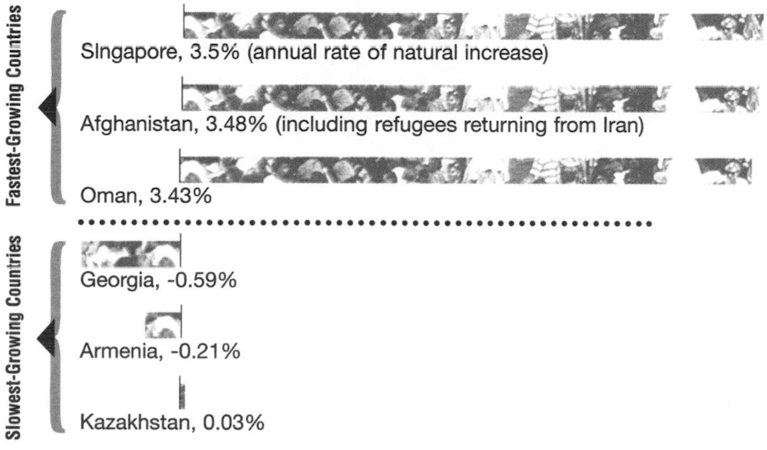

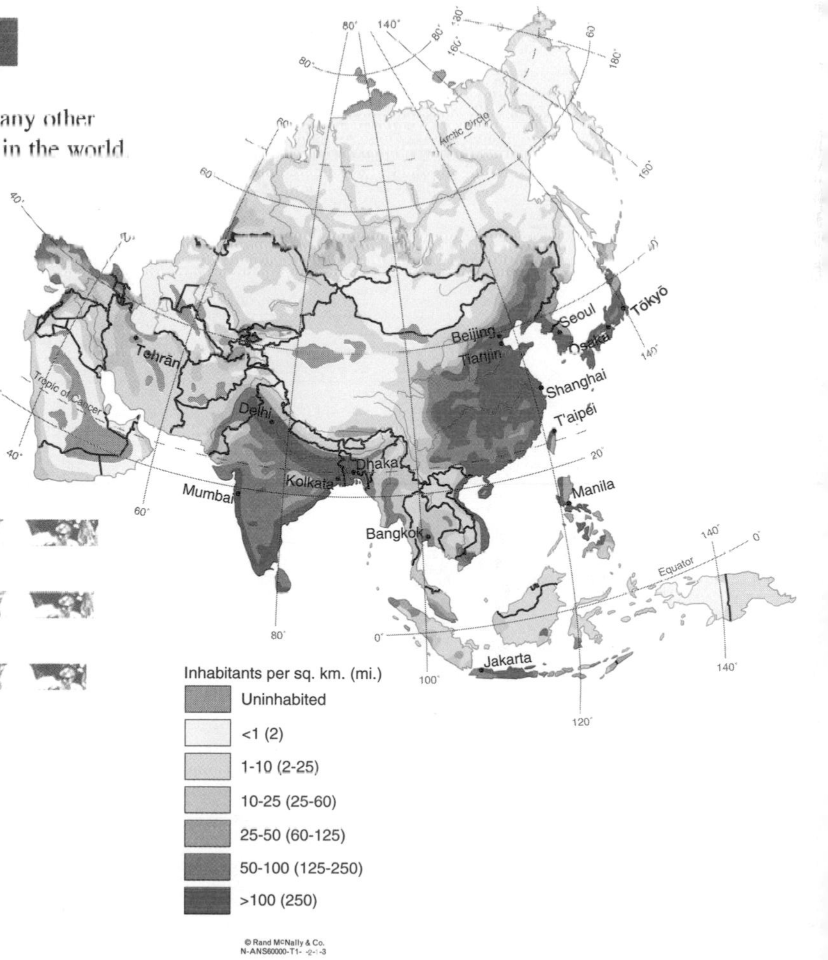

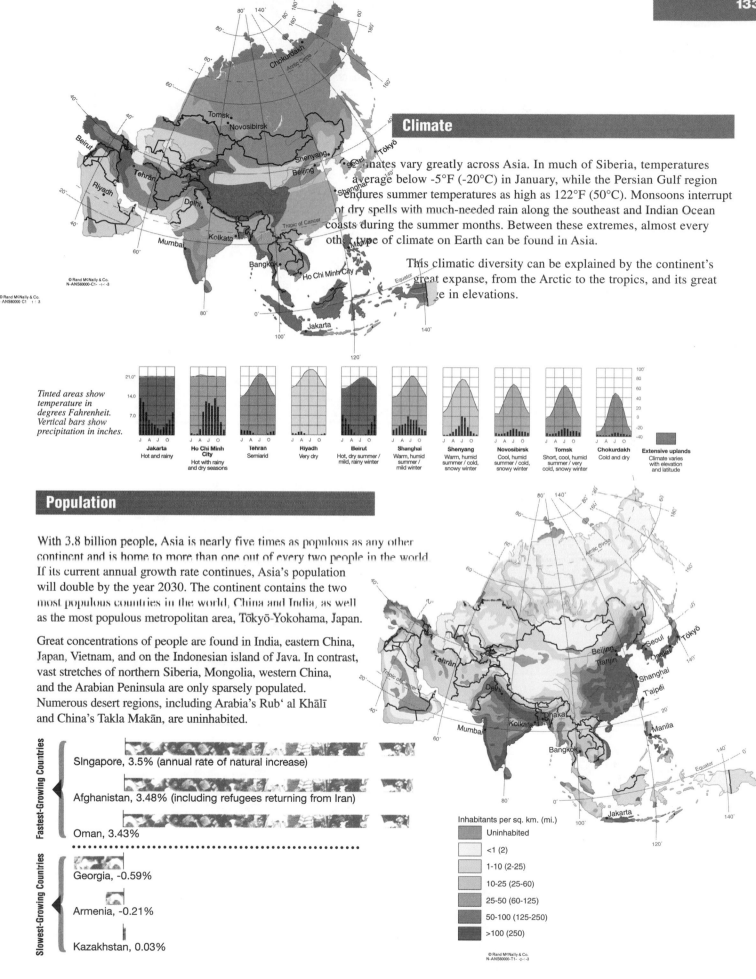

Environments and Land Use

Despite rapid industrialization in Japan, Korea, and Singapore, feeding the enormous and fast-growing population remains Asia's primary economic focus. In China, India, and Indonesia, two-thirds of the work force is engaged in farming. Where arable land exists, it is generally cultivated intensively. Rice is the most commonly grown crop: the continent produces more than 90% of the world's total. Other important crops include wheat, sorghum, millet, maize, and barley.

Asia's major agricultural regions are found in the fertile alluvial valleys, floodplains, and deltas of some of its greatest rivers, such as the Ganges and Brahmaputra in northern India, the Indus in Pakistan, the Huang (Yellow) and Yangtze in eastern China, the Irawaddy in Myanmar (Burma), the Mekong in Cambodia and Vietnam, and the Tigris and Euphrates in Iraq.

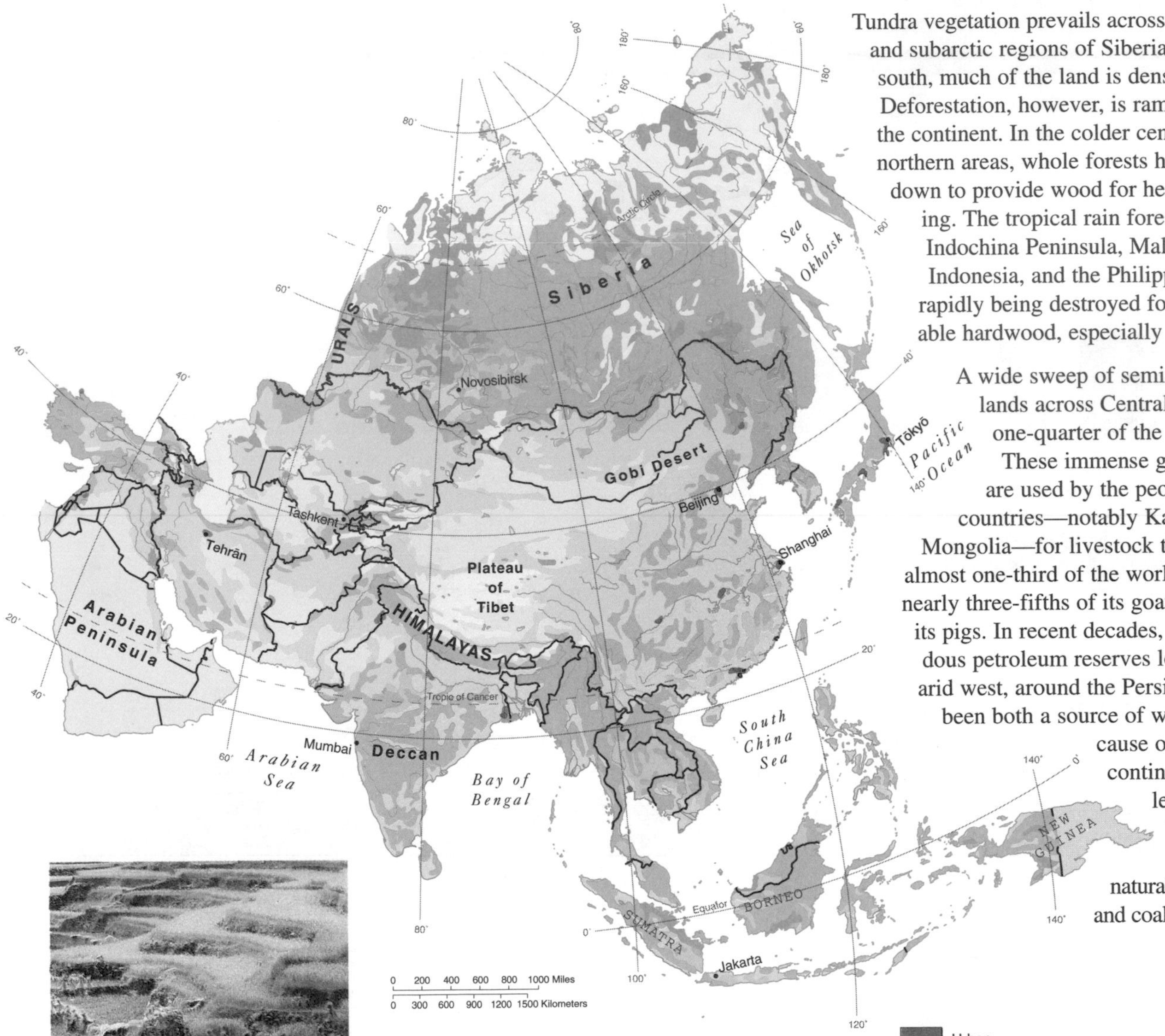

Tundra vegetation prevails across the arctic and subarctic regions of Siberia. Farther south, much of the land is densely forested. Deforestation, however, is rampant across the continent. In the colder central and northern areas, whole forests have been cut down to provide wood for heat and cooking. The tropical rain forests of the Indochina Peninsula, Malaysia, Indonesia, and the Philippines are rapidly being destroyed for their valuable hardwood, especially teak.

A wide sweep of semiarid grasslands across Central Asia covers one-quarter of the continent. These immense grazing lands are used by the people of many countries—notably Kazakhstan and Mongolia—for livestock that include almost one-third of the world's cattle, nearly three-fifths of its goats, and half of its pigs. In recent decades, the tremendous petroleum reserves located in the arid west, around the Persian Gulf, have been both a source of wealth and a cause of turmoil. The continent also has less exploited, but sizable reserves of natural gas in Siberia and coal in China.

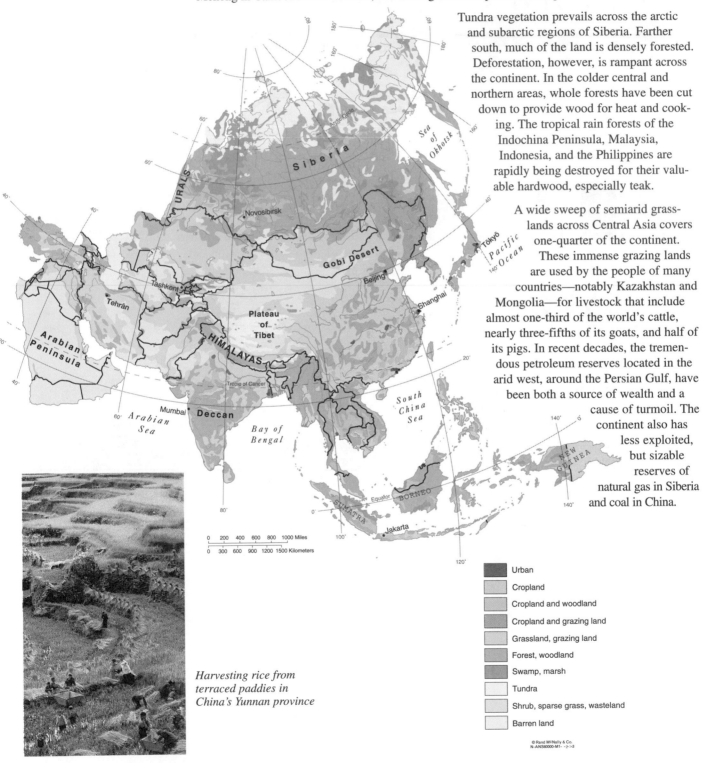

Harvesting rice from terraced paddies in China's Yunnan province

Asia and the Ring of Fire

Mt. Pinatubo, Philippines

"Ring of Fire" is the dramatic name given to the volcanoes that nearly encircle the Pacific Ocean. Its existence is explained by plate tectonic theory. According to the theory, Earth's thin crust is broken into sections or plates that move relative to each other. (See Plate Tectonics, pages 12 and 13.)

The giant Pacific plate submerges beneath other plates and plunges into Earth's hot interior, creating deep ocean trenches and causing magma to rise to the surface and erupt as volcanoes. The moving plates also trigger thousands of earthquakes that rumble along the Ring of Fire every year.

The Asian section of the Ring of Fire starts in the north on the Kamchatka Peninsula; swings down through the Kuril Islands; and includes Japan, Taiwan, the Philippines, and Indonesia.

The Kamchatka Peninsula, about the size of California, has more than 100 volcanoes. About 20 of these are active. Klyuchevskaya, the largest active volcano in Kamchatka, and in Eurasia, puts out about 60 million tons of basalt a year.

Japan is one of the most earthquake prone regions in the world. Four plates come together at Japan, and their movement against each other creates constant strain on the earth's crust. In 1995, an earthquake at Kōbe resulted in 5,500 fatalities. Japan's most deadly quake was in 1923, when more than 140,000 lives were lost.

The largest volcanic eruption in recorded history occurred in Indonesia. In 1815, Mt. Tambora spewed a column of ash 28 miles into the air. The fallout ruined crops, causing widespread famine. 82,000 people died as a result of Tambora's eruption, most of them from starvation. Gases from Tambora circled the globe and lowered world temperatures by as much as 3°. In 1816, the "year without summer", killing frosts during summer months destroyed crops in Europe and North America.

The 1991 eruption of Mt. Pinatubo in the Philippines was the second largest volcanic eruption of the 20th century, and approximately ten times as large as Mt. St. Helen's. Pinatubo blew an ash column about 21 miles into the sky. Although Pinatubo is near a heavily populated area not far from Manila, authorities were able to warn and evacuate residents in advance, preventing what could have been a major disaster.

Scale 1:40 000 000; one inch to 630 miles. Lambert's Azimuthal, Equal Area Projection

Elevations and depressions are given in feet

NORTH AMERICA
Bering Str.
M. DEZHNEVA (EAST CAPE)
ST. LAWRENCE
PRIBILOF IS. (U.S.A.)
CHUKOTSKIY P-OV
VRANGELYA (WRANGEL)
EAST SIBERIAN SEA
Arctic Circle
KORYAKSKIY KHREBET
BERING SEA
ALEUTIAN ISLANDS (U.S.A.)
ALEUTIAN TRENCH
KOMANDORSKIYE OSTROVA
KHREBET GYDAN
P-OV KAMCHATKA
Petropavlovsk-Kamchatskiy
Verkhoyansk
VERKHOYANSKIY KHREBET
Okhotsk
SEA OF OKHOTSK
Yakutsk
DZHUGDZHUR KHREBET
M. LOPATKA
SAKHALIN
KURIL ISLANDS
STANOVOY KHREBET
Komsomolsk
Tatar Strait
KURIL TRENCH
Amur
Blagoveshchensk
Sovetskaya Gavan
Khabarovsk
SIKHOTE ALIN'
HOKKAIDO
Hakodate
Nerchinsk
KHINGAN RANGE
MANCHURIA
HARBIN
CHANGCHUN
Jilin
Vladivostok
SEA OF JAPAN
JAPAN
HONSHŪ
Sendai
TOKYO
YOKOHAMA
GREATER KHINGAN RANGE
SHENYANG
NORTH KOREA
P'yongyang
SEOUL
SOUTH KOREA
KYOTO
KOBE
OSAKA
Zhangjiakou
BEIJING
TIANJIN
Dalian
Bo Hai
Jinan
QINGDAO
KITAKYŪSHŪ
Nagasaki
SHIKOKU
KYŪSHŪ
TAIYUAN
NANJING
EAST CHINA SEA
SHANGHAI
XI'AN
QIN LING
WUHAN
NANSEI SHOTŌ
PHILIPPINE SEA
Tropic of Cancer
PACIFIC OCEAN
Yichang
Changsha
Fuzhou
T'AIPEI
TAIWAN (FORMOSA)
Taiwan Strait
Xiamen
Shantou
NAN LING
GUANGZHOU
HONG KONG (Xianggang)
Wuzhou
Macau
Luzon Str.
BABUYAN IS.
LUZON
HAINAN DAO
Gulf of Tonkin
PHILIPPINES
Quezon City
MANILA
SAMAR
PHILIPPINE TRENCH
Hue
MINDORO
LEYTE
PANAY
MINDANAO
SOUTH CHINA SEA
PALAWAN
NEGROS
Phnom Penh
HO CHI MINH CITY (Saigon)
SULU SEA
SULU IS.
MUI BAI-BUNG
Kota Kinabalu
Sandakan
CELEBES SEA
HALMAHERA
Equator
NEW GUINEA
BRUNEI
MALAYSIA
Kuching
BORNEO
CELEBES (SULAWESI)
SINGAPORE
INDONESIA
Kuala Lumpur
West Longitude
East Longitude
120°
130°
0 200 400 600 800 1000 Miles
0 400 800 1200 1600 Kilometers

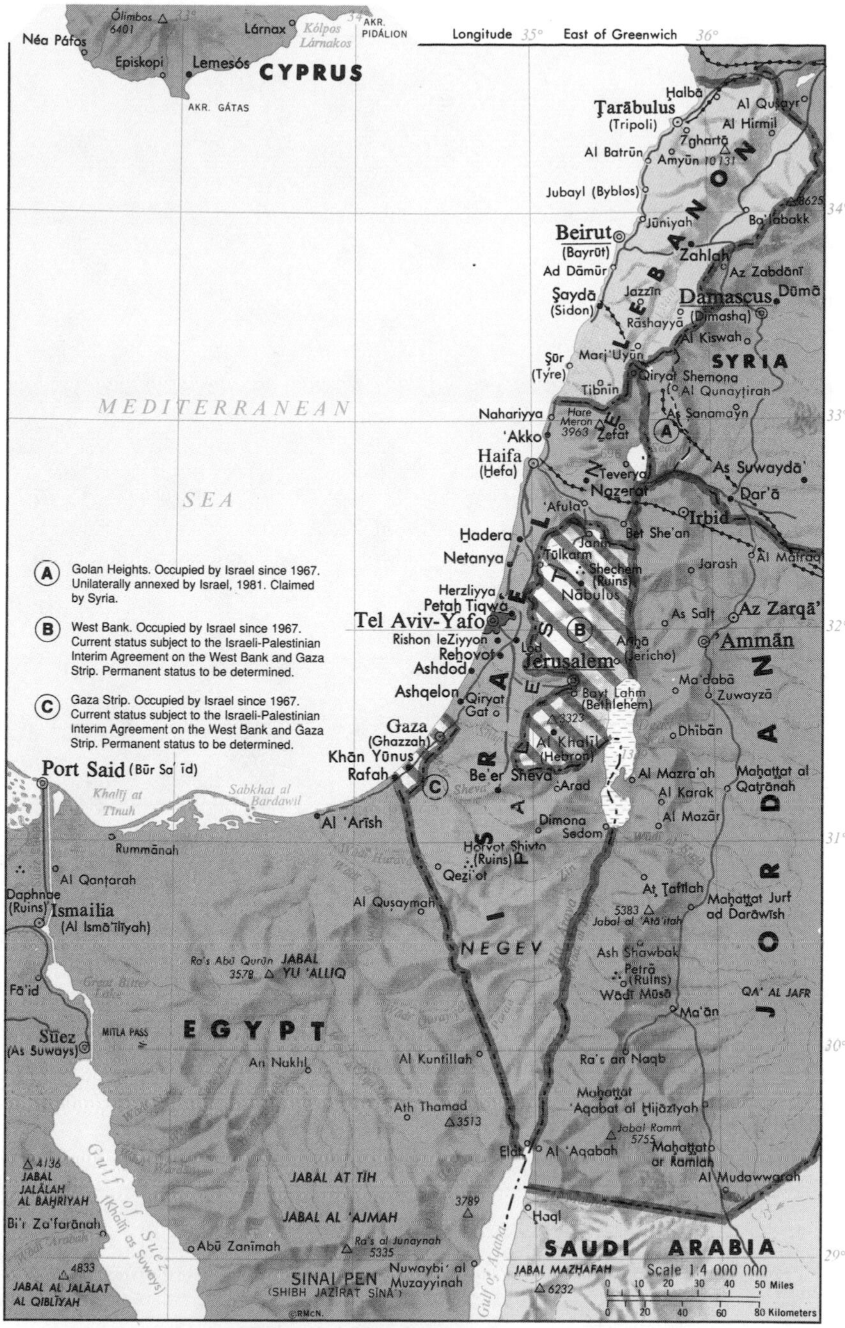
Longitude 35° East of Greenwich 36°
Ólimbos 6401
Néa Páfos
Lárnax
Kólpos Lárnakos
AKR. PIDÁLION
Episkopí
Lemesós
CYPRUS
AKR. GÁTAS
Halbā
Al Quşayr
Ţarābulus (Tripoli)
Al Hirmil
Zgharta
Al Batrūn
Amyūn
LEBANON
Jubayl (Byblos)
Beirut (Bayrūt)
Jūniyah
Ba'labakk
Zahlah
Ad Dāmūr
Az Zabdānī
Şaydā (Sidon)
Jazzīn
Damascus (Dimashq)
Dūmā
Rāshayyā
Al Kiswah
Şūr (Tyre)
Marj 'Uyūn
SYRIA
Tibnīn
Qiryat Shemona
Al Qunayţirah
MEDITERRANEAN SEA
Nahariyya
Hare Meron 3963
Zefat
As Sanamayn
'Akko
Haifa (Hefa)
Teverya
Nazerat
As Suwaydā'
Dar'ā
'Afula
Irbid
Hadera
Janin
Bet She'an
Netanya
Tūlkarm
Shechem (Ruins)
Nābulus
Jarash
Al Mafraq
Herzliyya
Petah Tiqwa
Tel Aviv-Yafo
As Salt
Az Zarqā'
Rishon leZiyyon
Rehovot
Lod
Arīhā (Jericho)
'Ammān
Ashdod
Jerusalem
Ma'dabā
Ashqelon
Qiryat Gat
Bayt Lahm (Bethlehem)
Zuwayzā
Gaza (Ghazzah)
Al Khalīl (Hebron)
Dhībān
Khān Yūnus
Rafah
Port Said (Būr Sa'īd)
Be'er Sheva
Arad
Maḩaţţat al Qaţrānah
Khalīj at Tīnah
Sabkhat al Bardawīl
Al 'Arīsh
Al Mazra'ah
Al Karak
Al Mazār
Dimona
Sedom
Rummānah
Horvot Shivta (Ruins)
Qezi'ot
ISRAEL
JORDAN
Al Qanţarah
Daphnae (Ruins)
Ismailia (Al Ismā'īlīyah)
Al Qusaymah
Aţ Ţafīlah
Maḩaţţat Jurf ad Darāwīsh
Jabal al 'Aţā'itah 5383
NEGEV
Ra's Abū Qurūn 3578
JABAL YU 'ALLIQ
Ash Shawbak
Petrā (Ruins)
Wādī Mūsā
Fā'id
Great Bitter Lake
QA' AL JAFR
Ma'ān
Suez (As Suways)
MITLA PASS
EGYPT
An Nakhl
Al Kuntillah
Ra's an Naqb
Maḩaţţat 'Aqabat al Ḩijāzīyah
Ath Thamad
3513
Jabal Ramm 5755
Maḩaţţat ar Ramlah
Elat
Al 'Aqabah
4136
JABAL JALĀLAH AL BAḨRĪYAH
JABAL AT TĪH
Al Mudawwarah
Gulf of Suez (Khalīj as Suways)
Bi'r Za'farānah
JABAL AL 'AJMAH
3789
Ḩaql
Abū Zanīmah
Ra's al Junaynah 5335
SAUDI ARABIA
4833
JABAL AL JALĀLAT AL QIBLĪYAH
SINAI PEN. (SHIBH JAZĪRAT SĪNĀ')
Nuwaybi' al Muzayyinah
Gulf of Aqaba
JABAL MAZḨAFAH
6232
Scale 1:4 000 000
0 10 20 30 40 50 Miles
0 20 40 60 80 Kilometers
©RMCN.
(A) Golan Heights. Occupied by Israel since 1967. Unilaterally annexed by Israel, 1981. Claimed by Syria.
(B) West Bank. Occupied by Israel since 1967. Current status subject to the Israeli-Palestinian Interim Agreement on the West Bank and Gaza Strip. Permanent status to be determined.
(C) Gaza Strip. Occupied by Israel since 1967. Current status subject to the Israeli-Palestinian Interim Agreement on the West Bank and Gaza Strip. Permanent status to be determined.
34°
33°
32°
31°
30°
29°

Kuala Lumpur
Kelang
Kajang
Kuala Klawang
PAHANG
Scale 1:4 000 000
0 10 20 30 40 50 Miles
0 20 40 60 80 Kilometers
SELANGOR
Gunung Telapa Burok 3915
TIOMAN
Gunung Kajang 3444
Telok Datok
NEGERI SEMBILAN
Bahau
Seremban
Sepang
Rantau
Rompin
Padang Endau
Port Dickson
Rembau
Gemas
PEMANGGIL
Tampin
Segamat
Gunung Besar 3403
CAPE RACHADO
Alor Gajah
Jasin
Mt. Ophir 4187
Labis
Mersing
AUR
Melaka (Malacca)
MELAKA
Panchor
MALAYSIA
2002
SOUTH CHINA SEA
TINGGI
STRAIT OF MALACCA
JOHOR
MALAY PENINSULA
Bandar Maharani
Keluang
Gunung Blumut 3312
Paloh
Rengam
Layang Layang
TANJONG TOHOR
Jumrah
RUPAT
Teluklecak
Batu Pahat
Ayer Hitam
Jason Bay
Kota Tinggi
Botupanjang
Dumai
Johor Baharu
Bengkalis
BENGKALIS
Bukitbatu
Pontian Kechil
TANJONG RAMUNIA
SINGAPORE
Singapore Strait
SUMATRA
Ketamputih
TANJONG PIAI
Kudap
TANJUNG BERAKIT
Pinggir
PADANG
Telesung
Philip Channel
BATAM
1181
1837
KARIMUN BESAR
KEPULAUAN RIAU
INDONESIA
BINTAN
RIAU
Tanjungbalai
Tanjungpinang
RANGSANG
REMPANG
Minas
TEBINGTINGGI
KUNDUR
Seranggung
341
Buatan
Siaksriinderapura
Baranpauh
©RMCN.
102°
103° Longitude East of Greenwich 104°
3°
2°
1°

Scale 1:40 000 000; one inch to 630 miles. Lambert's Azimuthal, Equal Area Projection

Elevations and depressions are given in feet

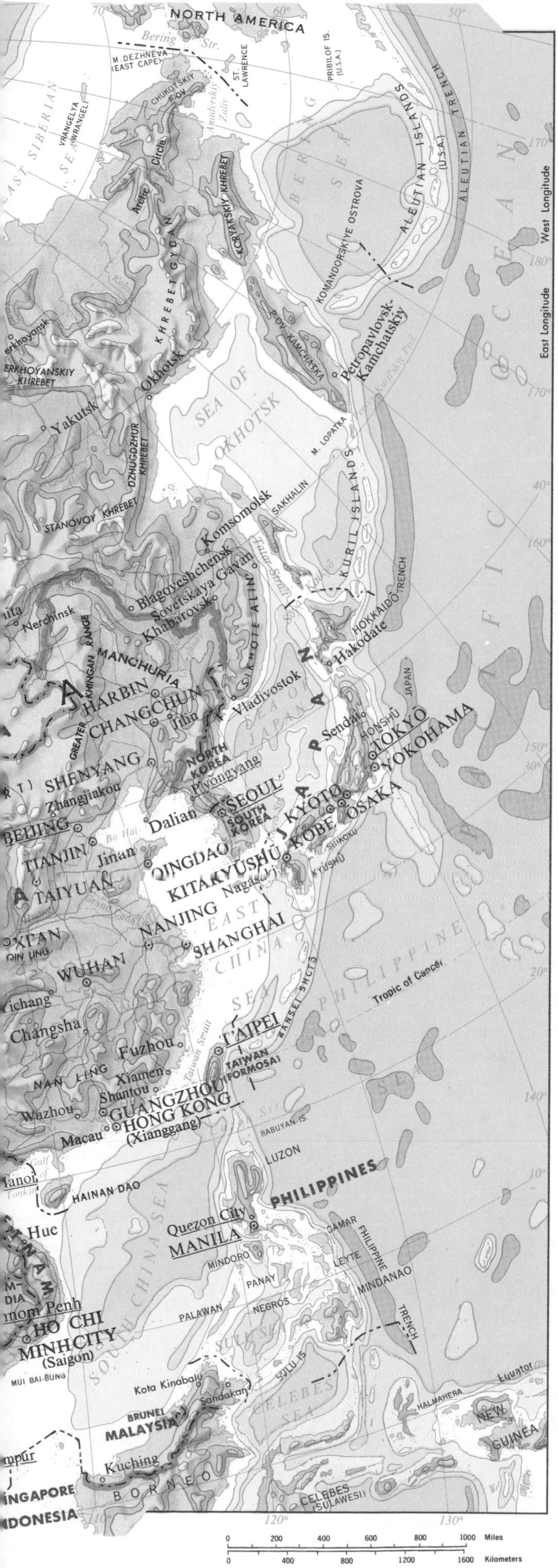

a

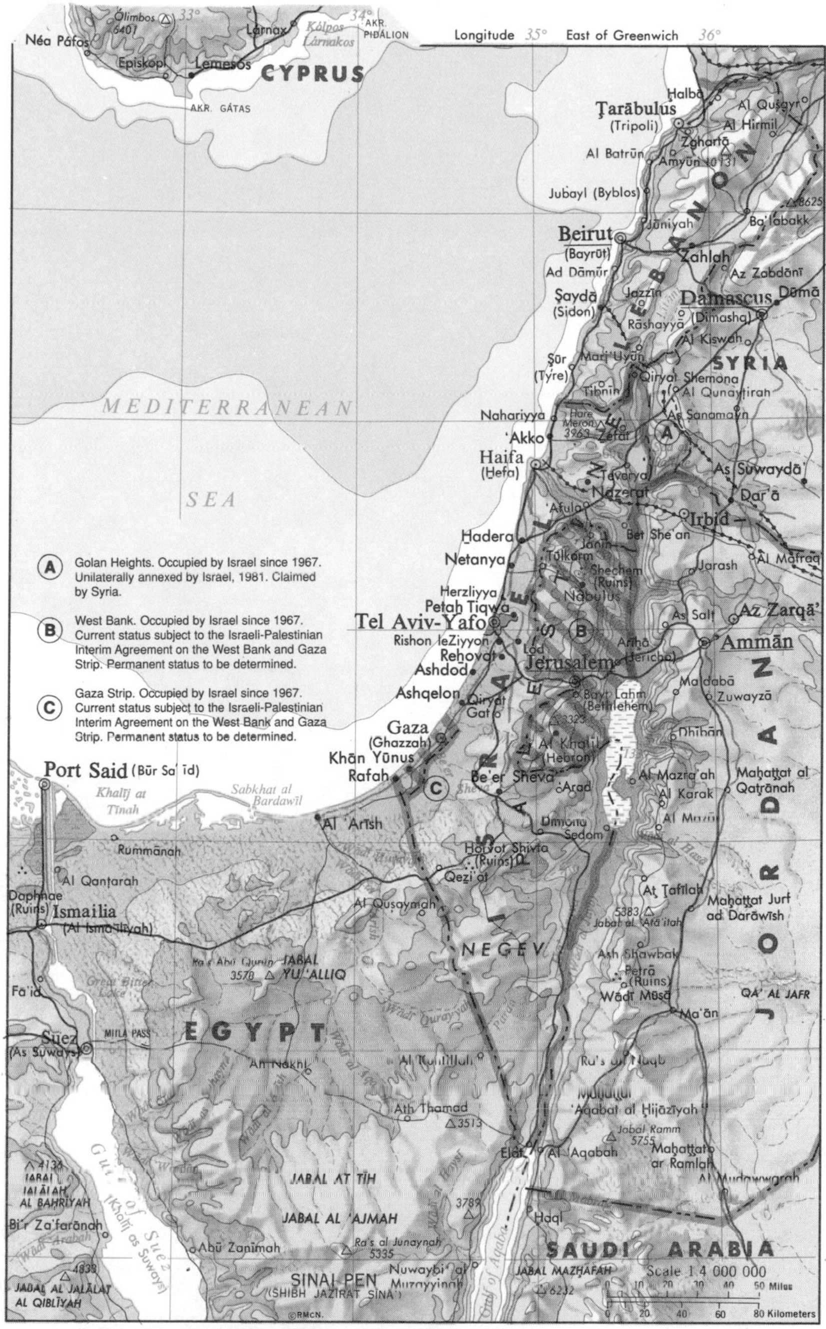

Ⓐ Golan Heights. Occupied by Israel since 1967. Unilaterally annexed by Israel, 1981. Claimed by Syria.

Ⓑ West Bank. Occupied by Israel since 1967. Current status subject to the Israeli-Palestinian Interim Agreement on the West Bank and Gaza Strip. Permanent status to be determined.

Ⓒ Gaza Strip. Occupied by Israel since 1967. Current status subject to the Israeli-Palestinian Interim Agreement on the West Bank and Gaza Strip. Permanent status to be determined.

b

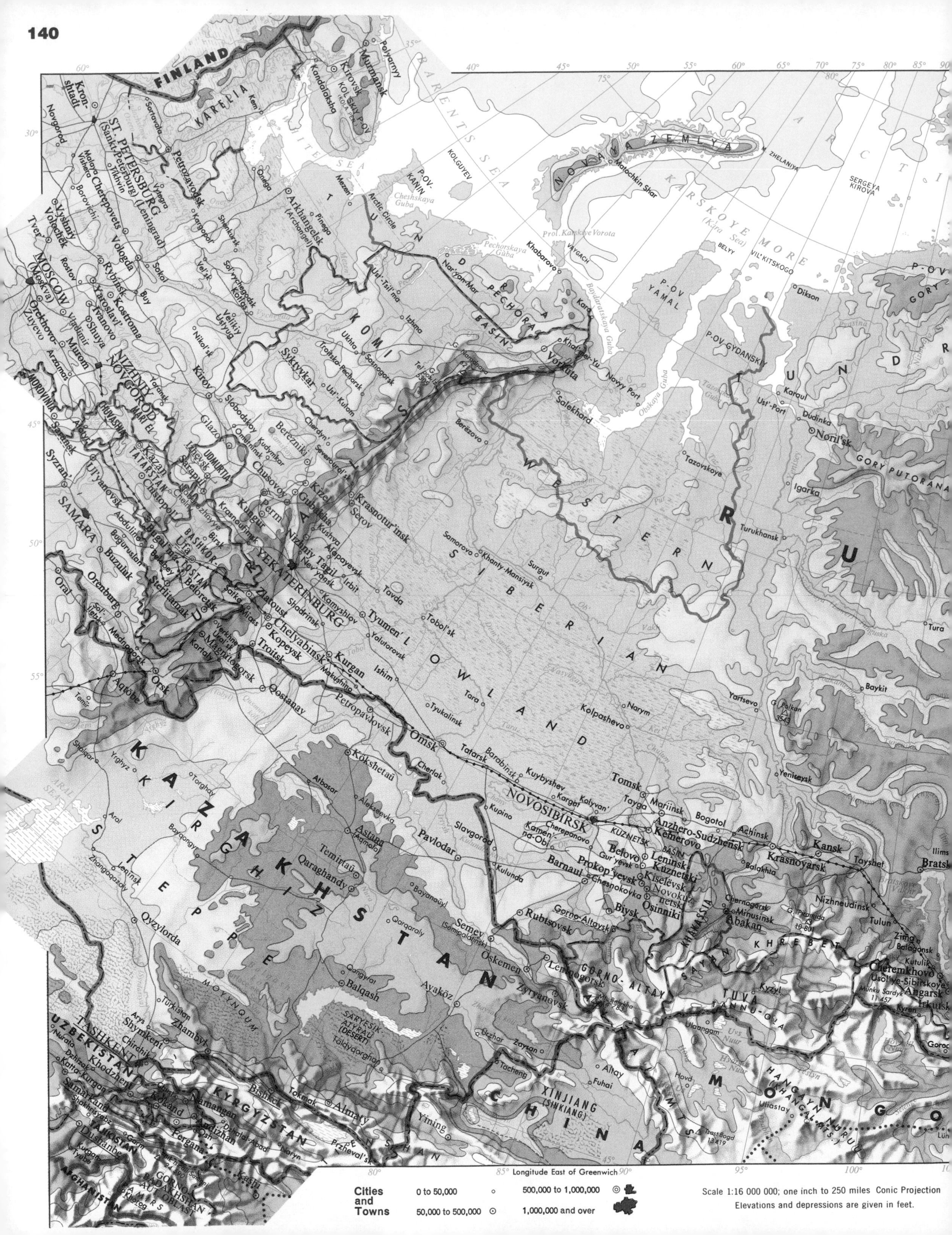
FINLAND
KARELIA
ST. PETERSBURG (Sankt-Peterburg) (Leningrad)
MOSCOW (Moskva)
NIZHNIY NOVGOROD
SAMARA
YEKATERINBURG
NOVOSIBIRSK
BARENTS SEA
WHITE SEA
NOVAYA ZEMLYA
KARSKOYE MORE (Kara Sea)
ARCTIC
TUNDRA
PECHORA BASIN
KOMI
URAL
WESTERN SIBERIAN LOWLAND
KAZAKHSTAN
KAZAKH STEPPE
KIRGHIZ STEPPE
KUZNETSK BASIN
GORNO-ALTAY
KHAKASSIA
TUVA
MONGOLIA
CHINA
XINJIANG (SINKIANG)
UZBEKISTAN
KYRGYZSTAN
TAJIKISTAN
AFGHANISTAN
ARAL SEA
Omsk
Tomsk
Krasnoyarsk
Irkutsk
Almaty
Astana (Aqmola)
Qaraghandy
Tashkent
Noril'sk
Murmansk
Arkhangel'sk (Archangel)
Longitude East of Greenwich
Cities and Towns
0 to 50,000
50,000 to 500,000
500,000 to 1,000,000
1,000,000 and over
Scale 1:16 000 000; one inch to 250 miles Conic Projection
Elevations and depressions are given in feet.

Bering Strait
VRANGELYA (WRANGEL)
CHUKOTSKIY P-OV
ANADYRSKIY ZALIV
Anadyr'
M. SHELAGSKIY
DE-LONGA
SEVERNAYA ZEMLYA (NORTHERN LAND)
MALYY TAMIR
M. CHELYUSKIN
OCEAN
NOVOSIBIRSKIYE O-VA (NEW SIBERIAN ISLANDS)
FADDEYA
NOVAYA SIBIR
BEL'KOVSKIY
KOTEL'NYY
MALYY LYAKHOVSKIYE
LYAKHOVSKIYE
EAST SIBERIAN SEA
MEDVEZH'I
AYON
Ambarchik
Chaunskaya Guba
CHUKOTSKOYE NAGOR'YE
KORYAKSKIY KHREBET
LAPTEV SEA
BYRRANGA
TAYMYR
BOL'SHOY BEGICHEV
Khatangskiy Zaliv
Nordvik
STOLBOVOY
M. SVYATOY NOS
G. Sellya Khskaya
M. BUOR-KHAYA
Guba Buor-Khaya
Ust'-Olenëk
Tiksi
Kazach'ye
Khatanga
Bulun
Allaykha
Nizhne-Kolymsk
Sredne-Kolymsk
Zyryanka
Arctic Circle
Penzhino
Ust'-Penzhino
Tilichiki
M. OLYUTORSKIY
KARAGIN
Gizhiga
KHREBET GYDAN (KOLYMSKIY)
KHREBET KULAR
Abyy
Verkhoyansk
Zashiversk
KHREBET CHERSKOGO
Gora Pobeda 10 174
VERKHOYANSKIY KHREBET
Zhigansk
Oymyakon
Magadan
Yamsk
M. TAYGONOS
ZALIV SHELEKHOVA
Penzhinskaya Guba
Palana
POLUOSTROV KAMCHATKA
Ust'-Kamchatsk
Klyuchevskaya (Vol.) 15 584
Verkhne-Kamchatsk
Petropavlovsk-Kamchatskiy
Ust'-Bol'sheretsk
M. ALEVINA
SEA OF OKHOTSK
ASIA
SAKHA
(YAKUTIA)
Vilyuysk
Yakutsk
Aldanskaya
Okhotsk
Suntar
Amga
Ust'-Maya
DZHUGDZHUR KHREBET
Mukhtuya
Olëkminsk
Tommot
Aldan
ALDAN PLATEAU
Nel'kan
Ayan
Peleduy
Vitim
PATOM PLATEAU
Kirensk
Bodaybo
STANOVOY KHREBET
Chumikan
Udskaya G.
SHANTAR
M. YELIZAVETY
Okha
SAKHALIN (Russia)
Nikolayevsk-na-Amure
Aleksandrovsk
Poronaysk
M. TERPENIYA
Uglegorsk
TATAR STRAIT
KURIL ISLANDS (Russia)
ITURUP
Dolinsk
Yuzhno-Sakhalinsk
Kholmsk
Korsakov
A-579300-76 -10 -22
COPYRIGHT BY RAND McNALLY & COMPANY MADE IN U.S.A.
Nizhne-Angarsk
Tyndinskiy
Zeya
Skovorodino
BURYATIA
Zhigalovo
Kachuga
Barguzin
Komsomol'sk-na-Amure
KHREBET BUREINSKIY
Svobodnyy
Belogorsk
Sovetskaya Gavan'
Ust'-Tyrma
Bureya
Raychikinsk
Birobidzhan
Khabarovsk
Zavitinsk
Blagoveshchensk
Aihui
Sretensk
NERCHINSKIY KHREBET
Nerchinskiy Zavod
Nerchinsk
Chita
Ulan-Ude
Babushkin
Petrovsk-Zabaykal'skiy
Kyakhta
Baley
Aginskoye
Borzya
Aksha
Manzhouli
Hailar
NEI MONGGOL
GREATER KHINGAN RANGE
LESSER KHINGAN RANGE
Longzhen
Goukou
CHINA
HEILUNGKIANG
Qiqihar
Hulan
HARBIN
Yilan
Choybalsan
Ulan Bator (Ulaanbaatar)
Öndörhaan
Dalnerechensk
SIKHOTE-ALIN
Spassk-Dal'niy
Arsen'yev
Ussuriysk
Artëm
Suchan
Nakhodka
Vladivostok
Ol'ga
Sui fenhe
Ning an
SEA OF JAPAN
HOKKAIDO
JAPAN
Sōya Kaikyō
Relief
Meters Feet
3050 10 000
1525 5000
610 2000
305 1000
152.5 500
0 Sea Level 0
152.5 500
1525 5000
3050 10 000
0 50 100 200 300 400 500 Miles
0 100 200 400 600 800 Kilometers

Scale 1:16 000 000; one inch to 250 miles. Polyconic Projection
Elevations and depressions are given in feet

a
AFGHANISTAN
PAKISTAN
Jalalabad
Dargai
Chārsadda
KHYBER PASS
MORGA RA.
Peshāwar
Scale 1:4 000 000
0 10 20 30 40 Miles
0 20 40 60 Kilometers
b
Scale 1:40 000 000
CHINA
XIZANG (TIBET)
AFGHANISTAN
JAMMU AND KASHMIR
HIMACHAL PRADESH
PUNJAB
UTTARANCHAL
PAKISTAN
HARYANA
RĀJASTHĀN
UTTAR PRADESH
NEPAL
SIKKIM
BHUTAN
ARUNACHAL PRADESH
ASSAM
NAGALAND
BIHĀR
BANGLADESH
MEGHALAYA
MIZORAM
Tropic of Cancer
GUJARAT
MADHYA PRADESH
JHARKHAND
WEST BENGAL
MYANMAR
CHHATTISGARH
ORISSA
MAHĀRĀSHTRA
ARABIAN SEA
BAY OF BENGAL
THAILAND
LAOS
KARNATAKA
ANDHRA PRADESH
TAMIL NADU
KERALA
SRI LANKA (CEYLON)
INDIA · POLITICAL
1-TRIPURA
2-MANIPUR
3-LAKSHADWEEP
4-DELHI
5-DĀDRA AND NAGAR HAVELI
6-PONDICHERRY
7-GOA, DAMĀN, AND DIU
c
Tiruchchirāppalli
Nāgappattinam
Thanjāvūr
Ernākulam
TAMIL NADU
KERALA
Madurai
Jaffna
Alleppey
Tuticorin
Mannar
Quilon
Tirunelveli
Trincomalee
Thiruvananthapuram
CAPE COMORIN
Anuradhapura
INDIAN OCEAN
SRI LANKA (CEYLON)
Colombo
Kandy
Galle
Matara
DONDRA HEAD
Same scale as main map
TASHKENT
KYRGYZSTAN
TAJIKISTAN
Bishkek
Dushanbe
PAMIRS
TAKLA MAKAN
XINJIANG UYGUR (SINKIANG)
KARAKORAM
HINDU KUSH
JAMMU AND KASHMIR
Islāmābād
Kābul
Srīnagar
Rāwalpindi
Peshāwar
Amritsar
LAHORE
Faisalabad
PAKISTAN
Multān
Quetta
Kandahār
XIZANG (TIBET)
GANGDISÊ SHAN
Lhasa
NEPAL
Kathmandu
SIKKIM
BHUTAN
Thimphu
ASSAM
NAGALAND
MEGHALAYA
DELHI
New Delhi
UTTAR PRADESH
Āgra
Lucknow
KĀNPUR
Jaipur
RĀJASTHĀN
GREAT INDIAN DESERT
Patna
BIHĀR
BANGLADESH
Dhaka
Hyderābād
KARĀCHI
INDIA
WEST BENGAL
KOLKATA (Calcutta)
Chittagong
MYANMAR (BURMA)
Mandalay
AHMADĀBĀD
GUJARAT
Bhopāl
MADHYA PRADESH
Nāgpur
Mouths of the Ganges
BAY OF BENGAL
MUMBAI (Bombay)
MAHĀRĀSHTRA
DECCAN
HYDERĀBĀD
Vishākhapatnam
Rangoon (Yangon)
Pune
Panaji (Panjim)
BANGALORE
CHENNAI (Madras)
Pondicherry
Coimbatore
Madurai
LAKSHADWEEP (LACCADIVE IS.) (India)
A Area occupied by Pakistan and claimed by India.
B Area claimed and occupied by India; status disputed by Pakistan.
C Area occupied by China and claimed by India.
D Area occupied by India and claimed by China.
0 50 100 200 300 400 500 Miles
0 100 200 400 600 800 Kilometers

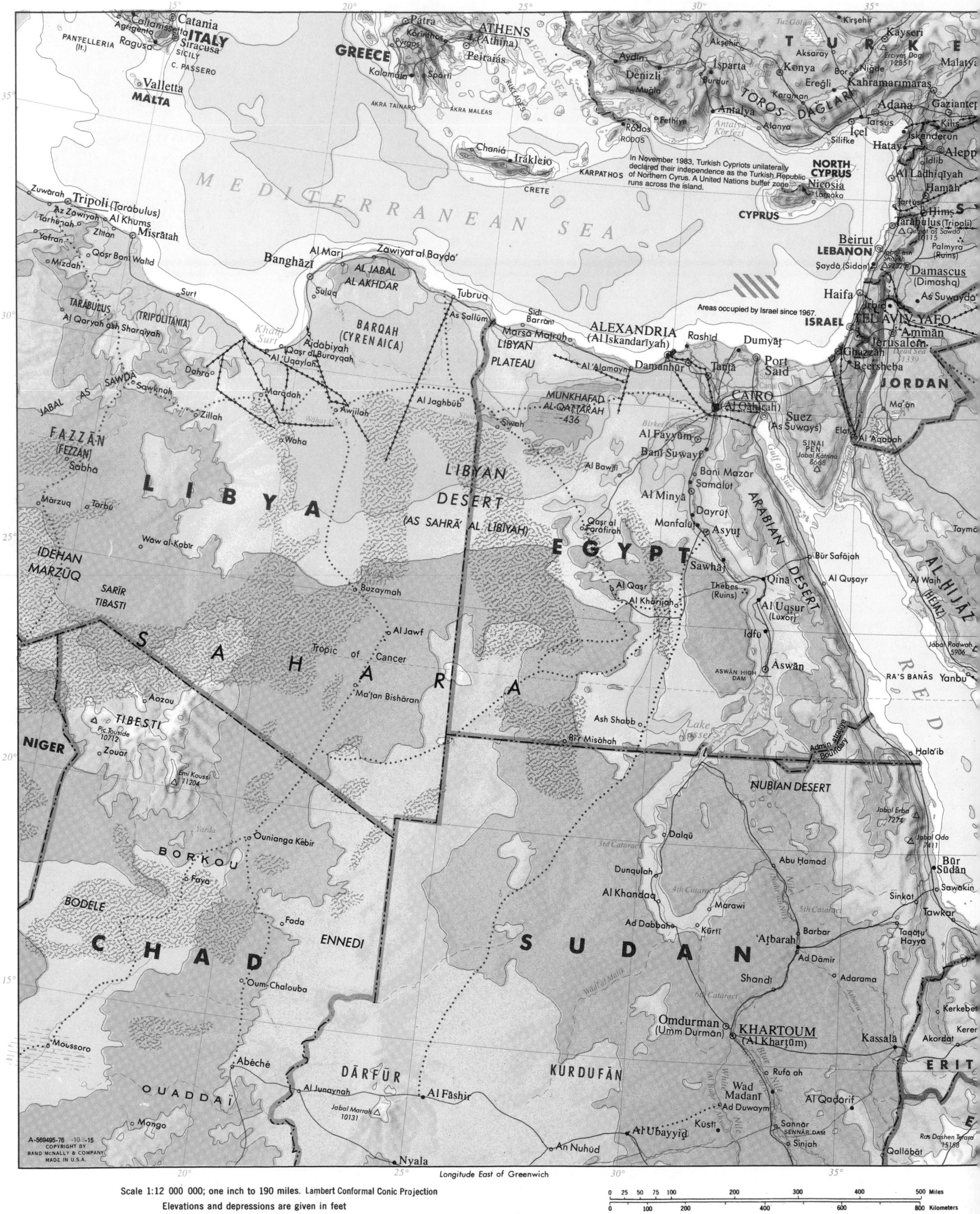

Scale 1:12 000 000; one inch to 190 miles. Lambert Conformal Conic Projection

Elevations and depressions are given in feet

0 25 50 75 100 200 300 400 500 Miles
0 100 200 400 600 800 Kilometers

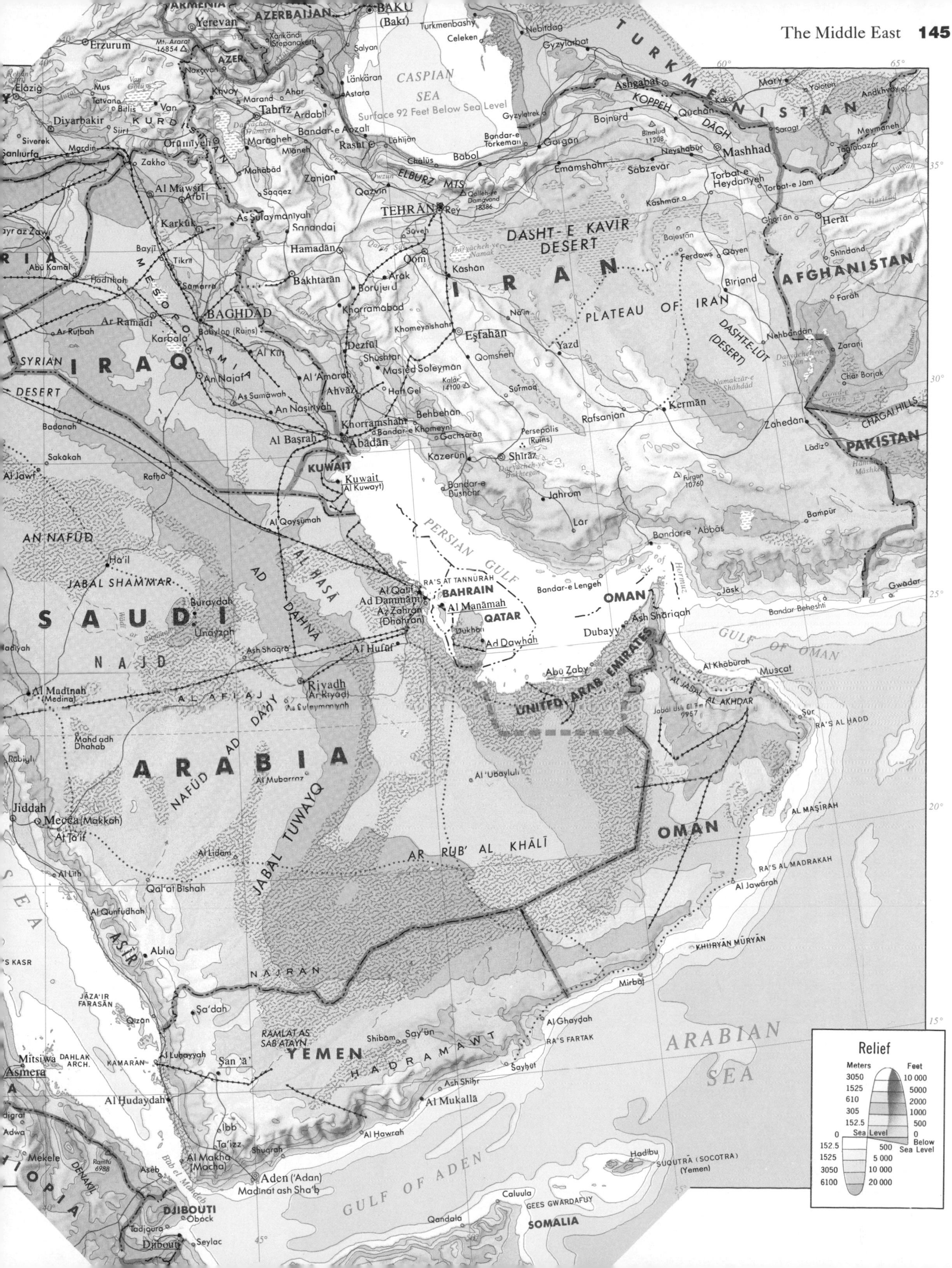
TURKMENISTAN
BAKU
(Bakı)
AZERBAIJAN
ARMENIA
Yerevan
Erzurum
Mt. Ararat
16854
Xankändi
(Stepanakert)
AZER.
Naxçıvan
Elâzığ
Muş
Tatvan
Bitlis
Van
Diyarbakir
Siirt
KURDISTAN
Siverek
Şanlıurfa
Mardin
Zakho
Khvoy
Marand
Ahar
Tabrīz
Ardabīl
Orūmīyeh
Maragheh
Mīāneh
Mahābād
Saqqez
Zanjān
Bandar-e Anzalī
Rasht
Lāhījān
Astara
Länkäran
Şalyan
Turkmenbashy
Celeken
Nebitdag
Gyzylarbat
CASPIAN
SEA
Surface 92 Feet Below Sea Level
Gyzyletrek
Bandar-e Torkeman
Gorgān
Bābol
Chālūs
ELBURZ MTS.
Qolleh-ye Damāvand
18386
Ashgabat
KOPPEH DĀGH
Qūchān
Bojnūrd
Binalud
11208
Neyshābūr
Mashhad
Emāmshahr
Sabzevār
Torbat-e Heydarīyeh
Torbat-e Jam
Kāshmar
Mary
Yoloten
Andkhvoy
Saragt
Meymaneh
Tagtabazar
Herāt
Ghūrīān
Shīndand
Farāh
AFGHANISTAN
Al Mawşil
Arbīl
As Sulaymānīyah
Karkūk
Sanandaj
Qazvīn
TEHRĀN
Rey
Saveh
Hamadān
Qom
Kāshān
Arāk
Bakhtarān
Borūjerd
Khorramābād
DASHT-E KAVĪR
DESERT
IRAN
Bajestān
Ferdows
Qāyen
Bīrjand
PLATEAU OF IRAN
DASHT-E-LŪT
(DESERT)
Nehbandān
Zaranj
Chār Borjak
Nā'īn
Khomeynīshahr
Eşfahān
Yazd
Dezfūl
Shūshtar
Masjed Soleymān
Qomsheh
Kalār
14100
Ahvāz
Haft Gel
Sūrmaq
Kermān
Rafsanjān
Zāhedān
CHAGAI HILLS
PAKISTAN
Lādīz
Dayr az Zawr
SYRIA
Abū Kamāl
Bayjī
Tikrīt
Sāmarrā'
Hadīthah
MESOPOTAMIA
BAGHDAD
Ar Ramādī
Ar Rutbah
Babylon (Ruins)
Karbalā'
Al Kūt
SYRIAN
DESERT
IRAQ
An Najaf
Al 'Amārah
As Samāwah
An Nāşirīyah
Badanah
Al Başrah
Khorramshahr
Ābādān
Bandar-e Khomeynī
Behbehān
Gachsārān
Persepolis
(Ruins)
Shīrāz
Kāzerūn
Furgun
10760
Bampūr
Sakākah
Al Jawf
Rafhā'
KUWAIT
Kuwait
(Al Kuwayt)
Bandar-e Būshehr
Jahrom
Lār
Bandar-e 'Abbās
Al Qayşūmah
PERSIAN GULF
Strait of Hormuz
AN NAFŪD
Ḥā'il
JABAL SHAMMAR
AD DAHNĀ
AL HASĀ
RA'S AT TANNŪRAH
Al Qaţīf
Ad Dammām
Az Zahrān
(Dhahran)
BAHRAIN
Al Manāmah
QATAR
Dukhān
Ad Dawḥah
Bandar-e Lengeh
OMAN
Jāsk
Gwādar
Bandar Beheshtī
Ash Shāriqah
Dubayy
GULF OF OMAN
Buraydah
'Unayzah
SAUDI
NAJD
Ash Shaqrā'
Al Hufūf
Abū Zaby
UNITED ARAB EMIRATES
Al Khābūrah
Muscat
AL JABAL AL AKHDAR
Şūr
RA'S AL HADD
Riyadh
(Ar Riyāḍ)
AL AFLĀJ
Al Madīnah
(Medina)
Mahd adh Dhahab
Rābigh
ARABIA
NAFŪD AD DAHY
Al Mubarraz
JABAL TUWAYQ
Al 'Ubaylah
Jiddah
Mecca (Makkah)
At Ṭā'if
OMAN
AL MAŞĪRAH
Al Līdām
AR RUB' AL KHĀLĪ
Al Līth
Qal'at Bīshah
RA'S AL MADRAKAH
Al Jawārah
RED SEA
Al Qunfudhah
'ASĪR
Abhā
KHURIYĀN MURIYĀN
NAJRĀN
Mirbāţ
JAZĀ'IR FARASĀN
Şa'dah
Qīzān
Al Ghayḍah
RAMLAT AS SAB'ATAYN
Shibām
Say'ūn
RA'S FARTAK
ARABIAN SEA
Mitsiwa
DAHLAK ARCH.
KAMARAN
Al Luḥayyah
Şan'ā'
YEMEN
HADRAMAWT
Sayhūt
Asmera
Ash Shiḥr
Al Mukallā
Al Ḥudaydah
Ibb
Al Ḥawrah
Ta'izz
Shuqrah
Hadibu
SUQUTRĀ (SOCOTRA)
(Yemen)
Mekele
Ramlu
6988
DENAKIL
Aseb
Al Mukhā
(Mocha)
Bab el Mandeb
Aden ('Adan)
Madīnat ash Sha'b
GULF OF ADEN
Caluula
GEES GWARDAFUY
Qandala
SOMALIA
DJIBOUTI
Obock
Tadjoura
Djibouti
Seylac
ETHIOPIA
Relief
Meters
Feet
3050
10 000
1525
5000
610
2000
305
1000
152.5
500
0
Sea Level
0
152.5
500
1525
5 000
3050
10 000
6100
20 000
Below Sea Level

Scale 1:16 000 000; one inch to 250 miles. Polyconic Projection
Elevations and depressions are given in feet

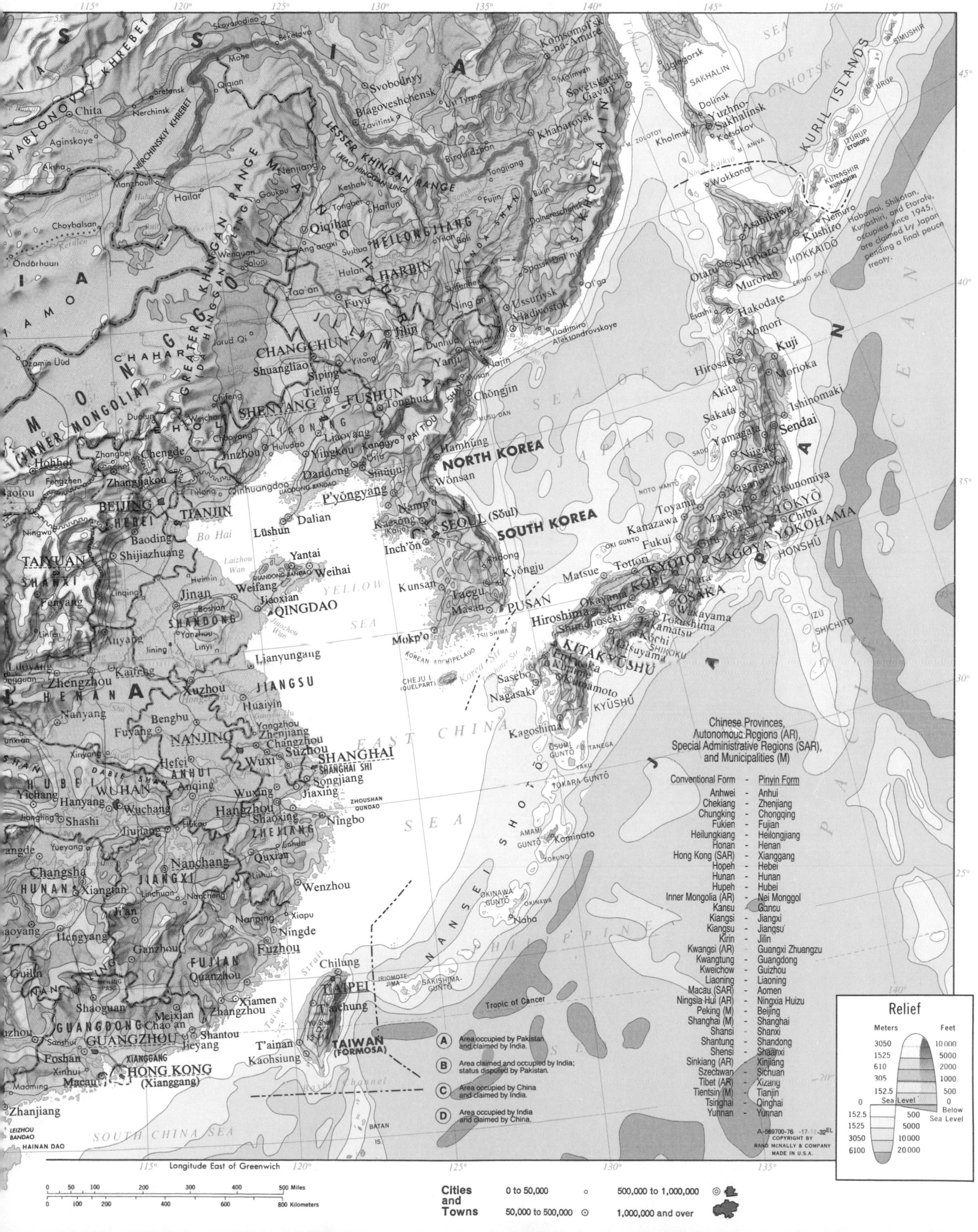
NORTH KOREA
SOUTH KOREA
TAIWAN (FORMOSA)
HONG KONG (Xianggang)
INNER MONGOLIA
HEILONGJIANG
JILIN
LIAONING
HEBEI
SHANXI
SHANDONG
HENAN
JIANGSU
ANHUI
HUBEI
HUNAN
JIANGXI
ZHEJIANG
FUJIAN
GUANGDONG
SHANGHAI SHI
BEIJING
TIANJIN
SHENYANG
HARBIN
CHANGCHUN
FUSHUN
QINGDAO
NANJING
SHANGHAI
WUHAN
GUANGZHOU
P'yŏngyang
SEOUL (Sŏul)
PUSAN
TŌKYŌ
YOKOHAMA
NAGOYA
KYŌTO
ŌSAKA
KŌBE
KITAKYŪSHŪ
SAKHALIN
KURIL ISLANDS
HOKKAIDŌ
HONSHŪ
SHIKOKU
KYŪSHŪ
SEA OF OKHOTSK
SEA OF JAPAN
YELLOW SEA
EAST CHINA SEA
SOUTH CHINA SEA
PACIFIC OCEAN
Bo Hai
NANSEI SHOTŌ
Tropic of Cancer
Habomai, Shikotan, Kunashiri, and Etorofu, occupied since 1945, are claimed by Japan pending a final peace treaty.
Chinese Provinces, Autonomous Regions (AR), Special Administrative Regions (SAR), and Municipalities (M)
Conventional Form - Pinyin Form
Anhwei - Anhui
Chekiang - Zhenjiang
Chungking - Chongqing
Fukien - Fujian
Heilungkiang - Heilongjiang
Honan - Henan
Hong Kong (SAR) - Xianggang
Hopeh - Hebei
Hunan - Hunan
Hupeh - Hubei
Inner Mongolia (AR) - Nei Monggol
Kansu - Gansu
Kiangsi - Jiangxi
Kiangsu - Jiangsu
Kirin - Jilin
Kwangsi (AR) - Guangxi Zhuangzu
Kwangtung - Guangdong
Kweichow - Guizhou
Liaoning - Liaoning
Macau (SAR) - Aomen
Ningsia Hui (AR) - Ningxia Huizu
Peking (M) - Beijing
Shanghai (M) - Shanghai
Shansi - Shanxi
Shantung - Shandong
Shensi - Shaanxi
Sinkiang (AR) - Xinjiang
Szechwan - Sichuan
Tibet (AR) - Xizang
Tientsin (M) - Tianjin
Tsinghai - Qinghai
Yunnan - Yunnan
A Area occupied by Pakistan and claimed by India.
B Area claimed and occupied by India; status disputed by Pakistan.
C Area occupied by China and claimed by India.
D Area occupied by India and claimed by China.
Relief
Meters Feet
3050 10000
1525 5000
610 2000
305 1000
152.5 500
0 Sea Level 0
Below Sea Level
152.5 500
1525 5000
3050 10000
6100 20000
A-569700-76 -17-10-32EL
COPYRIGHT BY RAND McNALLY & COMPANY MADE IN U.S.A.
Longitude East of Greenwich
0 50 100 200 300 400 500 Miles
0 100 200 400 600 800 Kilometers
Cities and Towns
0 to 50,000
50,000 to 500,000
500,000 to 1,000,000
1,000,000 and over

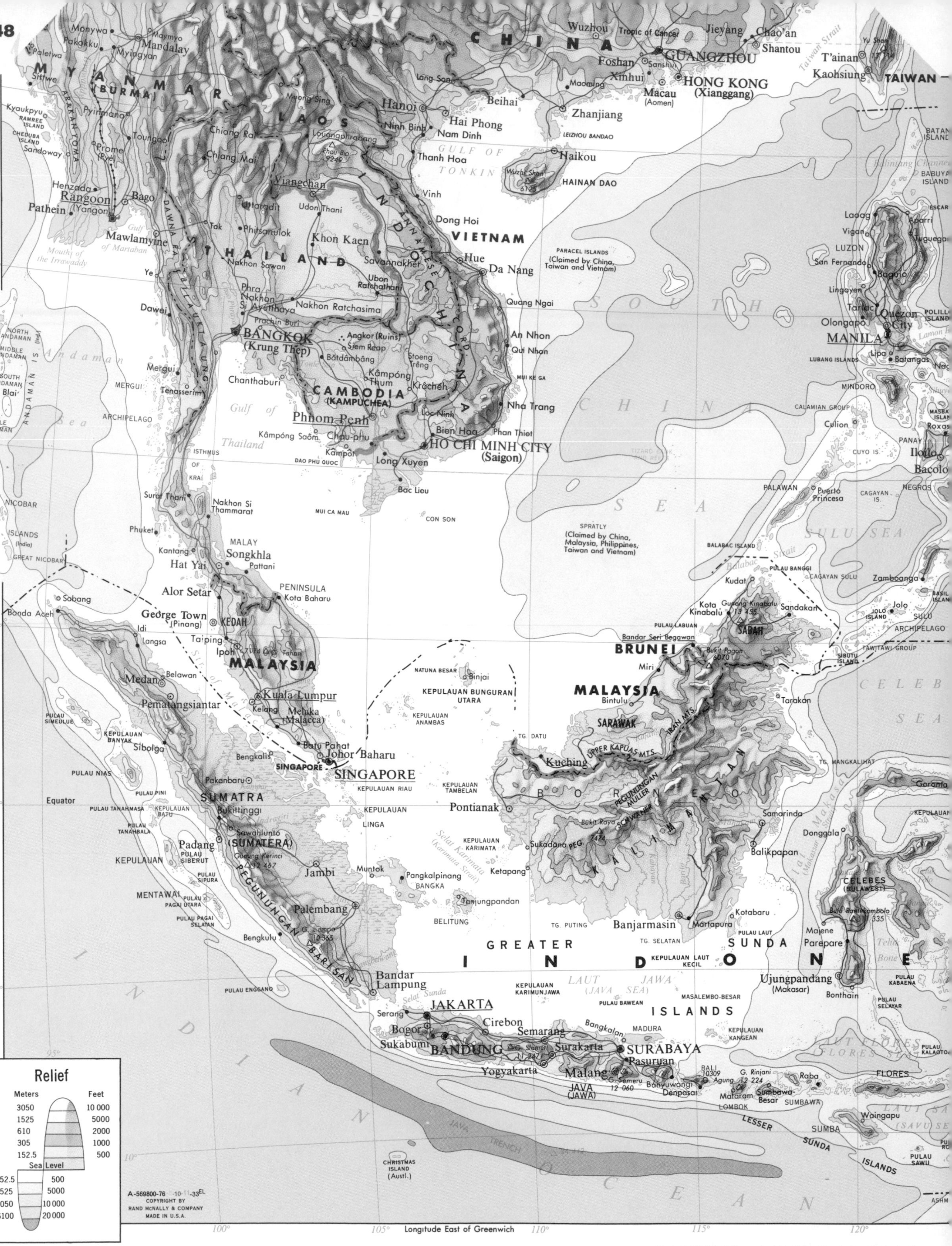

Scale 1:16 000 000; one inch to 250 miles. Polyconic Projection

Elevations and depressions are given in feet

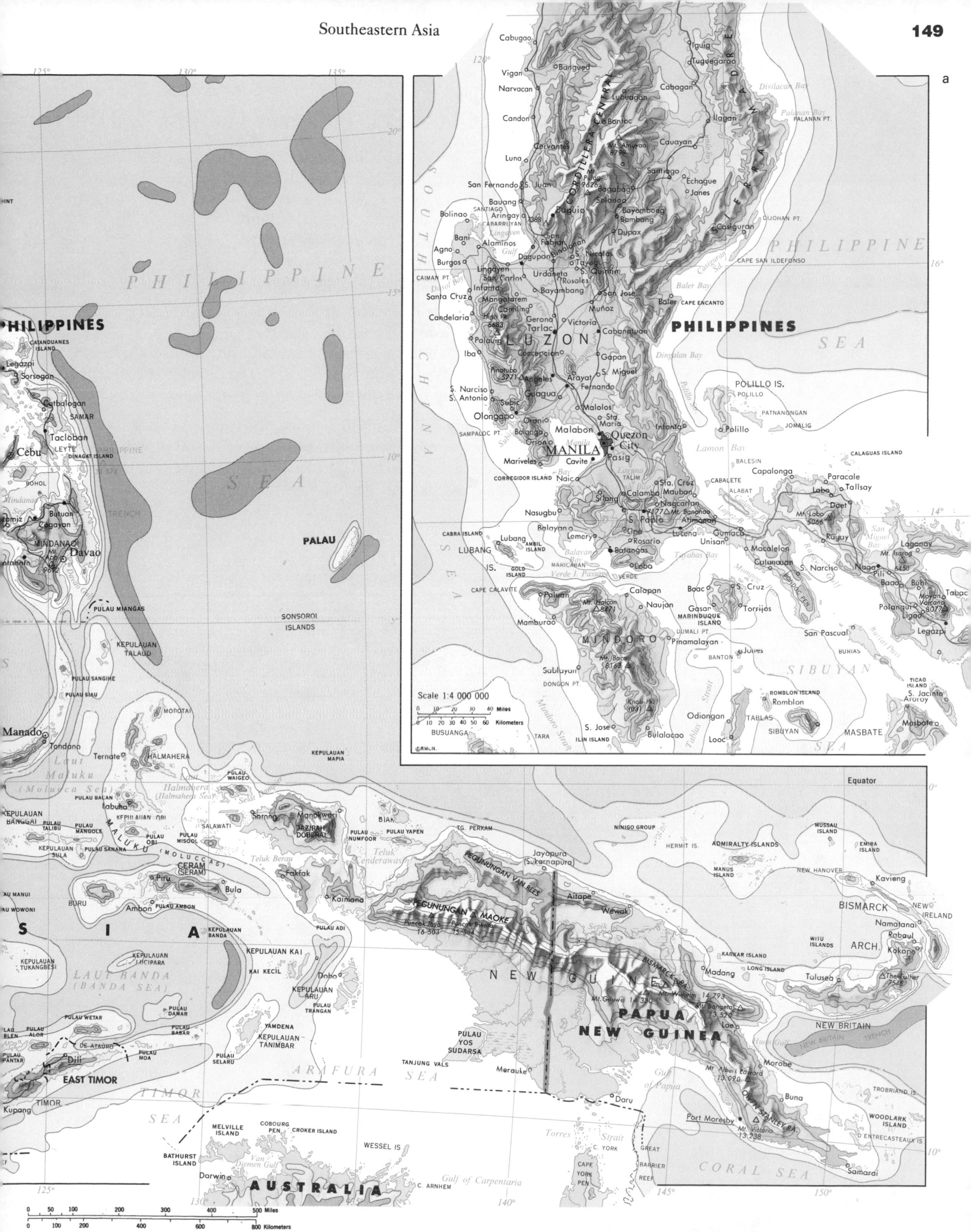
a
PHILIPPINES
PHILIPPINE SEA
LUZON
SOUTH CHINA SEA
Cabugao
Vigan
Narvacan
Candon
Luna
San Fernando
S. Juan
Bauang
Bolinao
Aringay
Baguio
Bani
Agno
Burgos
Alaminos
Lingayen Gulf
Dagupan
Lingayen
San Carlos
Urdaneta
Infanta
Santa Cruz
Mangatarem
Bayambang
Candelaria
Camiling
Gerona
Tarlac
Victoria
Cabanatuan
Palauig
Iba
Concepcion
Gapan
S. Miguel
Arayat
S. Fernando
Angeles
Guagua
Subic
S. Narciso
S. Antonio
Olongapo
Malolos
Sta. Maria
Orani
Balanga
Orion
Malabon
Quezon City
MANILA
Cavite
Pasig
Mariveles
Manila Bay
CORREGIDOR ISLAND
Naic
Nasugbu
Balayan
Lemery
Calamba
Sta. Cruz
Mauban
Nagcarlan
S. Pablo
Atimonan
Lipa
Rosario
Batangas
Lucena
Unisan
Gumaca
Lobo
Calapan
Naujan
Paluan
Mamburao
MINDORO
Sablayan
S. Jose
Bulalacao
Pinamalayan
Boac
Gasan
MARINDUQUE ISLAND
S. Cruz
Torrijos
Bangued
Luba
Bontoc
Cervantes
Mt. Pulog 9626
Mt. Amuyao 8799
Bagabag
Solano
Bayombong
Bambang
Dupax
San Fabian
Binalonan
S. Nicolas
Tayug
S. Quintin
Rosales
San Jose
Muñoz
CORDILLERA CENTRAL
SIERRA MADRE
Iguig
Tuguegarao
Cabagan
Ilagan
Cauayan
Santiago
Echague
Jones
Casiguran
Baler
Baler Bay
CAPE ENCANTO
CAPE SAN ILDEFONSO
Divilacan Bay
Palanan Bay
PALANAN PT.
DIJOHAN PT.
Dingalan Bay
POLILLO IS.
POLILLO
PATNANONGAN
JOMALIG
Polillo
Infanta
Lamon Bay
BALESIN
CALAGUAS ISLAND
Capalonga
Paracale
Labo
Tallsay
Daet
Mt. Labo 5066
Ragay
Lagonoy
Mt. Isarog 6450
Naga
Pili
Baao
Buhi
Tabaco
Mayon Volcano 8077
Polangui
Ligao
Legazpi
San Pascual
Macalelon
Calauag
S. Narciso
BONDOC PEN.
Tayabas Bay
Lubang
LUBANG IS.
CABRA ISLAND
AMBIL ISLAND
GOLD ISLAND
Verde I. Passage
CAPE CALAVITE
Mt. Halcon 8481
Mt. Baco 8163
Knob Pk. 3031
DONGON PT.
ILIN ISLAND
TARA
BUSUANGA
Tablas Strait
Mindoro Strait
Odiongan
Looc
TABLAS
ROMBLON ISLAND
Romblon
SIBUYAN
SIBUYAN SEA
MASBATE
Masbate
TICAO ISLAND
S. Jacinto
Aroroy
BURIAS
BANTON
Scale 1:4 000 000
Miles
Kilometers
©RMcN.
PHILIPPINES
CATANDUANES ISLAND
Legazpi
Sorsogan
Catbalogan
SAMAR
Tacloban
LEYTE
DINAGAT ISLAND
Cebu
BOHOL
Butuan
Cagayan
MINDANAO
Davao
Mt. Apo 9692
PHILIPPINE TRENCH
PHILIPPINE SEA
PALAU
PULAU MIANGAS
SONSOROL ISLANDS
KEPULAUAN TALAUD
PULAU SANGIHE
PULAU SIAU
MOROTAI
Manado
Tondano
Ternate
HALMAHERA
Laut Maluku (Molucca Sea)
Laut Halmahera (Halmahera Sea)
PULAU WAIGEO
KEPULAUAN MAPIA
PULAU BACAN
Labuha
KEPULAUAN OBI
KEPULAUAN BANGGAI
PULAU TALIBU
PULAU MANGOLE
KEPULAUAN SULA
PULAU SANANA
PULAU OBI
PULAU MISOOL
SALAWATI
Sorong
Manokwari
JAZIRAH DOBERAI
BIAK
PULAU NUMFOOR
PULAU YAPEN
Teluk Berau
Teluk Cenderawasih
MALUKU (MOLUCCAS)
CERAM (SERAM)
Piru
Bula
Fakfak
Kaimana
BURU
Ambon
PULAU AMBON
KEPULAUAN BANDA
PULAU ADI
KEPULAUAN KAI
KAI KECIL
Dobo
KEPULAUAN ARU
PULAU TRANGAN
KEPULAUAN LUCIPARA
KEPULAUAN TUKANGBESI
LAUT BANDA (BANDA SEA)
PULAU DAMAR
PULAU WETAR
PULAU ALOR
PULAU BABAR
YAMDENA
KEPULAUAN TANIMBAR
DE ATAURO
Dili
EAST TIMOR
PULAU MOA
PULAU SELARU
PULAU PANTAR
TIMOR
Kupang
TIMOR SEA
ARAFURA SEA
TANJUNG VALS
PULAU YOS SUDARSA
Merauke
MELVILLE ISLAND
BATHURST ISLAND
COBOURG PEN.
CROKER ISLAND
WESSEL IS
Van Diemen Gulf
Darwin
AUSTRALIA
C. ARNHEM
Gulf of Carpentaria
CAPE YORK PEN.
C. YORK
Torres Strait
GREAT BARRIER REEF
CORAL SEA
TG. PERKAM
Jayapura (Sukarnapura)
PEGUNUNGAN VAN REES
PEGUNUNGAN MAOKE
Puncak Jaya 16 503
Puncak Trikora 15 584
NEW GUINEA
Aitape
Wewak
Sepik
Digul
Fly
Madang
BISMARCK RA.
Mt. Wilhelm 14 793
Mt. Giluwe 14 330
Mt. Bangeta 13 520
Lae
PAPUA NEW GUINEA
Huon Gulf
Morobe
Mt. Albert Edward 13 090
OWEN STANLEY RA.
Buna
Port Moresby
Mt. Victoria 13 238
Gulf of Papua
Daru
Samarai
NINIGO GROUP
HERMIT IS.
ADMIRALTY ISLANDS
MANUS ISLAND
MUSSAU ISLAND
EMIRA ISLAND
NEW HANOVER
Kavieng
NEW IRELAND
BISMARCK ARCH.
Namatanai
Rabaul
Kokopo
WITU ISLANDS
KARKAR ISLAND
LONG ISLAND
Talasea
The Father 7546
NEW BRITAIN
NEW BRITAIN TRENCH
TROBRIAND IS.
WOODLARK ISLAND
D'ENTRECASTEAUX IS.
Equator
125°
130°
135°
140°
145°
150°
20°
15°
10°
5°
0°
Miles
Kilometers

Oceania (including Australia and New Zealand)

Bay of Islands, North Island, New Zealand

Oceania is comprised of Australia, New Zealand, eastern New Guinea, and approximately 25,000 other islands in the South Pacific, most of which are uninhabited. Many of the islands are coral atolls, formed by microscopic creatures over scores of centuries, while others are the result of volcanic action.

Oceania's largest landmass is Australia, which at three million square miles (7.7 million sq km) is the world's smallest continent. In fact, it is smaller than five countries—Russia, Canada, China, Brazil, and the United States. Australia is generally flat and dry. The interior is sparsely populated, with most people living in coastal cities such as Sydney.

The next-largest part of Oceania is Papua New Guinea, the country occupying the eastern half of the island of New Guinea, which has some of the most forbidding and remote terrain in the world. New Zealand, Oceania's third-largest country, is known for its natural beauty and its huge herds of sheep.

Oceania at a glance

Land area: 3,300,000 square miles (8,500,000 sq km)

Estimated population: 31,415,000

Population density: 9.5/square mile (3.7/sq km)

Mean elevation: 1,000 feet (305 m)

Highest point: Mt. Wilhelm, Papua New Guinea, 14,793 feet (4,509 m)

Lowest point: Lake Eyre, South Australia, 52 feet (16 m) below sea level

Longest river: Murray-Darling, 2,330 mi (3,750 km)

Number of countries (incl. dependencies): 33

Largest independent country: Australia, 2,969,910 square miles (7,692,030 sq km)

Smallest independent country: Nauru, 8.0 square miles (21 sq km)

Most populous independent country: Australia, 19,455,000

Least populous independent country: Tuvalu, 11,000

Largest city: Brisbane, pop. 806,746

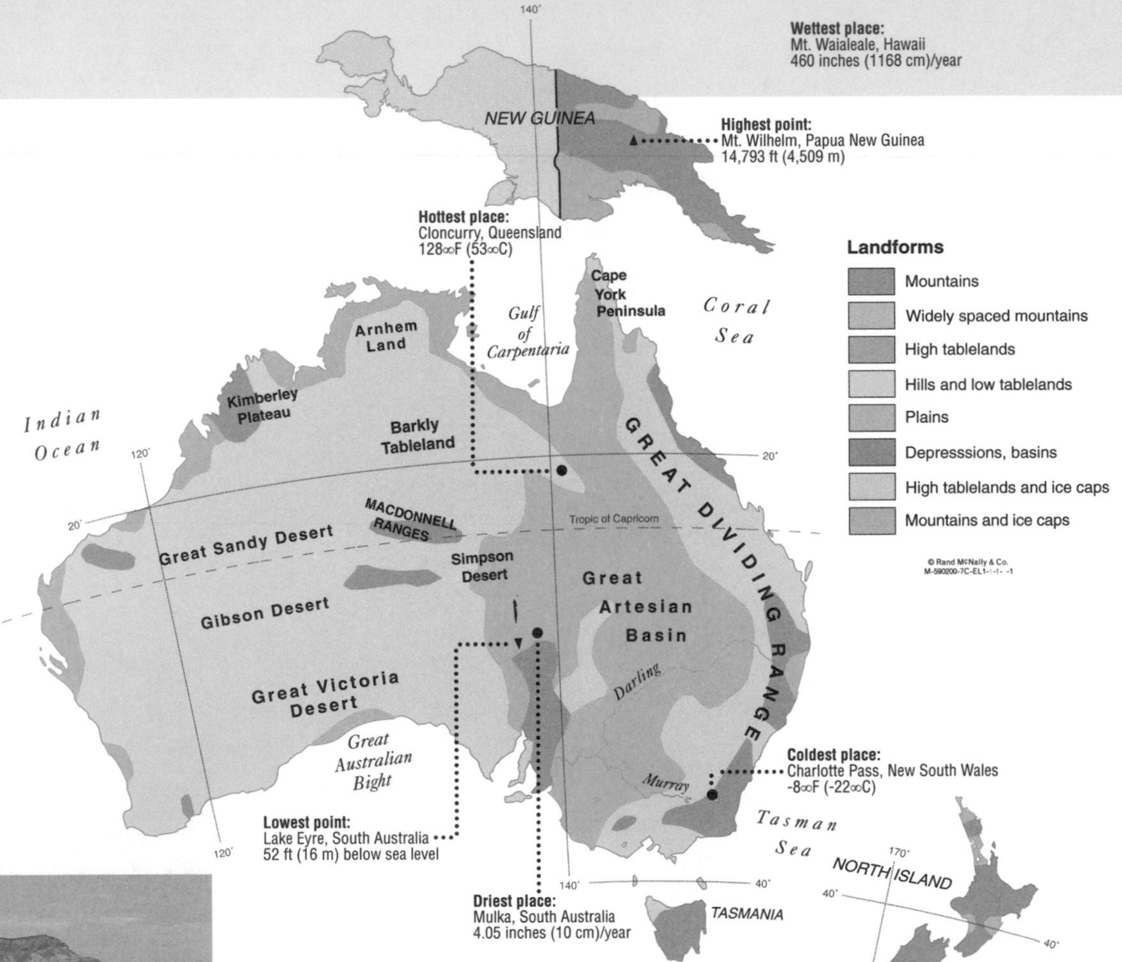

The Outback, Australia

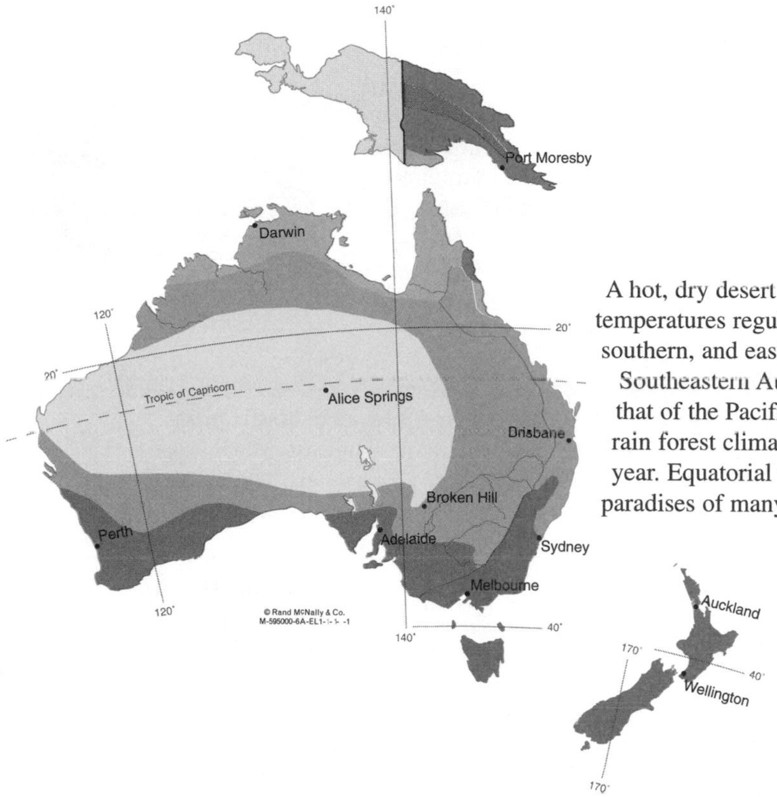

Climate

A hot, dry desert climate prevails in central and western Australia, where summer temperatures regularly rise above 100°F (40°C). Toward the continent's northern, southern, and eastern coasts, the climate becomes more temperate and less arid. Southeastern Australia and New Zealand enjoy a milder, rainier climate similar to that of the Pacific Northwest of the United States. New Guinea, which has a tropical rain forest climate, experiences heavy rainfall and high temperatures throughout the year. Equatorial warmth and moderating tradewinds combine to make tropical paradises of many of Oceania's islands.

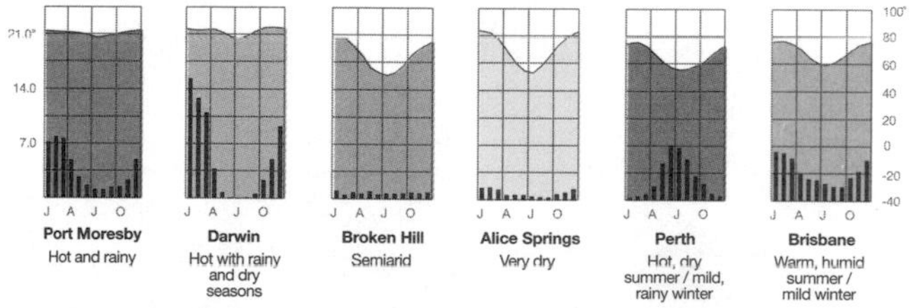

Tinted areas show temperature in degrees Fahrenheit. Vertical bars show precipitation in inches.

Population

Australia's population is concentrated in the coastal regions, especially along the stretch of southeastern coast that includes Adelaide, Melbourne, Sydney, and Brisbane. Almost all Australians speak English and are descendants of British settlers. In recent years, many immigrants have arrived from Asia, especially Hong Kong. Aboriginal people account for only about 1% of Australia's population. New Zealand has a similar ethnic make-up, but its indigenous people, the Maori, represent about 10% of the population. The North Island is home to approximately three out of four New Zealanders; the South Island, which is more mountainous and heavily forested, is sparsely populated.

Centuries of isolation have given rise to many distinctive cultures among the island groups of Oceania. There has been little immigration from other parts of the world.

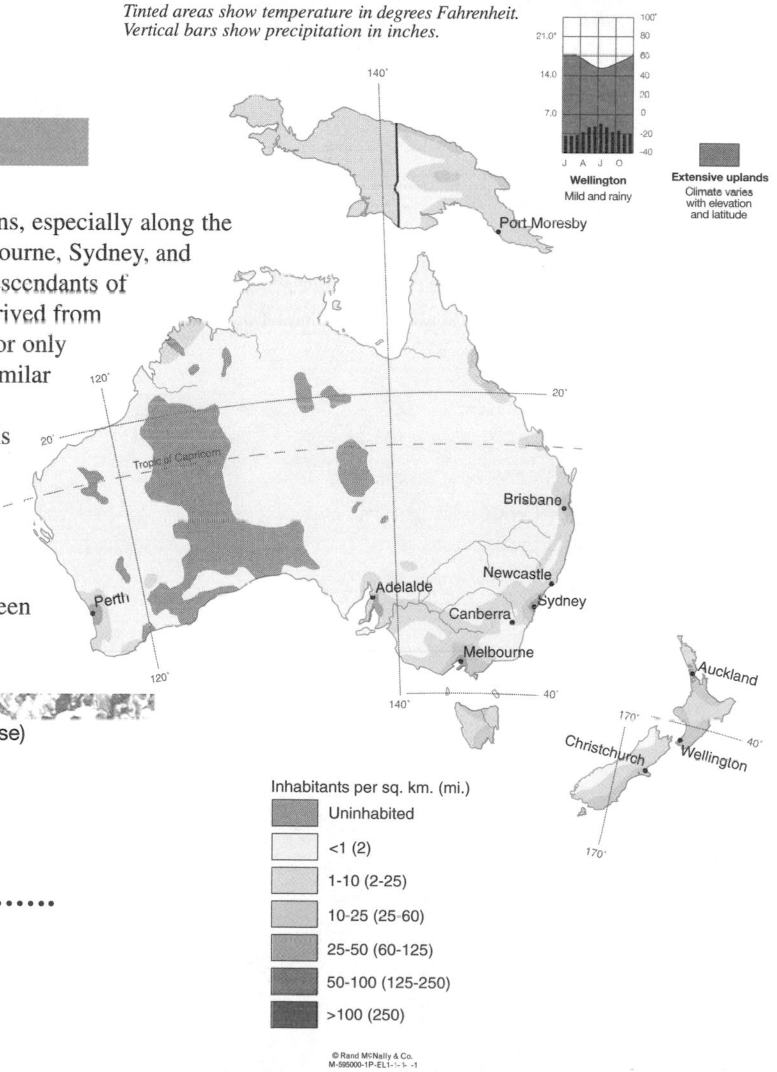

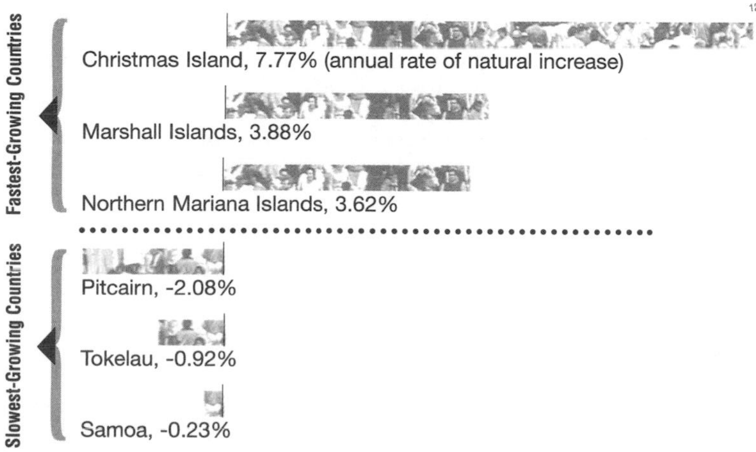

Environments and Land Use

Farmland on North Island, New Zealand

Much of central and western Australia is a dry, inhospitable land of sand, rocks, and scrub vegetation. Surrounding this desert region is a broad band of semiarid grassland that covers more than half of the continent and supports a huge livestock industry. Australia has more sheep—132 million—than any other country in the world, as well as sizable herds of cattle. The dry climate and sparse plant life, however, mean that each animal requires a dozen or more acres to survive. Six percent of the continent is suitable for crops; most of the arable land is found on fertile plains in the southeast. Major crops include wheat, sugar cane, oats, barley, sorghum, and rice.

Tourism plays an important role in Australia's economy. Among the continent's major attractions are its unusual wildlife, such as kangaroos, koalas, wombats, and platypuses; the Great Barrier Reef, which stretches for 1,250 miles (2,000 km) along the northeastern coast; and the ruggedly beautiful Outback, with its dramatic rock formations such as Ayers Rock (Uluru) and the Olga Rocks.

Thanks to its fertile land and temperate climate, New Zealand has a thriving livestock industry and is a leading world exporter of dairy products and lamb. Thinly populated and with little industry, it is one of the world's least polluted countries. Its pristine beauty encompasses a variety of scenery, including mountains, fjords, glaciers, rain forests, beaches and geysers. Only the country's relative isolation restrains its growing tourism industry.

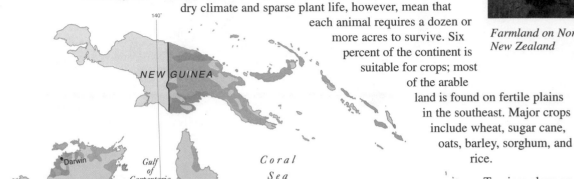

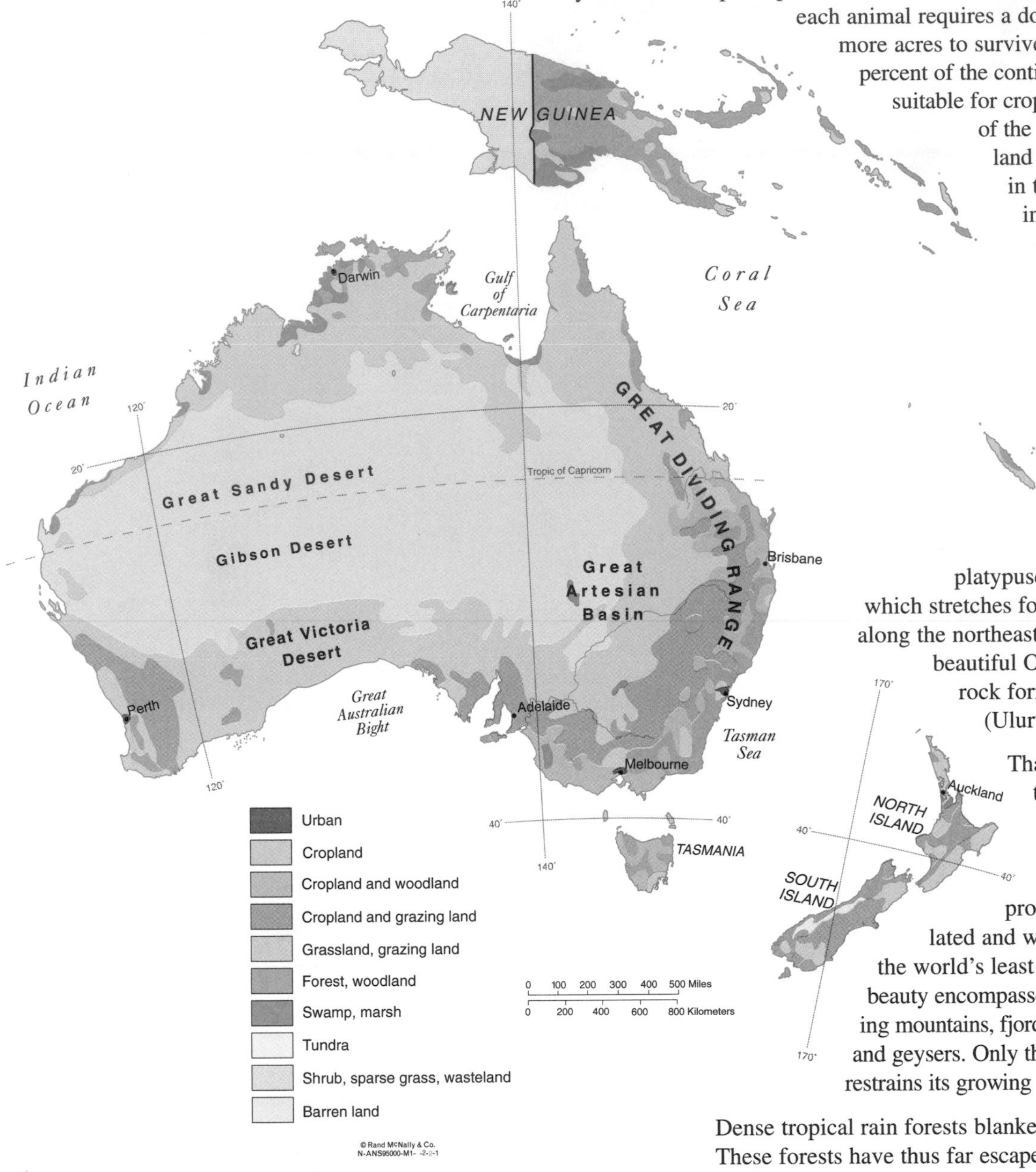

Dense tropical rain forests blanket much of Papua New Guinea. These forests have thus far escaped the large-scale deforestation that is taking place in other tropical forests around the world.

Tourism is central to the economies of many of the islands throughout Oceania. Abundant sunshine, pleasant temperatures, and beautiful beaches draw millions of visitors each year to islands such as Tahiti and Fiji. For islands with little or no tourism, the economic scene is less promising: many islanders rely on subsistence fishing and foreign aid from former colonial powers.

Herding sheep near Goulburn, New South Wales

The Original Australians and New Zealanders

Aboriginal boy with elders, Western Australia

Many anthropologists believe that Australia's Aborigines are the oldest race of people on Earth. During the 40,000 years since they migrated to the island continent from Asia, they have developed a rich culture with an intricate spiritual and social life.

The original New Zealanders, the Maoris, arrived from other Polynesian islands in the 10th century. At the beginning of large-scale immigration from Britain in the 1800s, the British government signed a treaty with the Maoris which granted them full rights as citizens. With the exception of some disputes over land, this agreement has paved the way for the historically harmonious relations between the races in New Zealand.

Relations between the Aborigines and whites in Australia have been less harmonious. The arrival of the first European colonists in 1788 set in motion a chain of events that decimated the Aborigines and threatened their unique culture. Disease and skirmishes killed Aborigines along the coast, and thousands of others were forced from their lands by settlers. Some sought refuge with Aborigines already living in Australia's interior, the Outback. Alcoholism and other social problems became common among the Aborigines as they found themselves confronted by a society they did not understand.

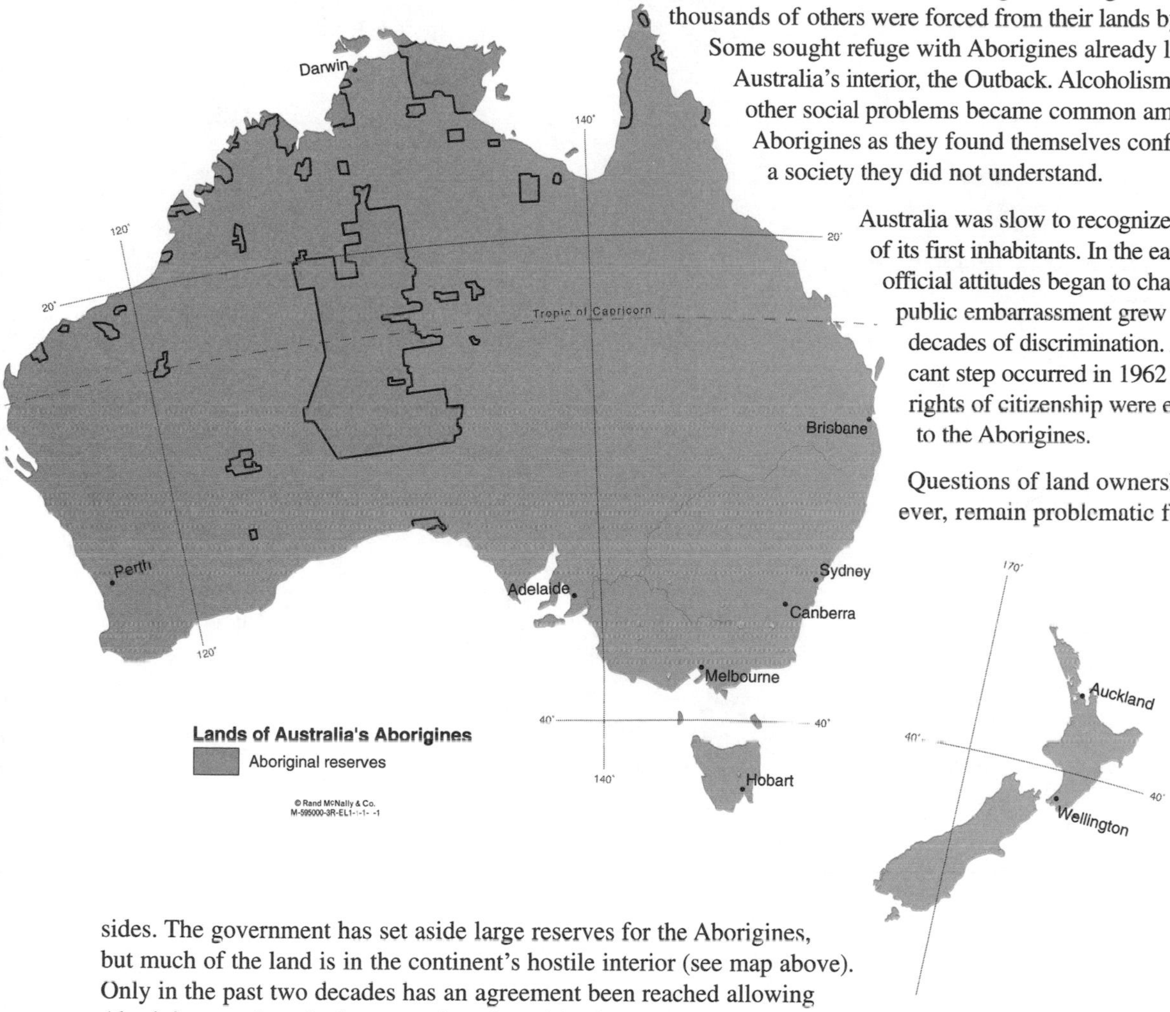

Australia was slow to recognize the rights of its first inhabitants. In the early 1960s, official attitudes began to change as public embarrassment grew over the decades of discrimination. A significant step occurred in 1962 when full rights of citizenship were extended to the Aborigines.

Questions of land ownership, however, remain problematic for both sides. The government has set aside large reserves for the Aborigines, but much of the land is in the continent's hostile interior (see map above). Only in the past two decades has an agreement been reached allowing Aborigines to share in the vast mineral wealth of their northern lands. Recent court decisions have awarded individual Aborigines rights to ancestral lands which were seized by settlers, but many local governments continue to fight these decisions.

In the face of indifference and hostility, there has recently been an upsurge of interest in cultural traditions among the approximately 240,000 Australians of aboriginal descent. Still, many of the traditions of the 500 different tribes that were present 200 years ago have been lost.

Scale 1:16 000 000; one inch to 250 miles. Lambert's Azimuthal, Equal Area Projection
Elevations and depressions are given in feet

PAPUA NEW GUINEA
NEW GUINEA
Mt. Albert Edward 13,100
Buna
Mt. Victoria 13,363
Port Moresby
OWEN STANLEY RA.
Torres Strait
MULGRAVE
BANKS
THURSDAY
HORN
PRINCE OF WALES
CAPE YORK
TROBRIAND IS.
WOODLARK
D'ENTRECASTEAUX ISLANDS
SOUTH CAPE
Samarai
LOUISIADE ARCHIPELAGO
TAGULA
ROSSEL
CHOISEUL
VELLA LAVELLA
NEW GEORGIA
RENDOVA
SANTA ISABEL
MALAITA
FLORIDA
TULAGI
SOLOMON ISLANDS
RUSSELL IS.
GUADALCANAL
Honiara
SAN CRISTÓBAL
RENNELL
SANTA CRUZ ISLANDS
Weipa
CAPE
YORK
PENINSULA
Princess Charlotte Bay
OSPREY REEF
CAPE MELVILLE
CORAL SEA
TORRES IS.
BANKS ISLANDS
Laura
Cooktown
Palmerville
GREAT BARRIER REEF
HOLMES REEFS
WILLIS IS.
ESPÍRITU SANTO
MAEWO
PENTECOST
NEW HEBRIDES
MALEKULA
AMBRIM
EPI
VANUATU
EFATE
Port Vila
EROMANGA
TANA
ANEITYUM
ATHERTON PLATEAU
Cairns
Mungana
Normanton
Croydon
Mt. Bartle Frere 5322
FLINDERS REEFS
LIHOU REEF
TREGROSSE IS.
Forsayth
Ingham
HINCHINBROOK
GREGORY RANGE
Halifax Bay
Townsville
MARION REEF
PACIFIC OCEAN
Charters Towers
Bowen
Richmond
Hughenden
WHITSUNDAY
CUMBERLAND IS.
CLARKE RA.
Repulse Bay
Mackay
Mt. Dalrymple 4190
CONNORS RANGE
ÎLES CHESTERFIELD (Fr.)
ÎLES BÉLEP
Kynuna
Winton
NORTHUMBERLAND IS.
SWAIN REEFS
Capricorn Chan.
WRECK REEFS
OUVÉA
LIFOU
NEW CALEDONIA (Fr.)
ÎLES LOYAUTÉ (French)
MARÉ
Nouméa
ÎLE DES PINS
Tropic of Capricorn
QUEENSLAND
GREAT ARTESIAN BASIN
GREAT DIVIDING RANGE
Clermont
Barcaldine
Emerald
Longreach
Jericho
Rockhampton
Mount Morgan
CURTIS
Gladstone
Dingo
Blackall
Yaraka
BUCKLAND TABLELAND
Tambo
Windorah
Bundaberg
Hervey Bay
SANDY CAPE
FRASER
Maryborough
Quilpie
Charleville
Gympie
GREY RANGE
Thargomindah
DARLING DOWNS
Toowoomba
Brisbane
N. STRADBROKE I.
Southport
Ipswich
Warwick
Cunnamulla
Dirranbandi
Hungerford
Mungindi
Mt. Roberts
Moree
Tenterfield
Lismore
Brewarrina
Bourke
Walgett
Glen Innes
Inverell
Grafton
NEW ENGLAND RANGE
MAIN BARRIER RANGE
Narrabri
Armidale
Coonamble
Tamworth
The Round Mountain
Wilcannia
Cobar
Nyngan
WARRUMBUNGLE
Kempsey
Broken Hill
Port Macquarie
Nymagee
LIVERPOOL RA.
LORD HOWE (NEW S. WALES)
NEW SOUTH WALES
Dubbo
MURRAY
Orange
Cessnock
Maitland
Newcastle
Wentworth
Forbes
Bathurst
West Wyalong
Lithgow
BLUE MTS.
SYDNEY
RIVERINA
Hay
Narrandera
Botany Bay
Wollongong
Swan Hill
Kerang
Goulburn
Wagga Wagga
Deniliquin
Echuca
Albury
Canberra
Jervis Bay
AUSTL. CAP. TER.
Bendigo
Benalla
Mt. Kosciusko 7316
SNOWY MTS.
Cooma
VICTORIA
Ararat
Ballarat
Maryborough
Bega
Bombala
TASMAN SEA
Geelong
MELBOURNE
CAPE HOWE
Warrnambool
Port Phillip Bay
Bairnsdale
NINETY MILE BEACH
CAPE OTWAY
Wonthaggi
WILSON'S PROMONTORY
KING
Bass Strait
FLINDERS
FURNEAUX GROUP
HUNTER IS.
CAPE BARREN
TASMANIA
Ulverstone
Burnie
Devonport
Launceston
Mt. Ossa 5305
Strahan
Risdon
New Norfolk
Hobart
BRUNY
SOUTH EAST CAPE
NORTH CAPE
Kaitaia
Russell
Hauraki Gulf
GREAT BARRIER
PACIFIC OCEAN
Devonport
Auckland
NORTH ISLAND
Hamilton
Bay of Plenty
EAST CAPE
North Taranaki Bight
NEW ZEALAND
New Plymouth
C. EGMONT
Mt. Ruapehu Vol. 9175
Gisborne
Hawke Bay
South Taranaki Bight
Napier
Hastings
Wanganui
Palmerston North
TASMAN SEA
CAPE FAREWELL
Tasman Bay
Nelson
Lower Hutt
Wellington
Karamea Bight
Cook Strait
CAPE FOULWIND
Greymouth
Hokitika
SOUTH ISLAND
SOUTHERN ALPS
Mt. Cook 12,316
Pegasus Bay
Christchurch
CASCADE PT.
Canterbury Bight
Timaru
RESOLUTION ISLAND
Dunedin
CAPE SAUNDERS
Foveaux Strait
Invercargill
STEWART ISLAND
SOUTHWEST CAPE
©RMCN.
Same scale as main map
Cities and Towns
0 to 50,000
50,000 to 500,000
500,000 to 1,000,000
1,000,000 and over
0 50 100 200 300 400 500 Miles
0 100 200 400 600 800 Kilometers

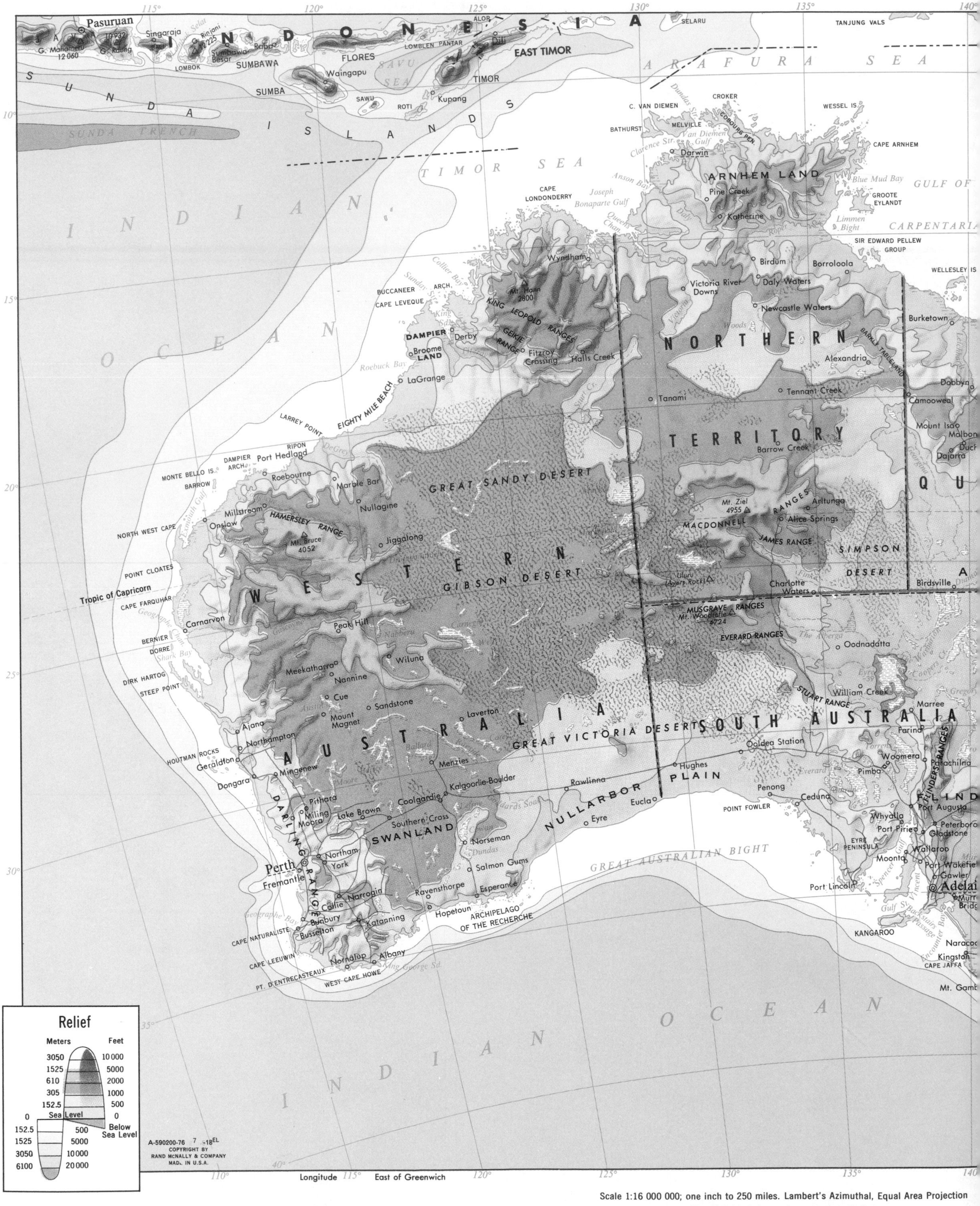

Scale 1:16 000 000; one inch to 250 miles. Lambert's Azimuthal, Equal Area Projection
Elevations and depressions are given in feet

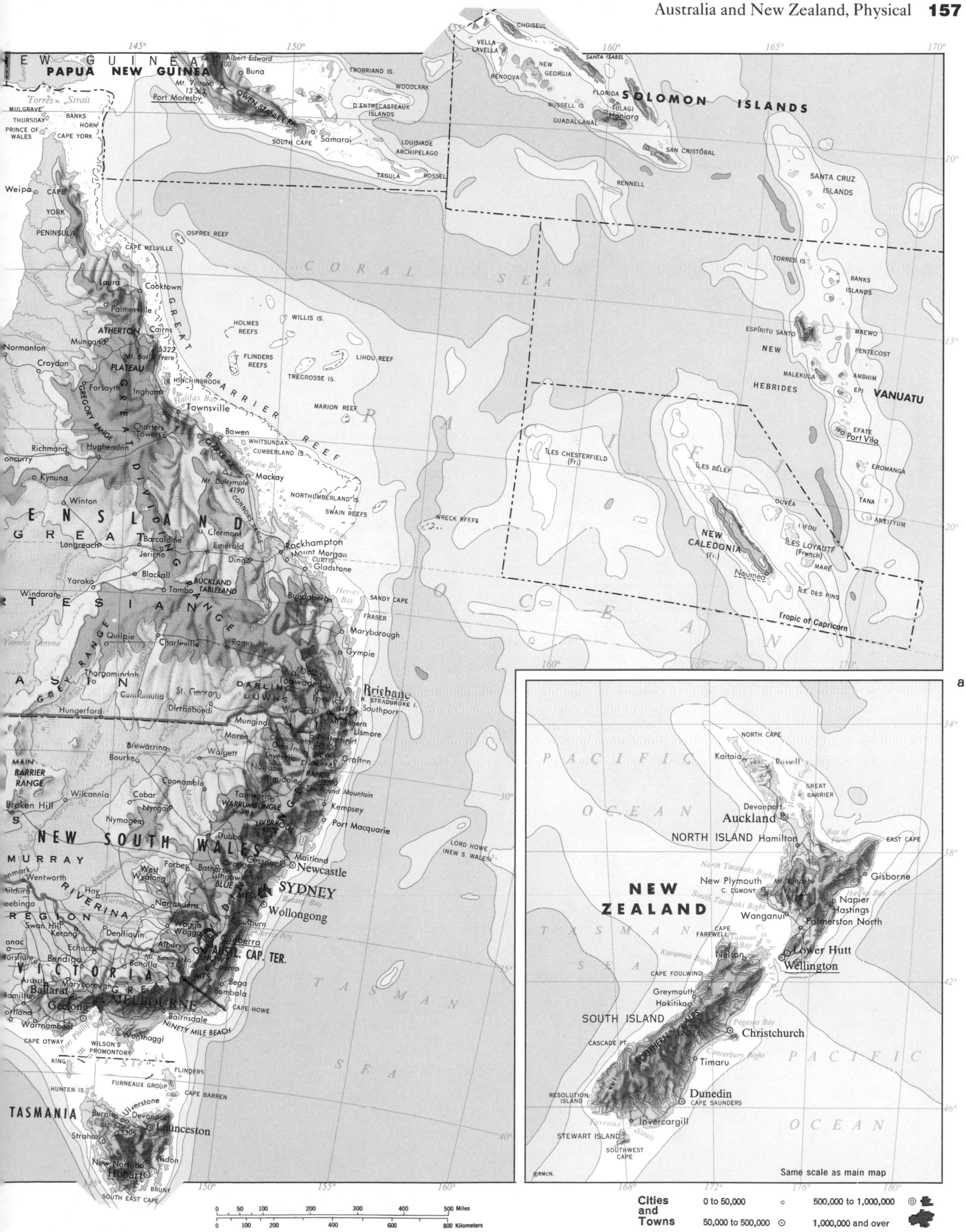
NEW GUINEA
PAPUA NEW GUINEA
Mt. Albert Edward
Buna
Mt. Victoria 13,363
Port Moresby
OWEN STANLEY RA.
TROBRIAND IS.
WOODLARK
D'ENTRECASTEAUX ISLANDS
Samarai
SOUTH CAPE
LOUISIADE ARCHIPELAGO
TAGULA
ROSSEL
CHOISEUL
VELLA LAVELLA
RENDOVA
NEW GEORGIA
SANTA ISABEL
FLORIDA
TULAGI
Honiara
RUSSELL IS.
GUADALCANAL
SOLOMON ISLANDS
SAN CRISTÓBAL
RENNELL
SANTA CRUZ ISLANDS
TORRES IS.
BANKS ISLANDS
ESPÍRITU SANTO
MAEWO
PENTECOST
NEW HEBRIDES
MALEKULA
AMBRIM
EPI
VANUATU
EFATE
Port Vila
EROMANGA
TANA
ANEITYUM
Torres Strait
MULGRAVE
THURSDAY
BANKS
HORN
PRINCE OF WALES
CAPE YORK
Weipa
CAPE YORK PENINSULA
Princess Charlotte Bay
OSPREY REEF
CAPE MELVILLE
CORAL SEA
Laura
Cooktown
Palmerville
GREAT BARRIER REEF
WILLIS IS.
HOLMES REEFS
FLINDERS REEFS
LIHOU REEF
TREGROSSE IS.
ATHERTON PLATEAU
Cairns
Mungana
Mt. Bartle Frere 5322
Normanton
Croydon
Forsayth
HINCHINBROOK
Ingham
Halifax Bay
Townsville
GREGORY RANGE
MARION REEF
Charters Towers
Hughenden
Richmond
Bowen
WHITSUNDAY
CUMBERLAND IS.
CLARKE RA.
Repulse Bay
Mackay
Mt. Dalrymple 4190
CONNORS RANGE
Kynuna
Winton
NORTHUMBERLAND IS.
SWAIN REEFS
Capricorn Chan.
WRECK REEFS
ÎLES CHESTERFIELD (Fr.)
ÎLES BÉLEP
OUVÉA
LIFOU
NEW CALEDONIA (Fr.)
ÎLES LOYAUTÉ (French)
MARÉ
Nouméa
ÎLE DES PINS
Tropic of Capricorn
PACIFIC OCEAN
QUEENSLAND
GREAT DIVIDING RANGE
Clermont
Barcaldine
Emerald
Longreach
Jericho
Dingo
Rockhampton
Mount Morgan
CURTIS
Gladstone
Blackall
Yaraka
BUCKLAND TABLELAND
Tambo
Windorah
GREAT ARTESIAN BASIN
Bundaberg
Hervey Bay
SANDY CAPE
FRASER
Maryborough
Gympie
Quilpie
Charleville
Roma
GREY RANGE
Thargomindah
Cunnamulla
St. George
Dirranbandi
DARLING DOWNS
Toowoomba
Ipswich
Brisbane
N. STRADBROKE I.
Southport
Warwick
Hungerford
Mungindi
Moree
Lismore
Tenterfield
Brewarrina
Bourke
Walgett
Inverell
NEW ENGLAND RANGE
Grafton
Armidale
MAIN BARRIER RANGE
Coonamble
Wilcannia
Cobar
Tamworth
Round Mountain
Kempsey
Broken Hill
WARRUMBUNGLE RA.
LIVERPOOL RA.
Nyngan
Nymagee
Port Macquarie
NEW SOUTH WALES
Dubbo
LORD HOWE (NEW S. WALES)
MURRAY
Maitland
Newcastle
Forbes
Orange
Bathurst
Cessnock
Lithgow
Wentworth
West Wyalong
BLUE MTS.
SYDNEY
RIVERINA
Hay
Narrandera
Wollongong
Botany Bay
REGION
Swan Hill
Wagga Wagga
Goulburn
Kerang
Deniliquin
Canberra
Jervis Bay
Echuca
Albury
AUSTL. CAP. TER.
Bendigo
Benalla
Mt. Kosciusko
SNOWY MTS.
Cooma
VICTORIA
GREAT DIVIDING RANGE
Bega
Bombala
Ballarat
Maryborough
Geelong
MELBOURNE
CAPE HOWE
TASMAN SEA
Warrnambool
Port Phillip Bay
Bairnsdale
NINETY MILE BEACH
Wonthaggi
CAPE OTWAY
WILSON'S PROMONTORY
KING
Bass Strait
FLINDERS
FURNEAUX GROUP
HUNTER IS.
CAPE BARREN
TASMANIA
Ulverstone
Burnie
Devonport
Launceston
Strahan
New Norfolk
Hobart
Risdon
BRUNY
SOUTH EAST CAPE
a
NORTH CAPE
Kaitaia
Russell
GREAT BARRIER
Hauraki Gulf
Devonport
Auckland
NORTH ISLAND
Hamilton
Bay of Plenty
EAST CAPE
North Taranaki Bight
New Plymouth
C. EGMONT
Mt. Ruapehu
Gisborne
Hawke Bay
NEW ZEALAND
South Taranaki Bight
Napier
Hastings
Wanganui
Palmerston North
CAPE FAREWELL
Tasman Bay
Nelson
Lower Hutt
Wellington
Cook Strait
Karamea Bight
CAPE FOULWIND
Greymouth
Hokitika
SOUTH ISLAND
SOUTHERN ALPS
Pegasus Bay
Christchurch
CASCADE PT.
Canterbury Bight
Timaru
RESOLUTION ISLAND
Dunedin
CAPE SAUNDERS
Foveaux Strait
Invercargill
STEWART ISLAND
SOUTHWEST CAPE
©RMCN.
Same scale as main map
0 50 100 200 300 400 500 Miles
0 100 200 400 600 800 Kilometers
Cities and Towns
0 to 50,000
50,000 to 500,000
500,000 to 1,000,000
1,000,000 and over

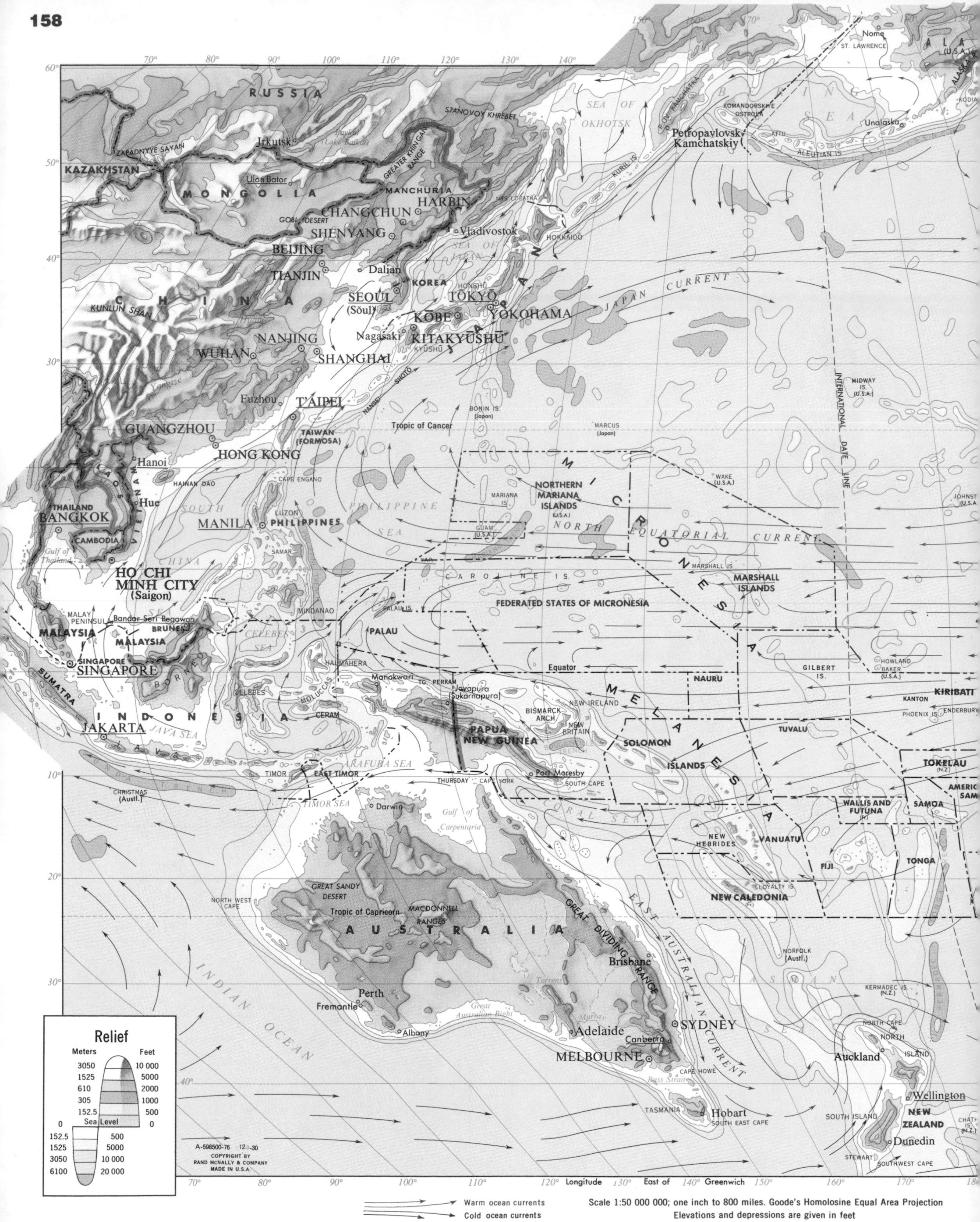

Warm ocean currents

Cold ocean currents

Scale 1:50 000 000; one inch to 800 miles. Goode's Homolosine Equal Area Projection

Elevations and depressions are given in feet

a
Scale 1:4 000 000
HAWAII (U.S.A.)
PACIFIC OCEAN
KAUA'I
NI'IHAU
O'AHU
Honolulu
MOLOKA'I
LĀNA'I
MAUI
KAHO'OLAWE
HAWAI'I
Hilo
CANADA
ROCKY MOUNTAINS
UNITED STATES
Vancouver
Victoria
SEATTLE
Portland
Salt Lake City
SAN FRANCISCO
LOS ANGELES
SAN DIEGO
ST. LOUIS
New Orleans
Galveston
GULF OF MEXICO
MEXICO
SIERRA MADRE OCCIDENTAL
Tampico
Mazatlan
MEXICO CITY
Veracruz
Acapulco
BELIZE
Guatemala
NICARAGUA
Managua
COSTA RICA
PANAMA
CARIBBEAN SEA
CALIFORNIA CURRENT
NORTH EQUATORIAL CURRENT
EQUATORIAL COUNTER CURRENT
SOUTH EQUATORIAL CURRENT
PERU CURRENT
WEST WIND DRIFT
Honolulu
HAWAI'IAN IS. (U.S.A.)
ISLAS REVILLAGIGEDO (Mex.)
ARCHIPÉLAGO DE COLÓN (GALÁPAGOS IS.) (Ecuador)
Buenaventura
Quito
ECUADOR
Guayaquil
COLOMBIA
PERU
LIMA
Callao
Arequipa
Mollendo
PERU-CHILE TRENCH
Iquique
Antofagasta
Coquimbo
Valparaíso
SANTIAGO
Concepción
Valdivia
Puerto Montt
CHILOE
CHILE
ARGENTINA
ANDES MOUNTAINS
Bahía Blanca
Punta Arenas
CABO DE HORNOS
ISLAS DE JUAN FERNANDEZ (Chile)
SAN FÉLIX (Chile)
I. SAN AMBROSIO (Chile)
ISLA DE PASCUA (EASTER) (Chile)
I. SALA Y GÓMEZ (Chile)
PITCAIRN (Br.)
DUCIE
MARQUESAS IS.
SOCIETY IS.
TAHITI
ÎLES TUAMOTU
FRENCH POLYNESIA
COOK ISLANDS (N.Z.)
MANIHIKI IS.
AITUTAKI
RAROTONGA
POLYNESIA
PALMYRA (U.S.A.)
TABUAERAN
KIRITIMATI
MALDEN
Longitude West of Greenwich
Miles
Kilometers

Relief
Meters
Feet
3050
10 000
1525
5000
610
2000
305
1000
0
Sea Level
0
152.5
500
Below Sea Level
1525
5000
3050
10 000
6100
20 000
A-594000-76
COPYRIGHT BY RAND McNALLY & COMPANY MADE IN U.S.A.
Tropic of Capricorn
I. SAN FÉLIX (Chile)
I. SAN AMBROSIO (Chile)
I. SALA Y GÓMEZ (Chile)
RAPA NUI (EASTER) (Chile)
IS. DE JUAN FERNÁNDEZ (Chile)
PERU
La Paz
BOLIVIA
Sucre
SOUTH AMERICA
BRAZIL
PARAGUAY
Asunción
Brasília
SANTIAGO
CHILE
LOS ANDES
ARGENTINA
Rosario
SÃO PAULO
BUENOS AIRES
URUGUAY
MONTEVIDEO
Santos
RIO DE JANEIRO
Río de la Plata
ARCH. DE LOS CHONOS
ÎLES TUAMOTU (Fr.)
Punta Arenas
Estr. de Magallanes
FALKLAND IS. (ISLAS MALVINAS) (Br.)
CABO DE HORNOS
Drake Passage
PACIFIC OCEAN
ATLANTIC OCEAN
INDIAN OCEAN
SOUTH SHETLAND ISLANDS (Br.)
BELLINGSHAUSEN SEA
ADELAIDE
SOUTH ORKNEY IS. (Br.)
SOUTH GEORGIA (Br.)
THURSTON I.
ALEXANDER I.
AMUNDSEN SEA
Mt. Rex 3 625
Mt. Ulmer 8 451
Mt. Siple 10 171
ELLSWORTH MTS.
Mt. Hope 1 513
Vinson Massif 16 066
SOUTH SANDWICH IS. (Br.)
TRISTAN DA CUNHA (Br.)
WEDDELL SEA
RONNE ICE SHELF
Antarctic Circle
EXECUTIVE COMMITTEE RANGE
Mt. Sidley 13 717
WHITMORE MTS.
BERKNER ISLAND
FILCHNER ICE SHELF
GOUGH (Br.)
ROCKEFELLER PLATEAU
THIEL MTS.
PENSACOLA MTS.
COATS LAND
CHATHAM IS. (N.Z.)
Little America
HORLICK MTS.
ROOSEVELT
QUEEN MAUD MTS.
SCOTT
ROSS SEA
ROSS ICE SHELF
South Pole
10 000
QUEEN MAUD LAND
MÜHLIG-HOFMANN MTS.
BOUNTY IS. (N.Z.)
Mt. Markham 14 049
Mt. Erebus 12 280
McMurdo
Mt. Sabine 12 201
Mt. Albert Markham 10 522
Mt. McClintock 11 457
BOUVETØYA (Nor.)
BALLENY IS.
VICTORIA LAND
ANTARCTICA
NEW ZEALAND
SOUTH ISLAND
CAMPBELL (N.Z.)
AUCKLAND IS. (N.Z.)
SØR RONDANE MTS.
BELGICA MTS.
QUEEN FABIOLA MTS.
MACQUARIE (Austl.)
TASMAN SEA
South Magnetic Pole
WILKES LAND
AMERICAN HIGHLAND
ENDERBY LAND
FRAMNES MTS.
NAPIER MTS.
AMERY ICE SHELF
C. OF GOOD HOPE
Cape Town
SHACKLETON ICE SHELF
WEST ICE SHELF
AFRICA
SOUTH AFRICA
PRINCE EDWARD IS. (S. Africa)
LESOTHO
Pretoria
Hobart
TASMANIA
Bass Str.
Durban
SWAZILAND
MELBOURNE
ÎLES CROZET (Fr.)
HEARD (Austl.)
McDONALD (Austl.)
MOZAMBIQUE
Adelaide
ÎLES KERGUÉLEN (Fr.)
Great Australian Bight
Mozambique Channel
C. STE. MARIE
AUSTRALIA
MADAGASCAR
COMOROS
C. LEEUWIN
ÎLE AMSTERDAM (Fr.)
GREAT VICTORIA DESERT
ÎLE ST. PAUL (Fr.)
Perth
Antananarivo
GREAT SANDY DESERT
RÉUNION (Fr.)
MASCARENE IS.
MAURITIUS
C. D'AMBRE
TIMOR SEA
TIMOR
NORTH WEST CAPE
AMIRANTE IS. (Sey.)
FLORES
INDONESIA
SEYCHELLES
Longitude West of Greenwich
Longitude East of Greenwich
ANTARCTICA IN PROFILE
SECTION ALONG LINE AB
15000
10000
5000
Feet (A)
5000
South Pole
Horlick Mts.
Framnes Mts.
Byrd Basin
Polar Basin
Sea Level
(B) Feet

Scale 1: 60 000 000; **(approximate)**
Lambert's Azimuthal, Equal Area Projection
Elevations and depressions are given in feet

Glossary

Foreign Geographical Terms

Afk. ... Afrikaans
Ara. ... Arabic
Ber. ... Berber
Blg. ... Bulgarian
Bur. ... Burmese
Cbd. ... Cambodian
Ch. ... Chinese
Czech ... Czech
Dan. ... Danish
Du. ... Dutch
Est. ... Estonian
Finn. ... Finnish
Fr. ... French
Gae. ... Gaelic
Ger. ... German
Gr. ... Greek
Heb. ... Hebrew
Ice. ... Icelandic
Indon. ... Indonesian
It. ... Italian
Jpn. ... Japanese
Kor. ... Korean
Lao. ... Laotian
Lapp. ... Lappish
Mal. ... Malay
Mong. ... Mongolian
Nor. ... Norwegian
Pas. ... Pashto
Per. ... Persian
Pol. ... Polish
Port. ... Portuguese
Rom. ... Romanian
Rus. ... Russian
S./C. ... Serbo-Croatian
Slo. ... Slovak
Sp. ... Spanish
Swe. ... Swedish
Thai ... Thai
Tib. ... Tibetan
Tur. ... Turkish
Ukr. ... Ukranian
Viet. ... Vietnamese

-å, Dan. , Nor. , Swe. ... river
ab, Per. ... river
ada(lar), Tur. ... island(s)
adrar, Ber. ... mountains
ákra, akrotírion, Gr. ... cape
altos, Sp. ... mountains, hills
-alv, -alven, Swe. ... river
-ån, Swe. ... river
archipel, Fr. ... archipelago
archipiélago, Sp. ... archipelago
arquipélago, Port. ... archipelago
arroyo, Sp. ... brook
-ås,-åsen, Swe. ... hills
baai, Du. ... bay
bab, Ara. ... strait
Bach, Ger. ... brook, creek
-backen, Swe. ... hill
bælt, Dan. ... strait
bahía, Sp. ... bay
bahr, baḩr, Ara. ... river, sea
baía, Port. ... bay
baie, Fr. ... bay
-bana, Jpn. ... cape
banco, Sp. ... bank
bandao, Ch. ... peninsula
bassin, Fr. ... basin
batang, Indon. ... river
bātlāq, Per. ... marsh
ben, Gae. ... mountain
Berg, Ger. ... mountain, hill
-berg, Afk. ... mountains
Berge, Ger. ... mountains
bi'r, Ara. ... well
birkat, Ara. ... lake
bocca, It. ... river mouth, pass
boğazı, Tur. ... strait
bogd, Mong. ... range
bolsón, Sp. ... enclosed basin
-breen, Nor. ... glacier
Brücke, Ger. ... bridge
Bucht, Ger. ... bay
bugt, Dan. ... bay
bukit, Indon. , Mal. .. mountain, hill
-bukten, Swe. ... bay
bulu, Indon. ... mountain
Burg, Ger. ... castle
burn, Gae. ... brook
burnu, burun, Tur. ... cape
cabezas, Sp. ... peaks
cabo, Port. , Sp. ... cape
campo, It. ... plain
cap, Fr. ... cape
capo, It. ... cape
catena, Sp. ... range
cayo(s), Sp. ... cay(s), islet(s)
cerro(s), Sp. ... mountain(s), hill(s)
chaîne, Fr. ... range
château, Fr. ... castle
chiang, Ch. ... harbor, harbour
chott, Ara. ... intermittent lake, salt marsh
cima, It. , Sp. ... peak
città, It. ... city
ciudad, Sp. ... city
co, Tib. ... lake
co. , cerro, Sp. ... mountain, hill
col, Fr. ... pass
colina(s), Sp. ... hill(s)
colline, It. ... hills
collines, Fr. ... hills
con, Viet. ... islands
cord. , cordillera, Sp. ... range
costa, Sp. ... coast
côte, Fr. ... coast, hills
cuchilla, Sp. ... hills, ridge
dağ, dağı, Tur. ... mountain
dāgh, Per. ... mountains
-dake, Jpn. ... mountain
-dal, -dalen, Nor. , Swe. ... valley
danau, Indon. ... lake
dao, Ch. , Viet. ... island
daryācheh, Per. ... lake
dasht, Per. ... desert
deniz, denizi, Tur. ... sea
desierto, Sp. ... desert
détroit, Fr. ... strait
dijk, Du. ... dike
distrito, Sp. ... district
djebel, Ara. ... mountain(s)
-do, Kor. ... island
-elv,-elva, Nor. ... river
embalse, Sp. ... reservoir
erg, Ara. ... sand desert
estrecho, Sp. ... strait
étang, Fr. ... pond
-ey, Ice. ... island
fjäll(en), Swe. ... mountain(s)
fjället, Swe. ... mountain
fjärden, Swe. ... fjord
-fjell, -fjellet, Nor. ... mountain
-fjord, Nor. ... fjord
-fjorden, Nor. , Swe. ... fjord, lake
-fjörur, Ice. ... fjord, bay
-flói, Ice. ... bay
foce, It. ... river mouth, pass
forêt, Fr. ... forest
forsen, Swe. ... waterfall
Forst, Ger. ... forest
-foss, Ice. ... waterfall
-fossen, Nor. ... waterfall
g. , gora, Rus. ... mountain, hill
g. , gunong, Mal. ... mountain
gang, Ch. ... bay
-gang, Kor. ... river
gave, Fr. ... mountain torrent
gebergte, Du. ... range
Gebirge, Ger. ... range
Gipfel, Ger. ... peak
göl, Tur. ... lake
golfe, Fr. ... gulf
golfete, Sp. ... bay
golfo, It. , Sp. ... gulf
gölü, Tur. ... lake
gora, Rus. ... mountain, hill
gora, S. \C. ... mountains
góra, Pol. ... mountain
gory, Rus. ... mountains, hills
góry, Pol. ... mountains
gr'ada, Rus. ... ridge
guba, Rus. ... bay
gunong, Mal. ... mountain
gunung, Indon. ... mountain
-guntō, Jpn. ... islands
Haff, Ger. ... lagoon
hai, Ch. ... sea, lake
-hama, Jpn. ... beach
hamada, Ara. ... desert
hāmūn, Per. ... lake, marsh
-hantō, Jpn. ... peninsula
hare, Heb. ... mountains, hills
-hav, Swe. ... sea, bay
havre, Fr. ... harbor, harbour
he, Ch. ... river
ho, Ch. ... river
-ho, Kor. ... reservoir
-holm, Dan. ... island
hora, Czech, Slo. ... mountain
Horn, Ger. ... point, peak
hu, Ch. ... lake, reservoir
Hügel, Ger. ... hill
-huk, Swe. ... cape
ig. , igarapé, Port. ... river
île(s), Fr. ... island(s)
îlet(s), Fr. ... islet(s)
ilha(s), Port. ... island(s)
ilhéu(s), Port. ... islet(s)
Insel(n), Ger. ... island(s)
isla(s), Sp. ... island(s)
isola, It. ... island
isole, It. ... islands
istmo, Sp. ... isthmus
jabal, Ara. ... mountain(s)
järv, Est. ... lake
-järvi, Finn. ... lake
jazā'ir, Ara. ... islands
jazirah, Indon. ... peninsula
jiang, Ch. ... river
-jima, Jpn. ... island
-joki, Finn. ... river
-jökull, Ice. ... glacier
-kai, Jpn. ... sea
-kaikyō, Jpn. ... strait
-kaise, Lapp. ... mountain
kali, Indon. ... brook
kandao, Pas. ... pass
-kang, Kor. ... river
-kapp, Nor. ... cape
kepulauan, Indon. ... islands
khalīj, Ara. ... gulf
khrebet, Russ. , Ukr. ... range
-ko, Jpn. ... lake, lagoon
-kō, Jpn. ... harbor, harbour
kólpos, Gr. ... bay
Kopf, Ger. ... peak
körfezi, Tur. ... gulf, bay
kosa, Rus. , Ukr. ... spit
kou, Ch. ... bay, pass
kuala, Mal. ... bay
kūh(ha), Per. ... mountain(s)
la, Tib. ... pass
lac(s), Fr. ... lake(s)
lag. , laguna, Sp. ... lagoon, lake
lago, It. , Port. , Sp. ... lake
lagoa, Port. ... lake, lagoon
laguna, Sp. ... lagoon, lake
lagune, Fr. ... lagoon
laht, Est. ... bay
-lahti, Finn. ... gulf
län, Swe. ... county
laut, Indon. ... sea
liedao, Ch. ... islands
liman, Rus. ... estuary
ling, Ch. ... mountain(s), peak
llano(s), Sp. ... plain(s)
loch, Gae. ... lake, inlet
lomas, Sp. ... hills
lough, Gae. ... lake
lyman, Ukr. ... estuary
-maa, Est. ... island
-man, Kor. ... bay
mar, Sp. , It. ... sea
marais, Fr. ... marsh
mare, It. ... sea
massif, Fr. ... massif
Meer, Ger. ... sea, lake
mer, Fr. ... sea
mesa, Sp. ... mesa
meseta, Sp. ... plateau
-misaki, Jpn. ... cape
mont, Fr. ... mount
montagna, It. ... mountain
montagne(s), Fr. ... mountain(s)
montaña(s), Sp. ... mountain(s)
monte, It. , Port. , Sp. ... mount
montes, Port. , Sp. ... mountains
monti, It. ... mountains
monts, Fr. ... mountains
more, Rus. , Ukr. ... sea
morne, Fr. ... mountain
morro, Port. , Sp. ... hill, mountain
mui, Viet. ... point
munkhafad, Ara. ... depression
munţii, Rom. ... mountains
-nada, Jpn. ... sea, gulf
nafūd, Ara. ... desert
nagor'ye, Rus. ... plateau, mountains
-näs, Swe. ... peninsula
ness, Gae. ... promontory
nos, Blg. ... cape
nuruu, Mong. ... mountains
nuur, Mong. ... lake
-ø, Dan. , Nor. ... island
-ö, Swe. ... island
o. , ostrov, Rus. ... island
óros, Gr. ... mountain(s)
ostriv, Ukr. ... island
ostrov(a), Rus. ... island(s)
otok, S. \C. ... island
ouadi, Ara. ... wadi
oued, Ara. ... wadi
-øy, -øya, Nor. ... island
oz. , ozero, Rus. , Ukr. ... lake
pampa, Sp. ... plain
pas, Fr. ... strait
paso, Sp. ... pass
Pass, Ger. ... pass
passe, Fr. ... passage
passo, It. ... pass
peg. , pegunungan, Indon. ... mountains
pélagos, Gr. ... sea
peña, Sp. ... peak, rock
península, Sp. ... peninsula
pertuis, Fr. ... strait
peski, Rus. ... sand desert
phnum, Cbd. ... mountain
phou, Lao. ... mountain
pic, Fr. ... peak
pico(s), Port. , Sp. ... peak(s)
-piggen, Nor. ... mountain
pik, Rus. ... peak
pique, Fr. ... peak
piton(s), Fr. ... peak(s)
pivostriv, Ukr. ... peninsula
planalto, Port. ... plateau
planina, S. \C. ... mountain, range
plato, Afk. , Blg. , Rus. ... plateau
playa, Sp. ... beach
pointe, Fr. ... point
polje, S. \C. ... plain, basin
poluostrov, Rus. ... peninsula
pont, Fr. ... bridge
ponta, pontal, Port. ... point
porto, It. ... port
presa, Sp. ... reservoir, dam
presqu'île, Fr. ... peninsula
proliv, Rus. ... strait
puerto, Sp. ... port
pulau, Indon. , Mal. ... island
puncak, Indon. ... peak
punta, It. , Sp. ... point, peak
qundao, Ch. ... islands
rão. , ribeirão, Port. ... river
ras, ra's, Ara. ... cape
rās, Per. ... cape
récif, Fr. ... reef
represa, Port. ... dam, reservoir
-retto, Jpn. ... islands
ría, Sp. ... ria (inlet)
rib. , ribeira, Port. ... brook
ribeirão, Port. ... river
rio, Port. ... river
río, Sp. ... river
riviera, It. ... coast
rivière, Fr. ... river
roca, Sp. ... rock
rocca, It. ... rock, mountain
rt, S. \C. ... cape
sa. , serra, Port. ... range
sahrā', Ara. ... desert
-saki, Jpn. ... cape
salar, Sp. ... salt flat
salina(s), Sp. ... salt marsh, salt flat
salto(s), Port. , Sp. ... waterfall
-sammyaku, Jpn. ... range
-san, Jpn. , Kor. ... mountain
-sanmaek, Kor. ... mountains
Schloss, Ger. ... castle
sebkha, Ara. ... salt flat
See(n), Ger. ... lake(s)
selat, Indon. ... strait
seno, Sp. ... sound
serra, Port. ... range, mountain
serranía(s), Sp. ... ridge(s)
shan, Ch. ... mountain(s), island
shanmo, Ch. ... mountains
-shima, Jpn. ... island
-shotō, Jpn. ... islands
sierra, Sp. ... range, ridge
-sjø, Nor. ... lake
-sjön, Swe. ... lake, bay
-sø, Dan. ... lake
Spitze, Ger. ... peak
sta. , santa, Port. , Sp. ... saint
ste. , sainte, Fr. ... saint
step', Rus. ... steppe
štít, Slo. ... peak
sto. , santo, Port. , Sp. ... saint
stretto, It. ... strait
Strom, Ger. ... stream
-ström, -strömmen, Swe. ... stream
-su, Kor. ... river
-suidō, Jpn. ... channel
Sund, Ger. ... sound
-sund, Swe. ... sound
-take, Jpn. ... mountain
Tal, Ger. ... valley
tanjong, Mal. ... cape
tanjung, Indon. ... cape
tao, Ch. ... island
teluk, Indon. ... bay
thale, Thai ... lagoon
-tō, Jpn. ... island
tônlé, Cbd. ... lake
-tunturi, Finn. ... hill, mountain
ujung, Indon. ... cape
-umi, Jpn. ... lagoon
-ura, Jpn. ... lake
valle, It. , Sp. ... valley
vallée, Fr. ... valley
vârful, Rom. ... mountain
-vatn, Ice. , Nor. ... lake
vdkhr. , vodokhranilishche, Rus. ... reservoir
-vesi, Finn. ... lake
-viken, Swe. ... gulf
vodokhranilishche, Rus. ... reservoir
vodoskhovyshche, Ukr. ... reservoir
vol. , volcán, Sp. ... volcano
wādī, Ara. ... wadi
wāhat, wāhāt, Ara. ... oasis
wan, Ch. , Jpn. ... bay
-yama, Jpn. ... mountain
yarımadası, Tur. ... peninsula
yoma, Bur. ... mountains
yumco, Tib. ... lake
yunhe, Ch. ... canal
-zaki, Jpn. ... point
zaliv, Rus. ... gulf, bay
zatoka, Ukr. ... gulf, bay
zee, Du. ... sea, lake

Abbreviations of Geographical Names and Terms

Ab., Can. Alberta, Can.
Afg. Afghanistan
Afr. Africa
Ak., U.S. Alaska, U.S.
Al., U.S. Alabama, U.S.
Alb. Albania
Alg. Algeria
Ang. Angola
Ant. Antarctica
Ar., U.S. Arkansas, U.S.
Arg. Argentina
Arm. Armenia
Aus. Austria
Austl. Australia
Az., U.S. Arizona, U.S.
Azer. Azerbaijan
B. Bay
Bah. Bahamas
Bahr. Bahrain
Barb. Barbados
B.C., Can. British Columbia, Can.
Bdi. Burundi
Bel. Belgium
Bela. Belarus
Bhu. Bhutan
Bngl. Bangladesh
Bol. Bolivia
Bos. Bosnia and Herzegovina
Bots. Botswana
Braz. Brazil
Bul. Bulgaria
Burkina Burkina Faso
C. Cape
Ca., U.S. California, U.S.
Camb. Cambodia
Can. Canada
C.A.R. Central African Republic
Cay. Is. Cayman Islands
C. Iv. Cote d'Ivoire
Co., U.S. Colorado, U.S.
Col. Colombia
C.R. Costa Rica
Cro. Croatia
Ct., U.S. Connecticut, U.S.
Ctry. Country
C.V. Cape Verde
Cyp. Cyprus
Czech Rep. Czech Republic
D.C., U.S. District of Columbia, U.S.
De., U.S. Delaware, U.S.
Den. Denmark
Dep. Dependency
Des. Desert
Dji. Djibouti
D.R.C. Democratic Republic of the Congo
Ec. Ecuador
El Sal. El Salvador
Eng., U.K. England, U.K.
Eq. Gui. Equatorial Guinea
Erit. Eritrea
Est. Estonia
Eth. Ethiopia
Eur. Europe
Falk. Is. Falkland Islands
Fin. Finland
Fl., U.S. Florida, U.S.
Fr. France
Fr. Gu. French Guiana
G. Gulf
Ga., U.S. Georgia, U.S.
Gam. The Gambia
Gaza Str. Gaza Strip
Geor. Georgia
Ger. Germany
Grc. Greece
Guad. Guadeloupe
Guat. Guatemala
Gui. Guinea
Gui.-B. Guinea-Bissau
Guy. Guyana
Hi., U.S. Hawaii, U.S.
Hond. Honduras
Hung. Hungary
I. Island
Ia., U.S. Iowa, U.S.
Ice. Iceland
Id., U.S. Idaho, U.S.
Il., U.S. Illinois, U.S.
In., U.S. Indiana, U.S.
Indon. Indonesia
Ire. Ireland
Is. Islands
Isr. Israel
Jam. Jamaica
Jord. Jordan
Kaz. Kazakhstan
Ks., U.S. Kansas, U.S.
Kuw. Kuwait
Ky., U.S. Kentucky, U.S.
Kyrg. Kyrgyzstan
L. Lake
La., U.S. Louisiana, U.S.
Lat. Latvia
Leb. Lebanon
Leso. Lesotho
Lib. Liberia
Lith. Lithuania
Lux. Luxembourg
Ma., U.S. Massachusetts, U.S.
Mac. Macedonia
Madag. Madagascar
Malay. Malaysia
Mart. Martinique
Maur. Mauritania
Mb., Can. Manitoba, Can.
Md., U.S. Maryland, U.S.
Me., U.S. Maine, U.S.
Mex. Mexico
Mi., U.S. Michigan, U.S.
Mn., U.S. Minnesota, U.S.
Mo., U.S. Missouri, U.S.
Mol. Moldova
Mong. Mongolia
Monts. Montserrat
Mor. Morocco
Moz. Mozambique
Ms., U.S. Mississippi, U.S.
Mt. Mountain
Mt., U.S. Montana, U.S.
Mts. Mountains
Mwi. Malawi
Myan. Myanmar
N.A. North America
N.B., Can. New Brunswick, Can.
N.C., U.S. North Carolina, U.S.
N. Cal. New Caledonia
N.D., U.S. North Dakota, U.S.
Ne., U.S. Nebraska, U.S.
Neth. Netherlands
Neth. Ant. Netherlands Antilles
N.H., U.S. New Hampshire, U.S.
Nic. Nicaragua
Nig. Nigeria
N. Ire., U.K. Northern Ireland, U.K.
N.J., U.S. New Jersey, U.S.
N. Kor. North Korea
N.L., Can. Newfoundland and Labrador, Can.
N.M., U.S. New Mexico, U.S.
Nmb. Namibia
Nor. Norway
N.S., Can. Nova Scotia, Can.
N.T., Can. Northwest Territories, Can.
Nu., Can. Nunavut, Can.
Nv., U.S. Nevada, U.S.
N.Y., U.S. New York, U.S.
N.Z. New Zealand
Oc. Oceania
Oh., U.S. Ohio, U.S.
Ok., U.S. Oklahoma, U.S.
On., Can. Ontario, Can.
Or., U.S. Oregon, U.S.
Pa., U.S. Pennsylvania, U.S.
Pak. Pakistan
Pan. Panama
Pap. N. Gui. Papua New Guinea
Para. Paraguay
P.E., Can. Prince Edward Island, Can.
Pen. Peninsula
Phil. Philippines
Pk. Peak
Plat. Plateau
Pol. Poland
Polit. Reg. Political Region
Port. Portugal
P.R. Puerto Rico
Prov. Province
Qc., Can. Quebec, Can.
R. River
Ra. Range
Reg. Region
Res. Reservoir
R.I., U.S. Rhode Island, U.S.
Rom. Romania
Rw. Rwanda
S.A. South America
S. Afr. South Africa
Sau. Ar. Saudi Arabia
S.C., U.S. South Carolina, U.S.
Scot., U.K. Scotland, U.K.
S.D., U.S. South Dakota, U.S.
Sen. Senegal
Serb. Serbia and Montenegro
Sk., Can. Saskatchewan, Can.
S. Kor. South Korea
S.L. Sierra Leone
Slvk. Slovakia
Slvn. Slovenia
Som. Somalia
Sp. N. Afr. Spanish North Africa
Sri L. Sri Lanka
Str. Strait
St. Vin. St. Vincent and the Grenadines
Sur. Suriname
Swaz. Swaziland
Swe. Sweden
Switz. Switzerland
Tai. Taiwan
Taj. Tajikistan
Tan. Tanzania
Ter. Territory
Thai. Thailand
Tn., U.S. Tennessee, U.S.
Trin. Trinidad and Tobago
Tun. Tunisia
Tur. Turkey
Turk. Turkmenistan
Tx., U.S. Texas, U.S.
U.A.E. United Arab Emirates
Ug. Uganda
U.K. United Kingdom
Ukr. Ukraine
Ur. Uruguay
U.S. United States
Ut., U.S. Utah, U.S.
Uzb. Uzbekistan
Va., U.S. Virginia, U.S.
Ven. Venezuela
Viet. Vietnam
V.I.U.S. Virgin Islands (U.S.)
Vol. Volcano
Vt., U.S. Vermont, U.S.
Wa., U.S. Washington, U.S.
Wal./F. Wallis and Futuna
W.B. West Bank
Wi., U.S. Wisconsin, U.S.
W. Sah. Western Sahara
W.V., U.S. West Virginia, U.S.
Wy., U.S. Wyoming, U.S.
Yk., Can. Yukon Territory, Can.
Zam. Zambia
Zimb. Zimbabwe

Index

This universal index includes in a single alphabetical list approximately 4,100 names of features that appear on the reference maps. Each name is followed by geographical coordinates and a page reference.

Abbreviation and Capitalization

Abbreviations of names on the maps have been standardized as much as possible. Names that are abbreviated on the maps are generally spelled out in full in the index. Periods are used after all abbreviations regardless of local practice. The abbreviation "St." is used only for "Saint". "Sankt" and other forms of this term are spelled out."

Most initial letters of names are capitalized, except for a few Dutch names, such as "'s-Gravenhage." Capitalization of non-initial words in a name generally follows local practice.

Alphabetization

Names are alphabetized in the order of the letters of the English alphabet. Spanish *ll* and *ch*, for example, are not treated as distinct letters. Furthermore, diacritical marks are disregarded in alphabetization. German or Scandinavian *ä* or *ö* are treated as *a* or *o*.

The names of physical features may appear inverted, since they are always alphabetized under the proper, not the generic, part of the name, thus: "Gibraltar, Strait of." Otherwise every entry, whether consisting of one word or more, is alphabetized as a single continuous entity. "Lakeland," for example, appears after "Lake Forest" and before "La Línea." Names beginning with articles (Le Havre, Al Manāmah, Ad Dawhah) are not inverted. Names beginning "St.," "Ste.'" and "Sainte" are alphabetized as though spelled "Saint."

In the case of identical names, towns are listed first, then political divisions, then physical features.

Generic Terms

Except for cities, the names of all features are followed by terms that represent broad classes of features, for example, *Mississippi, R.* or *Alabama, State.*

Country names and names of features that extend beyond the boundaries of one country are followed by the name of the continent in which each is located. Country designations follow the names of all other places in the index. The locations of places in the United States, Canada, and the United Kingdom are further defined by abbreviations that indicate the state, province, or political division in which each is located.

Page References and Geographical Coordinates

The geographical coordinates and page references are found in the last columns of each entry.

Latitude and longitude coordinates for point features, such as cities and mountain peaks, indicate the locations of the symbols. For extensive areal features, such as countries or mountain ranges, or linear features, such as canals and rivers, locations are given for the position of the type as it appears on the map.

Index

B

C

G

H

I

J

K

N

T

U

V